ORD'S
BOTHY SONGS AND BALLADS
OF
ABERDEEN BANFF AND MORAY
ANGUS AND THE MEARNS

WITH A NEW INTRODUCTION BY
ALEXANDER FENTON

JOHN DONALD PUBLISHERS LTD
EDINBURGH

John Donald Publishers Ltd.
138 St. Stephen Street
Edinburgh EH3 5AA

ISBN 0 85976 303 X

Printed in Great Britain by Bell and Bain Ltd., Glasgow

FOREWORD

NO man of our generation had a more intimate and loving knowledge of the by-ways of Scottish song than the late Superintendent JOHN ORD of the Glasgow Police Force. Distinguished in his profession, and an officer whose merit and ability earned for him both high promotion and the decoration which is the blue-ribbon of the Force, he found time to collect, to arrange, and to illustrate by apposite and illuminating comment the folk-song of his native county and its neighbours in the north-east of Scotland. He has not lived to witness the publication of what will be the classical work on a subject the importance of which is receiving wide recognition. We have here the real thing—the songs as actually sung in the bothies of the farms in the north. Their text may be evidence of the invasion of the vernacular by southern influence (though many words conventionally printed in English were, and are, pronounced as Scots), but their substance provides a living picture of Scottish rural life, absolutely sincere and free from any form of affectation. Food and drink, work and play, lovers' happiness and their tragedies (here and there their comedies as well), echoes of fairy tales and of civil war, the little incidents of daily life which vary with changing social custom—all of them things that might easily disappear and be lost—are here preserved with pious care in this Book of Remembrance.

A Northerner myself, I most cordially and gratefully commend Mr. ORD's admirable collection to all who are interested in the Scottish tongue, in Scots song, and in Scottish history and life.

ROBERT S. RAIT.

THE UNIVERSITY.
GLASGOW, *April, 1930.*

CONTENTS

v

CONTENTS.

CONTENTS.

(*b*) Songs of the Forsaken and Jilted.

Seven Years O'er Young, ... *Music* 170
On Longside Road, ... 172
Oh, Ye've been False, ... 173
The Fause Young Man, ... 174
It wasna My Fortune to get Her, ... 175
The Rambling Beauty, ... 176
I'll Cheer up my Heart, ... 177
The B ewer Lad, ... 178
The Days are awa that I hae seen, ... 179
When Fortune Turns Her Wheel, ... 180
Go and leave me if you wish it, ... 181
Green Grows the Laurel, ... 182
False Mallie, ... 183
The Bonnie Woods o' Hatton, ... 185
Blooming Caroline o' Edinburgh Town, ... 186
The Rose and the Thyme, ... 187
The Flower of France and England, O, ... 188
The Blaeberry Courtship, ... 190
The Flower o' Northumberland, ... 192
The Haughs o' Newe, ... 193
The Belt wi' Colours Three, ... 194
The Beauty of Garmouth, ... 195
For a' That and a' That, ... 196
The Duke of Argyle's Courtship, ... 197
My Mither she Feed me when I was O'er Young, ... 198
The Banks of Inverurie, ... 199
The Shannon Side, ... 200
It's Braw Sailin' on the Sea, ... 203
The Flower of Fochabers, ... 204
Geordie Asking Miss Tiptoe in Marriage, ... 204

PART II.

Songs relating to Farm Life and Work.

CONTENTS.

PART III.

Songs relating to Soldiers, Sailors, War, and Adventure.

CONTENTS.

INTRODUCTION

by

SANDY FENTON

When I worked on North-East farms as a youngster in the 1940s, earning a penny-fee on holidays from school, it was my good fortune to meet many fine people. They knew my interest in riddles and words and ferlies in general, but as a timmer-tuned laddie I was less able to keep up with them in song if things turned in that direction.

Two points stick in my mind in this respect, however. The first was the instrumental music of the Bruce family at Upper Pitglassie in Auchterless, a family big enough in itself to have its own dance band. Practising went on in the chaamer round the corner of the close. Here the rhythms of tunes to make your feet dance were driven well into my head. The second was an experience of a different, less publicly intended character. I used to hoe turnips sometimes with the son of a farmer up the road, Willie by name. Normally a shy, quiet man, the context of work seemed to slacken his inhibitions, and then he would sing song after song in an endless stream. Many of the lines and verses of songs, several of which are in John Ord's book, have stayed in my memory from that time, still flickering through my head at unexpected moments. But there was one difference from Ord. On page 3 of his Introduction, Ord deplores the coming of modern music-hall songs, and he firmly excluded them from his collection. Willie had no such worries. He was as happy to sing *The Muckin' o' Geordie's Byre* or *McGinty's Meal an' Ale* as he was to sing a traditional ballad.

This might seem like a weakening of the tradition. On the other hand, Ord was *selecting* his tradition, for the Victorian music-hall songs as well as others were fully alive also at his time. Perhaps it would make a truer reflection of the complex range of songs current on the lips of country folk if he had concentrated less on tradition, and been a little more catholic. To have done so would have been in line with modern thinking. A recent American scholar, discussing folk-music in the modern world, wrote that the 'cultural setting with which I am primarily concerned . . . is the modern world. This setting is responsive to both dramatic change and the stability afforded by tradition. It is a setting in which folk music thrives, albeit with only occasional resemblance to the pristine models advocated by conservative scholarship.'[1]

For us, dramatic change has come through the medium of the music-hall stage reinforced by radio and television, which have opened the pandora's box of the music world to the kitchens and sitting rooms of rural Scotland. The process was getting under way just about the time Ord was putting his collection into book form: as a North-east farmer noted in his diary on 8 April 1923, 'Harry & Geo. Wilson & Jim at Feithhill after dinner seeing the wireless receiver'.[2] No doubt they listened with as much fascinated attention as I paid to my first sight, as a young student, of a television set shown off to me by a hugely-grinning Gloucestershire farmer. It was the wireless that gave my friend Willie at least half of his songs; these, combined with the older ones, made up the reality of his musical world.

In concentrating more on the 'traditional', John Ord was following the method of approach of other well-known collectors like Gavin Greig, Whitehills (d.1914) and the Rev. James Bruce Duncan, Lynturk (d.1917). An edition of Greig's *Last Leaves of Traditional Ballads and Ballad Airs* appeared in 1925,[3] in the year when Ord finished penning the Introduction to his own collection (though it is only in the 1980s that a full and systematic publication of the over 3000 texts and over 3100 records of tunes in the Greig-Duncan Folk Song Collection has begun to be undertaken).[4]

It is no criticism of Ord, though, to say that he was following the pattern of scholarship of his time. The more widely comprehensive approach to collection is a child of very recent days. Ord's purpose was to record what was sung in bothies and farm-kitchens, at feeing-markets and harvest home suppers. The outcome is a fascinating picture of the world that farm-folk knew, especially in the nineteenth and first quarter of the twentieth centuries, before the radio began to leave its mark on the kind of songs sung, as well as lessening the need for self-made entertainment in the evenings.

In Ord's collecting days, the hard work of daytime hours was well balanced at times by a serious evening's entertainment, especially in winter. 'Billie & Ina over from Leggat kept up the roar through the evening' said James Hunter of a Saturday evening in January 1923.[5] It is clear from Ord's numerous footnotes that 'merry meetings' in farm-kitchens, bothies and chaamers were frequent and that performances were relished for both tunes and words over a very wide range of subjects. These are analysed and systematically presented by Ord in this volume. In his Introduction he also touches on some aspects of the daily environment — the hairst, the food, the young herd boys and lasses — but it is worth looking at the background in more detail, as it flows from the words of the texts themselves.

The bulk of the texts lie within the 63 years of Victoria's reign (1837–1901), with her successors Edward VII and George V taking us up to the date of publication. One song is even alleged to represent the feelings of one who had fallen in love with the teenage Victoria, and another welcomes her coming to Balmoral in Deeside.[6]

It is true that many of the events touched on, especially in the historical ballads, are of earlier centuries, and some of the songs, often distinguished by the quality of their structure and good use of language, have eighteenth-century antecedents. Robert Burns knew and made use of versions of some.[7] Nevertheless, as published here, the songs and ballads have the shape the singers gave them in the times of these three monarchs, and to a lesser extent of the three preceding (William IV, 1830–37; George IV, 1820–30; George III, 1760–1820).

The extent to which the songs can throw light on the society of their period lies, of course, within the limits of their own conventions. These include well-worn and internationally known and used motifs such as the opposition between youth and age, rich and poor, humble and noble birth, along with the trials and tribulations of courtship and marriage, acceptance and rejection, the disguised lover, the testing of love by a long-lost wanderer, and all the other aspects of the everlasting human situation that lie at the heart of most of our literature.

These conventions include symbolism. Colour figures largely. A gown of green marks the sorrow of being forsaken.[8] A green ribbon about a laddie's hat was a token of marriage.[9] Recovery from sorrow could involve moving in sequence from a coat of green to one of green and yellow to one of orange and blue.[10] The international perspective of such colour symbolism in relation to marriage is indicated by the painting of furniture in brides' dowries in places like Braunschweig in Germany: red marked a bride of the highest status, red and green a lower level, light and dark green followed, and two minor colours came at the bottom. The strictness of adherence to the system was breaking down there already by the end of the seventeenth century.[11] It is likely that the colour symbolism in Ord's collection preserves fragmentary relics of a similar old tradition, much wider than Scotland, and including the colours also of the world of fairy.[12] Amongst other symbols were love tokens, a ring from the finger, a garter from the knee, a brooch from the breast, a ring or piece of gold broken between a loving couple,[13] plants like rue and thyme, and red roses.[14]

Interesting as such relics are as pointers to an almost forgotten world, the major importance of Ord's collection nevertheless lies for us in the picture it gives of a particular society. With a few exceptions, the society reflected in the texts has a strongly rural basis. Farmers and their servants play a leading role and their presentation is in many ways the clearest. Farmers regularly appear fair and smiling at feeing markets as they press arles into a gullible hand and offer a glass in the ale tent, but turn into devils for work as they drive their men once they have them home to their chaamer or bothy.[15] Five o'clock rising and ten-hour days were the rule, and the horses had to be corned and combed on top of that. It is little wonder, or so it would seem from these texts, that the men were more than eager to move after six months, at the May or November term. There were examples of good places, indeed, where conditions and food were praised, as also the farmer's bonny daughter,[16] but more often sharp criticism was the rule. Some farmers fed their men on cold kail and potatoes, whilst they sat themselves at their tea and toast. At Sleepytown of Insch there was a strike when the men were expected to make their brose from the scrapings of the meal sacks. The gastronomic delicacies at the Barns o' Beneuchies were breakfast of buttermilk and meal, a drink of sour ale in the morning, for dinner sometimes beef-bree seasoned 'wi' three seeds o' barley and the smell o' a leek'.[17] One ballad tells of a farm run by a wife where the men supped their brose with spoons, but ben the hoose the knife and fork were used and there were breakfast delights like tea and coffee, butter, eggs and cheese.[18]

Such differences in diet between the men and the master's family are indicators of the real sense of hierarchy and prestige that lay within such rural communities, even if the distances between the status layers were slight. Clothing was another such marker. Farmers are depicted with broad-tailed coats and quaker hats, whips beneath their arms, and boots with spurs.[19] Part of the mental attitude of the men was a levelling, almost contemptuous, joking about the fashionable dress and habits of their superiors. The daughter might play the piano, wear a white veil to church, have a long gown trailing a yard behind her, and wear her hair tied up like a horse's tail.[20] One ballad mocks servant lasses who sought to outstrip their mistresses in dress and hair style;[21] but indeed it was part of the convention to rib the deem in such a way, and so in some degree maintain the perceptions of what was fitting at appropriate levels. You needn't look for gentlemen if you wanted the work done. And if a woman harvester came about the place with gaudy dress she could expect to be told about it, though she would give as good as she got. 'I'm nae prood. I'm tasty an' airy', answered one in the Cornhill district of Banffshire.[22]

Just as there were status differences between farmer and servants, so also was there a tightly hierarchical organisation among the men. There could be, depending on the size of the place, a gaffer, foreman, second and third lads, bailie, little bailie, orra loon or halflin, kitchen lass[23] and sometimes an orra woman, all jealously guarding their positions in the chain, but without question the role of ploughman was the coveted one. The praise of ploughmen is sung in many entries. They are toasted in an almost mystical fashion as the ones whose work provided the basis for human existence, all other standard crafts or trades — the gardener, smith, souter, miller, joiner, mason, tailor — being considered secondary or inferior.[24] If a girl turned up her nose at a mere ploughman as a marriage partner, she was seen as a 'maid of vain glory, with grandeur and pride'.[25] A ploughman was not lightly spurned according to the ploughmen, but it seems to be sadly true that a lass without a tocher might have to marry one, whilst a girl with a muckle tocher and a puckle gear would be too proud to do so.[26]

Ord's ballads provide revealing glimpses of social conditions and mental perspectives that go beyond the conventional attitudinising of the composers, known or unknown. A detailed analysis of the background to farm servant life has been given by Ian Carter, who also took the ballads into account to some degree;[27] but the same sources range more widely over the social scene also, and though sung in the North-East, do not deal exclusively with North-east matters. There was a bleacher lassie who worked at Cochrane's Bleachfields in Kelvinhaugh,[28] a collier laddie from Fife,[29] a hedger and ditcher who lived by undertaking farm work when not otherwise employed,[30] a roving baker from Mulguy,[31] a butcher laddie from Crieff,[32] sailors (often press-ganged to the sea) and whalers,[33] soldiers,[34] weavers who like ploughmen had good conceits of themselves,[35] and others. The songs and ballads are not wholly rural. There is, within their limits, a picture of a wider society, urban and industrial as well, to be got out of them.

Other groups also appear as parts of the social structure. In his Introduction, Ord draws attention to the beggars, the 'blue gowns' who operated under licence and were, at least lightly, tarred by James V's stick of royal favour. They and the packmen or chapmen played an important social role as disseminators of news, bringers of nicknacks for sale — buttons, needles, pins, ribbons and the like — and also the broadsheets that were a prime means of spreading knowledge of songs and ballads (as well as the prose stories of which Dougal Graham, the eighteenth-century 'skellat' bellman of Glasgow, is a leading exponent by the standards of any country of Europe),[36] many of which Ord annotates as being of broadsheet origin.[37] The theme of those of high degree in beggar's disguise continues,[38] with a lass of humble origin becoming elevated through marriage — perhaps an attractive fantasy — but the opposite could also happen, as when Lord Cassil's lady went off with the gipsies and a rich widow with a Deeside tinker. The different way of life of tinkers and gipsies, outside the normal conventions of society, readily gave rise to a kind of superstitious attitude towards them, within which a certain mesmeric influence over womenfolk, 'the pearlin ower my e'en', could be understandable.[39]

At another level again, coming under the heading of what might be called perceptions of identity, is the attitude towards the Highlanders and the Highlands that not uncommonly appears. The wife of 'a mannie Kempie' (the song makes insulting use of diminutives) stigmatised the shepherd at the farm as a 'cyaurd Hielan' thing'.[40] In fact shepherds of Highland origin were commonly employed on farms in North-East Scotland and places like Glenesk in Angus well through the twentieth century. But beyond such an employment situation is the mental concept of the Highlands held by Lowland folk, as expressed in several of the songs. The laddie offered enticements to the lass to join him in the Highlands, amongst the green woods, with plenty of sweet milk and curds, fresh mountain air, blaeberries to pull and eat, sheep in great plenty, black cattle, the deer and the roe to be hunted. On the other hand, the road to the Highlands was long, the mountains were high and ill to climb, the Highland tongue was strange, it was a place where reivers lived and perhaps the memory of the 50,000 Highland men under Donald, Lord of the Isles, though defeated by Lowlanders and burgesses of Aberdeen under Alexander Stewart, Earl of Mar, at Harlaw near Inverurie in 1411, did not fade easily.[41] Such points constitute perceptions or attitudes of a fairly natural kind, not directed by pressures of fashionable views underpinned by self-conscious literature,[42] and can be taken as general aspects of the popular culture of the times.

This is not to deny that some levels of literature influenced people's attitudes. John Paton, the Independent Labour Party's national organiser, claimed in 1936 that the most formative political and literary influences (on the party's adherents) were the works of Burns and the inspiration of the Bible.[43] There are no especially religious aspects to Ord's collection beyond the hymn-like *Dying Ploughboy*[44] which was in any case written by a minister (and remains popular), but Burns did sink deeply into the ballad mentality, verses being created that turned aspects of his life almost into symbols of the anguish of love and parting, not to mention convivial drinking.[45]

At a more ideological level also in this country of Scotland which is a nation without being a state is an aspect of its culture that, like 'tartan, speech, anthem, flag', reinforced its sense of nationhood.[46] This was the concept of 'brave auld kilted Caledon', the pride in the bayonet and kilt and the pibroch that stirred the blood to do valiant battle with the enemy, the ever-deceitful foreigner, at Waterloo, at Barossa, in Egypt and elsewhere, all compounded with the sorrow — which was also a kind of pride — of bereaved parents around the peat fires in the Highland glens.[47] Nearer home, Jacobite songs commemorate Culloden.[48] These songs, too, like those concerned with the sea — which, however, are less to do with glorifying battle and more with press-ganged lovers that proud parents had considered beneath their daughter's dignity — all help to portray the quality of the society of the time, at the level of the broad strata amongst whom the songs and ballads were popular.

Besides the picture of society to be gained, there are innumerable details of family and marriage, work and play, that help us to get inside the minds of the people involved and to understand the physical and mental settings within which they played out their lives. Such versified and sung forms of popular literature have to be set alongside the prose that appeared in great quantity in the popular press, especially after the repeal of the Stamp Act in 1855 that triggered off a revolutionary growth in the printing of papers,[49] for the picture — and its regional variations — to be filled out in even clearer detail. But to use the term 'popular literature' is not to demean the material Ord has assembled for us. In its wide variety, in its absorption of song from England, the Isle of Man and notably from Ireland (the last in some cases reflecting the presence of the tens of thousands of Irish seasonal migrants who came with their huiks to shear the Lowland hairsts), in its reflection of the attitudes and beliefs of a huge section of the population of Scotland, we have here important social historical material that lies waiting to be interpreted in deeper detail, with the added bonus that such a research tool as this is also a source of unlimited pleasure.

European Ethnological Research Centre,
National Museums of Scotland,
Edinburgh 1990

REFERENCES

1. P V Bohlman, *The Study of Folk Music in the Modern World* Indiana University Press 1988, xvi.
2. James Hunter, Brownhill, Auchterless, Turriff, *MS Diary.*
3. Alexander Keith, ed., *Last Leaves of Traditional Ballads and Ballad Airs collected in Aberdeenshire by the late Gavin Greig*, Aberdeen 1925.
4. E B Lyle, General Editor, *The Greig-Duncan Folk Song Collection*, Aberdeen, Vol. I, 1981; Vol. 2, 1984; Vol. 3, 1987. 8 volumes are planned, under the aegis of the University of Aberdeen and the School of Scottish Studies of Edinburgh University.
5. James Hunter, *MS Diary*, 13 January 1923.
6. *I'll Hang My Harp*, 56; *Queen Victoria's Welcome to Deeside*, 337.
7. *The Banks o' Deveron Water*, 29-30; *The Collier Laddie*, 40-42; *For A' That and A' That*, 196; *The Ploughman*, 217; *Harry Lumsdale's Courtship*, 427-29.
8. *Mormond Braes*, 62; *The Mantle so Green*, 155.
9. *My Bonnie Laddie's Lang, Lang o'Growing*, 112.
10. *The Unconstant Lover*, 133.
11. Cf. U Meiners, Forschungen zur historischen Sachkultur (Research in historical Material Culture), in *Der Deutschunterricht* XXXIX/6 (1987), 27-28.
12. *The King of the Fairies*, 166; *Sir John Gordon*, 423.
13. *Sweet Tayside*, 119; *False Mallie*, 183; *The Dark-Eyed Sailor*, 323; *The Brisk Young Sailor*, 327.
14. *Seven Years O'er Young*, 171; *The Rose and the Thyme*, 187.
15. Eg *Drumdelgie*, 209-211; *Swaggers*, 219-221.
16. *Broomhill's Bonnie Dochter*, 232-233; *The Guise o' Tough*, 236-237.
17. *The Weary Farmers*, 212; *The Barns o' Beneuchies*, 281.
18. *Auld Luckie of Brunties*, 246.
19. *The Weary Farmers*, 211.
20. *John Bruce o' the Corner*, 211.
21. *The Braw Servant Lasses*, 275-276.
22. See A Fenton, *Wirds an' Wark 'e Seasons Roon on an Aberdeenshire Farm*, Aberdeen 1987, 7.
23. *John Bruce o' the Corner*, 229-230; *The Guise o' Tough*, 236-237; *Sowens for Sap at Oor New Tap*, 251.
24. *The Bonnie Lad that Handles the Plough*, 81; *The Gairdner and the*

Ploughman, 94; *The Painful Plough*, 222-223; *The Praise of Ploughmen*, 242-243.

25. *Geordie Asking Miss Tiptoe in Marriage*, 204-205.
26. *Gien the Nowte their Fodder*, 228; *The Woods of Riccarton*, 253.
27. Ian Carter, *Farmlife in Northeast Scotland 1840-1914. The Poor Man's Country*, Edinburgh 1979: see especially Chapters 4-5.
28. *The Bleacher Lassie o'Kelvinhaugh*, 77.
29. *The Collier Laddie*, 40-42.
30. *The Hedger*, 48.
31. *The Feeing Time*, 82.
32. *The Wind Blew the Bonnie Lassie's Plaidie Awa'*, 96.
33. *The Foundling Baby*, 144-146; *It's Braw Sailin' on the Sea*, 203; *The Bonnie Ship the Diamond*, 312-313; *The Whalers' Song*, 317-318.
34. *The Plains of Waterloo*, 299-301 etc.
35. *The Calton Weaver*, 372-373; *The Wark o' the Weavers*, 381.
36. G MacGregor, *The Collected Writings of Dougal Graham*, 2 v., Glasgow 1883.
37. *The Pedlar*, 140-142.
38. *The Beggar Man*, 375-377; *The Beggar's Dawtie*, 382-383.
39. *The Gypsie Laddie*, 411-412; *Geordie Downie*, 461.
40. *The Barns o' Beneuchies*, 281-282.
41. *Bonnie Lassie, Come to the North Hielands*, 87; *There Cam' a Laddie Frae the North*, 103-105; *The Maid of Don*, 135; *The Blaeberry Courtship*, 190-191; *Gight's Ladye*, 408-410; *Harlaw*, 473-475.
42. Cf. L Leneman, A New Role for a Lost Cause: Lowland Romanticisation of the Jacobite Highlander, in L Leneman, ed., *Perspectives in Scottish Social History. Essays in Honour of Rosalind Mitchison*, Aberdeen 1988, 107-124.
43. Quoted in W Knox, The Red Clydesiders and the Scottish Political Tradition, in T Brotherstone, ed., *Covenant, Charter and Party: Traditions of Revolt and Protest in Modern Scottish History*, Aberdeen 1989, 93.
44. *The Dying Ploughboy*, 235, written by Rev R H Calder, minister of Glenlivet Parish Church.
45. *The Parting of Burns and Highland Mary*, 354-355; *Last Parting of Burns and Bonnie Jean*, 356; *A Wee Drappie O't*, 371 (additional verses).
46. Cf. D McCrone, S Kendrick and P Straw, *The Making of Scotland: Nation, Culture and Social Change*, Edinburgh 1989, 5 (Introduction).
47. Numerous examples in the section on Soldiers, Sailors, War and Adventure, 289ff.
48. *The Muir of Culloden*, 293; *The Highland Maid*, 297.
49. See W Donaldson, *Popular Literature in Victorian Scotland. Language, fiction and the press*, Aberdeen 1986.

John Ord

The men at Chapel of Seggat, Auchterless, 1917, outside the cart sheds. *Scottish Ethnological Archive.*

The bothie interior at Bethelnie, Aberdeenshire, 1907. *Scottish Ethnological Archive.*

Ploughing with a pair at Lumphanan, Aberdeenshire, in 1980. Photo. A. Fenton. *Scottish Ethnological Archive*.

Five pair and an orra beast, at Ingilston farm, Essie, Perthshire. Per Harry Davidson. *Scottish Ethnological Archive*.

A pair lowsed from the carts, on a Perthshire farm. Per Harry Davidson. *Scottish Ethnological Archive.*

A Fife pair under firm control. Per Alan Barron. *Scottish Ethnological Archive.*

Men and women servants among the grain on a South East farm. Per Mrs. A. Scott, Melrose. *Scottish Ethnological Archive.*

INTRODUCTION

———

A German antiquary once remarked that Scotland was a place where every stone had its history, and where there is no mouldering castle, nor heap of ruined stones, which had formed a few cottages, that is not memorable for some story of war or piety, some gleam of long past love, or dark with tale of revenge. That the German gentleman's description of our country is correct, there can be no manner of doubt, and he would have been equally correct if he had stated that the stories of fire, flood, and battle, piety and devotion, love and hate, connected with the ruins he referred to, had been transmitted from one generation to another by the medium of our ballads and folk-songs.

This compilation consists principally of Folk-songs and Ballads collected in the bothies and farm-kitchens in the counties of Aberdeen, Banff, and Moray, although a goodly number of them are common to the counties of Kincardine, Forfar, and Perth.

Bothy-song is just another name for folk-song, and folk-song means briefly that body of minstrelsy which circulates among the common people of a country, and has originated among them. It is a communal product and not, as a rule, the result of individual effort. There are, however, some exceptions to the general rule, for example " The Dying Ploughboy," a bothy-song exceedingly popular all over the north-east of Scotland, the author of which is still alive.

A ballad is a species of minor epic, that is, it narrates a story, real or fictitious, representing some heroic action, or event of lasting importance in the history of a nation or race, or it may be some long forgotten love tragedy, or dark deed of revenge. Like our ballads, our Scottish love-songs generally tell a story, while their English analogues are simply sentiments in rhyme. To hear folk-songs to the best advantage, they should be sung and not read.

In the days of long ago the peasantry of Scotland had songs for every occupation, and every sentiment; war songs commemorating every battle, from Bannockburn to Alma; songs of love, hatred, courtship and marriage; songs of domestic life; ploughing matches and feeing markets; of poaching, begging, and drinking; cradle songs and lullabies; and even whale-fishers' songs. While milking the cows the women crooned their milking songs:—

> Pbroo, pbroo, my bonnie cow,
> Pbroo, hawkie, ho, hawkie,
> Ye ken the han' that's kind to you,
> Sae let the drappie go, hawkie.

At the time when every farmer and crofter kept his own sheep, for the purpose of providing wool to be spun into cloth to make the clothing of both sexes, there were faulding songs, and buchting songs, such as, "Will ye gang to the ewe-buchts, Marion?"

The whale-fishing industry, chiefly from the ports of Aberdeen, Peterhead, and Dundee, was responsible for quite a large number of songs, now almost forgotten. The Peterhead whalers' song was perhaps the most popular. It describes the departure and home-coming of those hardy toilers of the deep.

> Once more for Greenland we are bound,
> To leave you all behind:
> Wi' timbers firm, and hearts so warm,
> We sail before the wind.

> A blowing breeze comes frae the south,
> Our sails all seem asleep,
> Wi' three cheers more we leave the shore,
> And float upon the deep.

> .   .   .   .

> And now we pass the Orkney Isles,
> The pilot-boat draws near,
> We see our sweethearts and our wives,
> All waiting on the pier.

> And now in harbour safely moored,
> We next shall go on shore,
> An' wi' plenty o' brass and a bonnie lass,
> We'll mak yon taverns roar.

Bothy songs deal with the every day affairs of the country people, depicting their life with its lights and its shadows, its occupations, amusements and recreations, its joys and its sorrows. And although the rhythm halts, and the rhyme does not run smoothly, and in many cases they are pure doggerel, the melodies to which they are sung are in many cases exceptionally fine, and often superior to all except the very best of our standard Scottish songs. It has been truly said that our Scottish folk-tunes, originally of one strain only, have a sweetness which delights every ear unspoiled by the complex productions of the laborious ingenuity of the modern band-master.

As the flowers of the hot-house and garden may be compared with the songs of the drawing-room and the concert hall, so the wild flowers of the fields and the woodlands compare with the simple lays of the farm-kitchen, the bothy, and the feeing market. No doubt we admire the flowers of the hot-house and the garden, but do we not occasionally love to turn to the fields and the glens of our native land, and pluck the wild flowers which are only to be found there?

There is no comparison between the folk-songs and ballads of our country and the modern music-hall songs, which in many cases are simply a string of pure nonsense, highly seasoned with indelicate double meaning, and sometimes grossly offensive and obscene.

Many of the bothy-songs in vogue in the past have fallen into disuse as the circumstances and modes of life that called them into being have passed away. Shearing songs and harvest songs have passed with the advent of the reaping machine. The Poor Law and Vagrancy Acts swept away any romance which existed in connection with the begging profession, while the Education Act of 1872 practically abolished herding, and the songs and superstitions of the herd passed into the limbo of forgotten things. In the words of a modern poet:—

> They sang the songs with a cheerful zest,
> In the days that have passed away,
> Each one had a song that suited him best,
> In that happiest yesterday.
> They sang of the wonders their ancestors wrought,
> They sang of the freedom their full blood had bought
> In the wars that are legend now.
> Oh, they sang with zest, and they sang with the best
> The songs that are legend now.

Feeing markets and ploughing matches were two of the most important events in the life of a ploughman. The foreman at a large first-class farm attached great importance to his position.

> " I had a hat upon my heid,
> It cost me mair than half a guinea;
> Held a' the lassies in Brannan Fair
> Gazing at the foremost man of Milne o' Beenie."

At a ploughing match his horses, plough, and the kind of ground the match is held on, comes in for more attention than the man himself:—

> Then some wi' pins and some wi' props,
> They a' began a-feerin',
> Some o' them seemed to be well pleased;
> And some began a-swearin';
> Some said their rigs were fearfu' teuch,
> Some said that theirs were stony,
> The furs wad neither cut nor grip,
> Nor yet look square nor bonnie.

In his own estimation, according to his songs, he comes out an easy first when comparing himself with other workmen:—

> The mason he's a laddie that's proud o' his post,
> Gin it werena for the mason we wad a' dee wi' frost,
> But the mason's like the rest he'd get little for to do,
> Gin it werena for the bonnie lad that handles the plough.
>
> The tailor he's a laddie that sews at a cloot,
> He'll tak' an auld coat an' he'll turn't inside out,
> He'll turn't inside out, and he'll mak' it look like new,
> But he's far frae like the bonnie lad that handles the plough.

He even quotes both sacred and secular history in support of this contention:—

> Samson was the strongest man,
> And Solomon was wise;
> Alexander for to conquer
> Was all his daily prize;
> King David was a valiant man
> And many thousands slew,
> But none of those bold heroes
> Could live without the plough.

After this it may be fairly presumed that the fair sex prefer the ploughman to any other tradesman:—

> The tailor he's been seekin' me,
> The sailor's seekin' me;
> But I think I'll tak' my ploughman lad
> And lat the rest gang free.
> For what can a poor tailor do
> When he want's candle light?
> The ploughman can water his two bonnie steeds
> Any hour in a' the night.

Not only does he place himself on a higher plane than other tradesmen, but he is continually poking fun, in his songs, at some of them, and in particular at the tailors:—

> The tailor cam' to clout the claes,
> Sic a braw fellow;
> An' he filled the hoose a' fu' o' flaes,
> Daffan doun an' dilly.

The song from which this verse is quoted refers to the time when tailors moved about from place to place, and made clothing from the farmer's own home-spun cloth.

Even at church, the ploughman, according to his songs, is continually attracting the attention of the fair sex:—

> When I go to the kirk on Sunday,
> Mony a bonnie lass I see,
> Prim, sitting by her daddy's side,
> And winking o'er the pews at me.

That he is sometimes given to boasting will be seen from the following verse:—

> I can drink and not be drunk,
> I can fight and not be slain;
> I can court another's lass,
> And aye be welcome to my ain.

Many bothy songs refer to the food supplied by the farmers to his servants, which, in a great many cases, was of the very poorest quality. Thus the breakfast:—

> Meg M'Pherson made the brose,
> And her and me could ne'er agree,
> 'Twas first a knot, and then a mote,
> An' aye the ither splash o' bree.

Even where the foreman made the brose, he did not always give satisfaction:—

> In the mornin' we got brose,
> As mony's we could belly in:
> Willie Buchan made the brose,
> And faith he did not mak' them thin.

If the breakfast was poor, the dinner was no better:—

> The breid was thick, the brose was thin,
> The broth they were like bree;
> I chased the barley roun' the plate,
> And a' I got were three.

In the counties of Aberdeen and Banff, fifty years ago, supper, as a rule, consisted of oatmeal porridge or brose made with boiling milk, or with boiling ale with a glass of whisky added by way of seasoning. This was varied at times by sowens, boiled till they were of the same consistency as porridge or made like gruel and sweetened with syrup.

Other dishes were served, though less frequently; mashed turnips when in season; green kail (colewort) boiled in water and seasoned with pepper and salt with the addition of a little cream; rice boiled in skim milk and sweetened with a little sugar. At some farms, however, the servants were simply

allowed six and a half bolls of oatmeal per annum, and one
Scotch pint of sweet milk per day, and they had to make their
own food in the bothies. In such cases it was brose for breakfast, dinner, and supper.

The instruction of a Buchan farmer to his kitchen-maid as
to the feeding of the servants of another farmer, who were
coming to his assistance to get the remainder of his crop into
the stackyard, is described in the song as follows: —

> " You, Annie Scott, ye'll get on the muckle pot,
>   An' you'll mak' milk porridge a-plenty;
> For thae hungry brosers are coming frae Pitgair,
>   An' they're keepit aye sae bare and sae scanty."

The greedy farmer's broken promises, and the miserable way
in which he feeds his horses, is also described in terse
language: —

> He promised me the ae best pair
>   That ever I clapt e'en upon;
> When I went home to Barnyards,
>   There was naething there but skin and bone.

Again: —

> Darra's horse were very poor,
>   They got their corn ance a day,
> And ither twice got neeps and cauf (chaff)
>   To gar them nab their pickle strae.

The next verse, from a different song, is even better than those
quoted: —

> We did drive on his horses,
>   Till they were out o' breath,
> They were fitter for the tannerie,
>   Than for to be in graith.
> For want o' corn they did lie hard,
>   And he with us did chide,
> And he swore we had neglected them
>   Upon sweet Bogieside.

It naturally follows that servants did not renew their engage-
ments with this class of farmer. At some farms the foreman
was given the best horses, supplied with the best tools, and was
paid much higher wages than the other servants. In return for
this treatment, the farmer expected him " to carry on the work "
and get as much out of the other servants—mostly youths—as
possible.

> An' aye he told the foreman cheil
>   To keep the steady grind,
> An' no to lat the orra lads
>   Fa' idle back behind.
> For I pay ye a' guid wages,
>   An' I wish ye to get on;
> And when ye are not able,
>   There's another when you're done.

At other farms, the greedy farmer had a different way of getting as much work out of his men as could be got:—

> There's nae a chiel here ca'd a foreman,
>   Drawing a muckle, big pay,
> The man that's first oot in the mornin',
>   He's the foreman for the day.

When work was plentiful, such farmers had a difficulty in getting men to engage with, and often could get none in the district where they were known, consequently they had to go to distant markets, and with smiling faces and false promises, which they never meant to keep, they had to engage strangers to fill up their vacancies:—

> But they'll gang on some twenty miles,
>   Where people disna ken them,
> An' there they'll fee their harvest hands,
>   An' bring them far frae hame.

This is how the average farm-servant warns his colleagues about such farmers:—

> Come a' ye jolly ploughman lads,
>   That whistle through the fair,
> Beware o' gaun to Swaggers,
>   He'll be in Porter Fair;
> He's aye lauch, lauchin',
>   He'll aye be lauchin' there,
> An' he'll hae on the blithest face
>   In a' Porter Fair.
>
> He'll tell ye a fine story,
>   Sae little ye'll hae tae dae,
> An' he'll ca' in the ither gill,
>   Get you for little fee;
> An' he'll ca' in the ither gill,
>   Until he gets you fu ,
> But gin ye gang tae Swaggers,
>   Sae sune's he'll gar ye rue.

Domestic life naturally furnishes much matter for bothy song, even the discomfort of the washing day comes in for attention:—

> My Kate she is a bonnie wife, there's nane mair free frae evil,
> Except upon the washing day, and then she is the deevil;
> The very kittens on the hearth, they dare not even play,
> Away they jump, wi' mony a thump, upon the washing day.
> For it's thump, thump, scold, scold, thump, thump away,
> The deil a bit o' comfort there's upon the washing day.

The next song I quote from illustrates the merits of a good wife:—

> He that gets a gude, gude wife,
>   Gets gear eneuch, gets gear eneuch,
> An' he that gets an ill, ill wife,
>   Gets care eneuch, gets care eneuch.

> A man may spend and hae money to lend,
>   If his wife be ocht, if his wife be ocht,
> But a man may spare and aye be bare,
>   If his wife be nocht, if his wife be nocht.

On the whole the wife of the average farm servant escapes the lash of the local poetaster more easily than the unmarried servant girl does:—

> When schoolin' is over to service she goes,
>   For the greed o' high wages as you may suppose,
> And the first of it goes for a white muslin goon,
>   And a hat that would keep the munelicht frae a toon.
> And noo she's rigged oot like a ship in full sail,
>   Wi' six, seven flounces abune her goon-tail,
> And the very first Sunday the buckle goes on,
>   Says Jock to his neighbour, losh, wha is she yon?
> Wi' my tiddy, fu' liddy, fu' liddy fu' e'e.

The old farm servant, who has grown grey in his master's service, enquires of his younger colleague:—

> What think ye o' oor lassies noo,
>   Wi' their bicycles sae braw, man?
> It wasna sae in their mither's day,
>   When shank's mare did it a', man.

If the servant maid does not escape criticism from the rural poet, neither does her mistress. One guid-wife is made to express herself in disgust, in the following words:—

> It is a most disgraceful thing,
>   It wad provoke a saunt,
> To see a' the servant girls wi' lads.
>   When the gentle anes maun want.
> Providence has acted wrang
>   Sic pleasure for to gie
> To ony servant lad or lass
>   Just workin' for a fee.

The eldest daughter of an Aberdeenshire farmer was known as the maiden, thus the maiden of Gushetneuk, and she held a higher status than her sisters did, and although as a general rule, she was on good terms with her father's men-servants, she sometimes came in for a slating:—

> At the kirk on Sunday she wears a white veil,
>   An' a yard o' her goon ahin her does trail;
> An' her hair is tied up like my auld horse's tail,
>   To charm the lads o' the corner.

The treatment of the mistress and daughter is mild in comparison with that of the farmer himself. In a well-known bothy-song, entitled "The Weary Farmers," there occurs the following severe criticism:—

> They'll tip you on the shoulder
> And speir gin ye're to fee:
> And they'll tell ye a fine story.
> That's every word a lee;
>
> They'll tak' ye to an alehouse
> And gie ye some sma' beer:
> And they'll tak' a drap unto themsel's
> Till they get better cheer.
>
> And when the bargain's ended
> They'll toll ye out twa shillin's,
> And grunt and say that siller's scarce—
> The set o' leein' villains.
>
> Wi' cauld kail and tatties,
> They feed ye up like pigs,
> While they sit at their tea and toast,
> Or ride into their gigs.

In another popular bothy-song we have a similar description of the farmer:—

> Dinna gang to the Barns if ye want to dae weel.
> A' the days o' your life, ye ne'er saw sic a chiel;
> He'll treat you to a breakfast o' buttermilk an' meal.
> Wi' a drink o' sour ale in the mornin'.

After all this severe criticism one would have liked to hear the farmer's opinion of the average farm-servant, but in the case of the farmer poet it is his landlord that he has a grievance against:—

> Cauld blaws the win' owre the Knock and the Bin;
> A' the earth is asleep in its blanket o' snaw;
> I ance had a hame I could aye ca' my ain,
> But the laird and his factor have turned me awa'.
>
> My wife she grat sair, an' it whitened her hair,
> When forced frae the craft we had laboured sae lang,
> But her soul is at rest in the land o' the blest,
> And her body is laid where the richest maun gang.

For a time the feeling of injustice rankled sore in the hearts of the smaller Scottish farmers and crofters:—

> For if we but shoot but a hare or a muircock,
> Or mak' but a bushel or twa of our bere,
> The gauger or gamekeeper they come to hear o't,
> They're on wi' a vengeance ye then may be sh'er.
>
> And then we are dragged to the courts they ca' justice,
> But justice I'm sure is foreign to them;
> For judge hoo they like, they aye get the best o't,
> The puir man aye maun be put in the blame.

In the north-east of Scotland, half a century ago, there was a feeling amongst the people that the scales of justice were not very evenly balanced, the general opinion being that when there was litigation between the farmer and his landlord, the latter nearly always got the best of it. Whereas, when there was a dispute between a farmer and one of his servants, the former was generally successful in the Law Courts.

Only a few years ago I noticed in a north country newspaper, in a report of criminal trials in a Sheriff Court, two men, who were convicted of poaching, were each fined in forty shillings with expenses in addition. At the same court, on the same day, a man convicted of stealing a number of hens from a farmer's fowl-house got off with a fine of fifteen shillings. Comment in such cases is needless. They speak for themselves.

Even when he has found a prosperous home in a new country, such as America or Australia, the Scottish crofter still sighs for his lost home in the Highlands:—

> In the dreams o' the nicht the peat-reek I smell,
> In fancy I see the sweet nodding blue-bell,
> The bloom o' the heather, and I hear the wild bee;
> But the Hielands o' Scotland nae mair I shall see.

As the Canadian boat song puts it:—

> Fair these green meads, these hoary woods are grand,
> But we are exiles from our fatherland.

Referring to the love songs of the farm-servants in the counties of Aberdeen, Banff, and Moray, my friend, the late Gavin Greig, in a note to one of the songs in his *Folk-Songs of the North-East*, says:—

" The folk-songist of these parts is not a fervid lover, and if he feels the tender passion he does not care to be too frank about it. While he may in the ordinary affairs of life be rather confident, and sometimes aggressive, when he enters the domain of the feelings he begins to be somewhat reticent."

While agreeing with Mr. Greig, in a general way, I am still of opinion that many of the farm servants' love songs are of real merit, and lack not the expression of the finer feelings in choice language.

The following verses from well known bothy-songs are, in my opinion, fairly expressive. In the first verse, the rustic lover describes his sweetheart as follows:—

> Queen Mary on her Scottish throne
> Was never half so fair,
> As round her brow hang mony a curl
> And lock o' raven hair;
> Her cheeks were like the roses
> Below her rolling e'e,
> And aye she sighed for Sinnahard,
> And fair Drummallochie.

From another song I cull an example of a similar kind:—

> My Peggie she's fair, my Peggie she's fine,
> Her cheeks are like lilies all dipped in the wine;
> Her eyes, how they sparkle, how brightly they shine,
> Like the stars on a fine frosty morning.

Unlike the lyric poet, who writes for the drawing-room and the concert hall, the ploughman poet seldom describes his sweetheart as having cherry lips, lily hands, a mouth like a rose-bud, a complexion like a peach, and breath fragrant as the honeysuckle. He is much more honest and straight forward. The following may be taken as good examples of the ploughman's love lilts:—

> My life's sweetest treasure, my ain charming lassie,
> To you I'll be ever devoted and true;
> The heart that is beating so fast in this bosom
> Is a heart that could never love ony but you.
>
> The ox may hang in the plough, love,
> The cow may drown in the mire,
> But the laddie will never want his riches
> That marries his heart's desire.
>
> Love for love is the bargain for me,
> And the wee cot hoose to haud me;
> And the warld before me to win my bread,
> And to share wi' my ploughman laddie.*

Whilst it must be confessed that the efforts of the folk-song writers do not appear, in many cases, to have been particularly happy in giving full expression to love sentiments, some of the many effusions concerning the jilted lover and the false lover "hit the nail on the head." In one ditty, entitled "Mormand Braes," which is still a great favourite in the farm kitchens and bothies in the north-eastern counties, the deserted heroine,

* This verse was touched up by Burns and was used by him in his version of the "Collier Laddie."

made of too stern material to give way to grief, commendably
shows her resolution in the following stanzas:—

> O, I'll put on the gown o' green,
>   It's a forsaken token,
> And that will let the young men know
>   That the bands o' love are broken.
>
> There's as good fish into the sea
>   As ever yet was taken;
> I'll cast my line and try again,
>   I'm only ance forsaken.

There is nothing of " I'll lay me doun and dee feeling " about
that young woman.

Another well known bothy-song shows the deserted lover, a
woman, in a forgiving mood, which is seldom the case where
the fair sex is concerned:—

> Another maid now fills your arms,
>   Those arms which once were mine;
> And she enjoys the favours now,
>   That I did monys the time.
> Oh! may she flourish in your arms,
>   And happy may she be,
> For she's innocent and ignorant
>   Of what she's done to me.

In the next song from which I quote, the victim, also a
woman, gives expression to her feelings in so vindictive a spirit
as to almost make a person shiver:—

> Tomorrow is my love's wedding day,
>   Mony wonders do we see;
> Tomorrow is my love's wedding day,
>   And a dowie day to me.
>
> The minister that marries my bonnie love,
>   O red-mad may he run,
> And the kirk that my love's kirkit in.
>   In a red lowe may she burn.

Then comes the final curse on the newly married couple:—

> Mony bonnie bairns may they hae,
>   And ill, ill may they thrive,
> And may a funeral leave their house
>   Every year till they bury five.
>
> For the sinnerin' o' me and my bonnie love,
>   For the sinnerin' o' him and me;
> I wish that their heids may ne'er be hale
>   That sinnert him and me.

The next song depicts the deserted girl in a state of despair:—

> Well, since he's gane, joy gang wi' him,
> It's ne'er be he shall gar me complain,
> I'll cheer up my heart, and I'll get anither,
> I'll never lay a' my love upon ane.
>
> I couldna get sleepin' yestreen for weepin',
> The tears ran doun like showers o' rain,
> An' had I nae got greetin' my heart would hae broken,
> And oh, but love's a tormenting thing.

Then we have the girl who is wearying for the right man to come along, but is not prepared to take any one that asks her:—

> O! but I'm weary, weary, weary,
> O! but I'm weary, nicht and day,
> O, mither gie me the man
> Will tak' this weariness away.
>
> O, daughter dear, wad ye marry a man
> Wha mak's his living by the plough?
> "O! no, mither," she says,
> "The ploughman's wife has much to do."

The mother goes over all the various tradesmen she can think of and finally asks:—

> O, daughter dear, wad ye marry a man
> Wha mak's his living by the pen?
> "O! yes, mither," she says,
> "I dearly love young gentlemen."

But it is in giving advice as to choosing a wife or a husband, that the folk-song writers excel themselves:—

> Young women they are fickle things,
> When young men gang to woo;
> The more you follow after them,
> The more they fly from you;
> But dinna follow after them,
> Nor dinna them pursue,
> Gie them the gouns o' green to wear,
> And then they'll follow you.

The following verse from a song, which for want of a better name is known as "The Toom Wa's," is excellent in its way:—

> Dinna tak' ane that is owre auld,
> Or than wi' her ye may catch cauld;
> And dinna tak' ane that is owre young,
> Or she may deeve ye wi' her tongue;
> Dinna tak' ane for the sake o' her siller,
> Gin that be the thing that's drawin' ye till her;
> And dinna tak' ane that's fond o' braws,
> She'll never dae weel in yon toom wa's.

The next verses give advice to young women as to the choosing of husbands:—

> Come a' ye maids o' quality,
>   And a' ye that are bonnie,
> Don't lay your love on an auld man
>   For the sake o' gowd or money;
> But lay it on a beardless youth
>   Wi' nae hair on his chin,
> And he's the lad will learn you
>   The courting to begin.

Our national poet, Burns, tried his hand at giving advice on the same subject:—

> Some will spend and some will spare,
>   And wilfu' folk maun hae their will;
> Syne as ye brew, my maiden fair,
>   Keep mind that ye maun drink the yill. (ale)

But the bothy poet is just as expressive when he wrote:—

> We'll set her in a reekie hoose.
>   And lat her greet her fill;
> And say, "Lassie, gin ye'd brew'd it weel,
>   Ye'd had the better yill."

The humours of country courtship have never, perhaps, been more graphically set forth than in the bothy songs known as " The Bonnie Wee Window " and " Kissing in the Dark." In the former the lover, to get a parting kiss from his sweetheart, pushes his head through a broken pane in a window of her grandmother's cottage, and is unable to withdraw it again:—

> A kiss Johnny got, and sweet was the smack,
>   But for his dear life he couldna get his head back,
> He ruggit, he tuggit, he bawled, and he curst,
>   Till Nell's sides wi' lauchin' were baith like to burst
>
>   At his head in the window,
>   The sweet little window,
>   The bonniest window
>   That ever ye saw.

In " Kissing in the Dark," the rustic lover mistakes his sweetheart's mother for herself, and hugs and kisses the old woman before he discovers his mistake:—

> She ruggit, and she tuggit, and she tried to get awa,
> But I held her aye the closer, and I gave ither twa,
> Then oot she burst a-lauchin', says—" This is awfa' wark,
> To touzle an aul' body, and to kiss her in the dark."

The bothy poet is perhaps at his best when dealing with the affairs of his daily life in a humoursome manner, but when dealing with the life of other tradesmen his language is

sometimes extravagant. A good example of this is to be found
in a song entitled " The Souters' Feast ":—

> Souters they cam' hine frae Perth,
>   Tanteerie orum,
> And souters cam' frae 'neath the earth,
>   The eedle, and the orum;
> Souters cam' frae Peterhead,
>   Tanteerie orum,
> Wi' fent a tooth in a' their heid,
>   The eedle and the orum,
>   Thee-a-noddle, thee-a-num,
>   The eedle and the orum.

Harvest songs were a special class of bothy-song, and many of
them were only of local interest, but " The Band o' Shearers,"
which is one of the oldest and best of its kind, was known in
every county in Scotland. It is a true folk-song, and there are
many variants of it. It belongs to the days of the shearing-
hook:—

> Autumn comes wi' heather bells,
> And bonnie ower yon mountain dells,
> Wi' yellow corn ripe Lothian vales
> Are ready for the shearing.
>   So, bonnie lassie, will ye gang,
>   And shear wi' me the hale day lang,
>   And love will cheer us as we gang
>   To join yon band o' shearers.
>
> For blythe and lichtsome is the toil,
> Your bonnie e'en my care beguile;
> We'll meet together 'yont the style,
>   And join yon band o' shearers.
>
> And when the harvest days are done,
> And slowly sets yon wintry sun,
> Ye'll be my ain till life is run,
>   Nae mair to join the shearers.

The reaping scythe was introduced into the North of Scotland by William Anderson, farmer, Hatton of Fintray,
Aberdeenshire, in 1810, but the old shearing hook was not quite
superseded by the scythe for many years afterwards. The
shearing was mostly done by women. The value of a day's
work was calculated by the number of thraives cut. A thraive
consisted of two stooks of twelve sheaves each. To cut seven
or eight thraives was considered a good day's work for a shearer.

After the introduction of the scythe, the best men cut the
corn, the women gathered it into sheaves, and made the bands,
while younger men, as a rule, bound and stooked the sheaves.
The bandster could claim a kiss from the gatherer for each band
whose knot slipped in the binding, and a well known Aberdeenshire author remarks that where both were young, and the girl

fair to look upon, such forfeits occurred with amazing rapidity.

This is depicted in the following verses from the same author's poetical works:—

> The saft winds played springs in the barley,
>   And sweet was the swish of the scythe,
> And never a lassie that gather't
>   Had bandster sae strappin' and blythe;
> Sae herty he bun' and he stookit,
>   And sairly my bands he wad try;
> And though sicker I made them, yet aften
>   I wished in my hert they wad fly.
>
> Then oh! to be ance mair a lassie,
>   And hairstin' sae lichtsome and blythe,
> And liftin' the gowd-tappit corn
>   Frae aff o' the neb o' the scythe;
> And oh! to be makin' a slip knot,
>   And Donal' my bandster to be,
> Ae hairst on the banks o' the Bogie
>   Was worth a' my lifetime to me.

Amongst the harvest songs peculiar to the counties of Aberdeen, Banff, and Moray, the chief favourites were " The Bogend Hairst," which, under the title of " Linten Lourin," has been harmonised and is printed in *The Songs of the North*; " The Hairst o' Rettie," and " The Lothian Hairst." The last, according to tradition, was written about seventy years ago by a Highland Lassie, one of a band of Deeside harvesters to the Lothians, where grain cutting began several weeks earlier than in the north-east.

Upwards of half a century ago it was usual for harvest contractors to visit the Lothians during the summer, and undertake to cut, gather, and stook grain crops at an arranged price per acre. The contractor, or maister as he was called by the workers, engaged a foreman, who was held responsible by the contractor for carrying out the various contracts. The foreman was in every case expected to act like " Logan " in the song, and to see that the male reapers visiting their female co-workers at their bothies terminated their visits at a given hour. The rules referred to in the song are all against the charges made some years ago by a writer, who claimed that in the reaping-hook days, and later in the days of the scythe, bands of workers of both sexes occupied bothies indiscriminately. A few verses of the song will suffice to prove my case:—

> On August twelfth frae Aberdeen,
>   We sailed upon the Prince,
> And safe arrived at Clifford's fields,
>   The harvest to commence.

INTRODUCTION. 17

For sax lang weeks the country roun',
   Frae toon to toon we went,
And I took richt weel wi' the Lothian fare,
   And aye was weel content.

Oor maister, William Mathieson,
   Frae sweet Deeside he came;
Oor foreman cam' frae the same place,
   And Logan was his name.

I followed Logan on the point
   Sae weel's he laid it doon,
And sae boldly as he led oor squad
   Ower mony's the thrissly toon.

My mate and I could get nae chance,
   For Logan's watchful eye,
And wi' the lads we got nae sport,
   For Logan was so sly.

He cleared oor bothy every nicht
   Before he went to sleep,
And he never left behind him one,
   But strict his rules did keep.

When we come to Aberdeen,
   He weel deserves a spree,
For herding o' us a' sae weel,
   Frae the Lothian lads we're free.

The first innovation upon the old shearing hook was the scythe; then, in the late " sixties " and the early " seventies " of the last century, came the reaping machine which swept away scythes and shearing hooks never to return. The last decade of the nineteenth century saw self-binding machines on all large farms.

There is little fun now on the harvest rig—four men and two self binders will handle a crop which took all the farm hands, and a band of specially hired helpers to take off. So clyacks. kirns, and harvest home festivals have passed into the limbo of forgotten things.

In connection with the " Lothian Hairsts " the following excerpt from the *Glasgow Evening Times* newspaper of 29th March, 1923, is interesting:—

" The death has taken place at Tininver, Dufftown, Banff-shire, of Mr. John Gordon, who on February 2nd, celebrated his 99th birthday. A native of the parish of Grange, Banff-shire, he entered farm service at an early age, and when a young man would walk to Aberdeen and proceed by boat to Leith to engage in the Lothian Harvests. He had been for many years manager of farms in Banffshire."

This appears to have been the last of the Lothian harvesters,
who used to sing:—

> We'll fill a glass and drink it roun',
> Before the boat will start,
> And may we safely reach the shore,
> And all in friendship part.

Another topic tolerably popular with bothy rhymsters, was
the open herding of cattle and sheep existing before the fencing
period, which did not begin in many parts of Scotland till the
passing of the Education Act of 1872.   Prior to that date there
were employed, on most farms, a herd, and in some cases two.   In
some cases a girl was employed to herd the cows, while a boy
looked after the rest of the cattle, thus:—

> When wee Jeanie used to be keeping the kye,
> O, wha was so happy as Jeanie and I?
> We gaed doon to the burnie on yon hallow green,
> And puddled till we were baith wet to the e'en.

The farmer's daughter sometimes herded her father's cows and
courted her sweetheart at the same time, as will be seen from the
following verses:—

> Once on a fine summer's evening,
> A young couple I did spy,
> 'Twas a young man and a maiden—
> A-courting amang the kye.

> And aye as he kissed and caressed her,
> An aye as he bade her comply,
> "Bonnie lassie, think o' your sweetheart,
> An' leave aff keeping the kye."

The herding song, which has been harmonised, and printed in
the second volume of *The Songs of the North*, is a fine example
of this class of lyric.

The herd boy carried a club, having engraved thereon a
mystic figure which somewhat resembled a fancy knot, and was
known as the Meltie-Bow.   This figure, it was understood, was
able to prevent the club from doing a serious injury to an animal
if it by chance was struck on a vital part.   The following
characters, known as Jocky and his Owsen, were cut in notches
on the club, viz.:—II I III V II II IV I I III X II II,
followed by a figure supposed to represent Jocky himself.

This is how the notches were read by the initiated.   Twa
afore ane, three afore five, first twa and syne twa, then four
comes belyve, noo ane and then ane, and three at a cast, double
ane, and twice twa and Jocky comes at last.

In one of the many songs relating to the life of a herd, an old man looks back, with regret, to his young days when he followed the occupation of a herd laddie: —

> O for the innocent days I hae seen,
> When a' my young thoughts they were happy and keen;
> When up in the morning I raise frae my bed,
> An' I got my full sarin o' milk and o' bread.
>
> Syne awa to the fauld an' I drove out my nowt,
> Sae merrily as they gaed friskin' about;
> They licked their fat sides as they fed on the sward,
> When I led the life of a jovial young herd.

Another herd's song shows the other side of the picture: —

> I weary fu' sair, and the days appear lang,
> When I min' o' the playmates that I ran amang;
> And wi' them fu' sunner again I wad be,
> Than herdin' thae kye on this bleak whinny lea.
>
> The claes I hae on me are a' worn dune,
> They're maist as far through as my stockin's and shune
> An' ae leg o' my breekies is aff at the knee,
> An' can bring me nae bield on this bleak whinny lea.
>
> The folk that I'm servin' are scrimpin' an' bare,
> An' there's few o' their dainties that come to my share,
> But the grun' o' my stamack, that aften I feel,
> Gars their auld mouldy bannocks aye taste unco weel.

Not only were there female cow-herds, but there were also female shepherds. "The Broom of the Cowden Knowes," a well known Scottish folk-song, depicts a pastoral love scene, in which the shepherdess laments the absence of her lover. This song appears in Herd's collection of Scottish song, printed in 1769, and under the title of "The Lovely Northern Lass," it was printed in London as a Scotch Ballad as far back as 1621.

There is a considerable number of Jacobite songs belonging to Aberdeenshire, which are never heard except in the bothies and the farm-kitchens of the north-east. Among others may be mentioned "The Muir of Culloden": —

> The Gordons, MacGregors, and the MacDonalds,
> The Camerons, MacPhersons, and the Clan-Ronalds,
> Rushed fierce to the charge, where down thousands were trodden,
> Determined to conquer or die at Culloden.
>
> Nae mair the pipes play Prince Charlie a-comin',
> Nae mair they hurrah, and the Southrons are runnin'.
> And noo for our Prince ilka Scotch heart is throbbin',
> But cauld lie our lads on the Muir o' Culloden.

The "Highland Maid," one of the most pathetic of our Jacobite songs, I have never heard sung except in the farm-kitchens of Aberdeen, Banff, and Moray.   In no other part of the country was the Jacobite spirit so strong.   It was in Aberdeenshire that the Earl of Mar raised the Old Pretender's standard in 1715.

> The standard on the braes o' Mar,
>   Is up and streaming rarely.

It was at Peterhead, in the same county, that the Old Pretender himself landed some months later.   It was also in Aberdeenshire that Lord Gordon, son of the Marquis of Huntly, disbanded the Jacobite army, after the Old Pretender and the Earl of Mar had fled to the Continent.   To this period belongs the Aberdeenshire mustering song known locally as "The Trooper and the Maid."

> The trumpet sounds at Burreldales,
>   Says, "man and horse mak' ready,"
> The drums do beat on Staneman Hill,
>   "Lads, leave your mam' and daddy; "
> The pipes do play at Cromlet Banks—
>   "Lads, leave the Lews o' Fyvie,"
> The trooper to the fair maid said—
>   "O lassie, I maun lea' you."

Writing of the rebellion of 1745, an Aberdeenshire author describes "Bonnie Prince Charlie" as the idol of Jacobite love and devotion, and it is an historic fact that in no other county did the Stuart cause find such favour with the common people.

While the Prince's army was lying at Glasgow Green during Christmas week, 1745, Lord Lewis Gordon at the head of a force, composed chiefly of young farmers and farm-servants from the Gordon estates of Aberdeen, Banff, and Moray, defeated MacLeod of MacLeod at the Battle of Inverurie, on the banks of the River Don.   MacLeod's army consisted of 450 of his own clan and 200 of the clan Munro.   MacLeod had 40 men killed and 60 made prisoners, including his famous piper, MacCrimmon.   He had a narrow escape from being captured himself.   He lost his targe, and the bridle was torn off his horse. A great many of his clansmen were wounded.   The fight is commemorated by a long ballad, three verses of which will suffice:—

> The godless Whigs wi' their intrigues,
>   Together did convene, man,
> At Inverurie, on the Riggs,
>   On Thursday afterneen, man.

> MacLeod cam' doun frae Inverness,
>   Wi' a' his Clan and mair, man,
> The loyal Gordons to supress,
>   And tirr their hurdies bare, man,
>
> The second chieftain of Munros
>   Cam' 'cross the Moray Firth, man,
> But ye shall hear before ye go,
>   The Gordons marred their mirth, man.

Four Aberdeenshire regiments fought for the Prince at Culloden. They were respectively commanded by Gordon of Avochy, Moir of Stoneywood, Gordon of Glenbuchat, and Farquharson of Monaltrie, who is described by Jacobite writers as "Bonnie Monaltrie wi' the gowden locks," owing to the colour of his hair. Besides these foot regiments there was a troop of horse commanded by Forbes of Pitsligo, who has been described as the last of the Scottish Cavaliers.

If the Scottish peasant is anything, he is a patriot, and the songs and ballads relating to his country's battles have always been favourites with him. Almost every battle fought in Scotland from Stirling Bridge to Culloden has been commemorated in song. This country's intervention in European politics, and more particularly its participation in the German wars, commenced with the accession of the Houses of Orange and Hanover to the throne of Great Britain. As late as the beginning of the last century, "The Wars of Germany" were a favourite theme with Scottish lyric poets. Allan Cunningham gave us a song in which occurs the following verse:—

> Oh! wae be to the cruel wars,
>   That ever they began,
> For they have swept my native Isle
>   Of mony a pretty man;
> For first they took my brethren twain,
>   Then wiled my love frae me;
> Woe, woe unto the cruel wars
>   Of low Germanie.

Hector M'Neil wrote:—

> My luve's in Germanie,
>   Send him hame, send him hame.

And Motherwell's "Wars of Germanie" is described as his lyric masterpiece:—

> O' wae to the orders that marched my luve awa',
> And wae be to the cruel cause that gars my tears down fa',
> And wae be to the bludy wars in Hie Germanie,
> For they hae taen my luve and left a broken heart to me.

These songs can scarcely be classed as folk-songs, being
individual and not communal productions, but the songs relating
to the Napoleonic Wars, commencing with the Battle of Aboukir
in 1801, and finishing with Waterloo in 1815, are genuine
bothy-songs, and have never been sung in the drawing-room or
the concert hall. Sir Robert Abercrombie's victory at Aboukir
is commemorated by a song, entitled "The Banks o' the Nile,"
which depicts the parting scene between a soldier and his sweetheart. The girl proposes to enlist and accompany her lover to
Egypt, and he naturally objects to the proposal:—

> I'll put on my velveteens, and go along with you,
> I'll volunteer my services, and go to Egypt too,
> I'll fight beneath your banner, love, kind fortune yet may smile,
> And I'll be your loyal comrade on the banks o' the Nile.
>
> Your waist is rather slender, your complexion is too fine,
> Your constitution is too weak to stand the hot campaign;
> The sultry suns o' Egypt your precious health would spoil,
> And the hot sandy deserts on the banks o' the Nile.

The storming of Fort St. Michael at Burgos inspired the
writing of the pathetic ballad of "Young Jamie Foyers," which
has been sung in almost every feeing market in the country,
while a ballad commemorating Sir Thomas Graham's victory at
Barossa, on 5th March, 1811, is still to be heard in the farm
kitchens of Buchan and Moray. In one of the verses of this
ballad there is a gibe at our then allies, the Spanish:—

> The Spaniards said they'd take the front,
>   Their country for to free,
> And let bold Britain take the rear.
>   That glorious day to see;
> But when Barossa's plains appeared.
>   We never saw them more,
> Their columns drew behind a wood,
>   Along some hidden shore.

In a letter from a soldier at the front to his sweetheart at
home, in a song entitled "Nairn's River Banks," there is given
a narrative of the Spanish War:—

> Like midges in the summer sun,
>   The French around us lie,
> But with our British bayonets,
>   We'll make them fight or fly,
> We'll make them fight or fly, my love,
>   And drive them out of Spain,
> That wars may cease, and bring us peace,
>   And send us home again

There were a great many popular bothy songs relating to begging half a century ago, and this is probably accounted for by the fact that in the olden time the beggar was a member of a privileged class, and had a recognised place in our social system. The King patronised him, and went the length of creating an aristocratic order of beggars, known as Blue-Gowns, or King's Bedeman. As the means of identification, the members of this class were supplied with a brass or pewter badge, on which was engraved the Scottish Thistle, surmounted by a Crown. On the left of the crown was the initial of the reigning Sovereign, and on the right the letter " R " for Rex or King. The beggar's name, with the words " PASS AND REPASS " was also engraved on the badge. In the absence of newspapers, the Blue-Gown was a recognised carrier of news, consequently he was a welcome visitor, and sure of a hearty greeting from the farmers' wives and daughters:—

> When beggars o' the gangrel corps.
> Are driven from the hallan doors,
> The gude-wife cries, "Come ye in ower,
> Auld Eddie Ochiltree."
>
> He tells wha's bridal's to be neist,
> An' wha has little time to waste,
> An' wha's to stan' afore the priest,
> Auld Eddie Ochiltree.

King James V. of Scotland went about the country disguised as a beggar, and he is given the credit of having written two of our best-known begging songs, viz.:—" The Jolly Beggar," and " The Gaberlunzie Man." At several periods in the history of our country, stern measures had to be taken to suppress begging and vagrancy. At the end of the seventeenth and the beginning of the eighteenth centuries, following upon the civil and religious wars, vagrancy seems to have reached its height. According to Fletcher of Saltoun, about one-tenth of the population of Scotland, at that period, lived by begging and sorning. Magistrates of Burghs and Kirk Sessions of country parishes issued badges to their own poor. Persons found begging without having such badges were imprisoned, and under an Act of the Scottish Parliament of 1606, they could be seized and compelled to work in the coal mines. Notwithstanding those laws, begging continued to be popular, as a profession, right down to the establishment of a regular police force.

> O' a' the trades that I do ken,
> The begging is the best,
> For when a beggar's weary,
> He can sit down and rest.

It was, however, at village and country weddings that the professional beggar made his harvest:—

> If there's a wedding in the town,
>   I'll airt me to be there,
> And pour my kindest benison
>   Upon the winsome pair;
> And some will give me breid and beef,
>   And some will give me cheese,
> And I'll slip out amang the folk
>   And gather bawbees.
>
>   To the begging we will go, etc.

As a rule, the country folks were kind to the gangrel:—

> The beggar's bed was made at e'en
>   Wi' clean pea stra',
> And in ahint the ha' door,
>   And there the beggar lay.

According to several of our bothy songs, it was a practice among gentlemen, in the olden time, when on the lookout for a suitable wife, to disguise themselves as beggars, and court their sweethearts in that disguise:—

> It's ye'll cast aff your robes o' red,
> And ye'll put on a beggar's weed,
> And ye'll follow me, and ye'll beg your breid,
>   And be a beggar's dawtie.

In answer to this request the girl replies:—

> I love you just as manifold
> As Jesse loved the cups of gold,
> And as Jacob loved Rachel of old,
>   And I'll be a beggar's dawtie.

The belief in the supernatural still lingers in the straths and glens of the north-east of Scotland, and some of the old folk will tell in confidence that they have heard the fairy music at the dead of night, about lone paths and mystic places, where the shining circles are traced on the grass by the feet of the little people. The abduction of Sir John Gordon, a scion of the great house of Gordon, by the Fairy Queen, is the subject of one of the best known romantic ballads common in Aberdeenshire. Sir John, while hunting in the forest, becomes fatigued, lies down and falls asleep, under the elfin-tree. On waking he finds the Elfin Queen bending over him, and at first mistakes her for the "Virgin Mary." She tempts him to kiss her, which he does,

and he is immediately brought under her spell.   Then we have
a description of their journey to Fairyland:—

> And they rode on, and further on,
>   Till it was mirk, mirk nicht,
> And horrid vipers round them twined,
>   And hissed wi' a' their micht.

> And they rode on and further on,
>   Through plains fu' o' dead men's banes,
> And horrid hags wi' ravenous claws,
>   Picked the banes o' unchristened weans.

> What think ye, think ye now, Sir John,
>   O' the kiss ye gae to me?
> Fu' weel I see ye dearly rue
>   The love that blin's the e'e.

Before leaving the subject of ballads as distinguished from
folk-song, and the border line between them is a very narrow
one, as they both as a general rule tell a story, I may mention
that in selecting specimens for this collection I have simply
noted down those which are still being sung in the bothies and
farm kitchens, and have refrained from copying from collections
already in print.   Aberdeenshire has been a fruitful field for the
ballad hunter.   During the past century and a half many
collections have been made.   Amongst the principal collectors
may be mentioned Miss Annie Gordon, daughter of Professor
Gordon, King's College, Aberdeen, who afterwards was known
as Mrs. Brown of Falkland.   Many of the ballads gleaned by
this lady were used by Sir Walter Scott in his *Border
Minstrelsy*, and by Jamieson in his collection of Scottish
ballads.   After Miss Gordon came Peter Buchan, and then Dean
Christie, and lately the late Gavin Greig did a great work,
principally in the Buchan district, where he collected hundreds
of ballads, folk-songs, and folk-melodies, many of which had
not been previously published.

In conclusion I would point out, that the attention of the
cultured and learned classes has been drawn to our Scottish folk-
songs and folk-airs, and they are being systematically collected,
edited, and printed, and in a humble way I have assisted in this
interesting work.   The question is, what is to be the result of all
this searching and collecting?   The wild flowers, that is our
folk-songs and ballads, have been gathered and issued in book
form for the information of the public.   Will they live to
entertain our children and our grand-children, as they did our
forefathers, or will they pine and die?   We recognise that many

of them may, after being transplanted from their native soil, linger for a time, and then die and be forgotten. But the hope and justification of those of us who have taken an interest in the matter is that many of the songs in this, and other collections of a similar kind, will live to gladden the hearts of generations yet unborn, and teach them something of the lives and customs of their countrymen of past generations, which cannot be learned from histories and school books.

For some of the old and familiar melodies which appear in this work, and many of them are in print for the first time, I am indebted to Mr. James B. Allan, A.L.C.M., L.T.S.C., music teacher, Newlands, Glasgow; and the late Mr. Gavin Greig, M.A., New Deer, Aberdeenshire. My grateful thanks are accorded to Mr. Allan for his help in arranging the melodies to suit the words of the various songs.

JOHN ORD.

Glasgow, 1925.

PART I.

(a) **Songs relating to Love, Courtship, Marriage and Domestic Life**

(b) **Songs of the Forsaken and the Jilted**

PART I.

(a) Songs relating to Love, Courtship, Marriage, and Domestic Life.

THE BANKS O' DEVERON WATER.

As I went out to take the air,
  'Twas on the banks o' Deveron Water;
I chose a maid to be my love,
  Were it my fortune for to get her.

Her equal's not on Deveronside,
  Nor any part o' Gadie Water;
I dinna care what may betide
  In any way, if I could get her.

She's of a genteel middle size,
  Her body's always neat and slender;
Her lips are sweet as honey pear,
  To which I am an oft pretender.

When I look to her weel-faur'd face,
  Her lily hands and lovely fingers;
I clasp her in my arms twa,
  Saying, " Wae's my heart that we maun sinder."

Her cheeks are like the crimson rose,
  Her eyes like stars when brightly shining;
She is the girl I dearly love,
  And I've wish'd lang out o' this pining.

She has possession of my heart,
  The keys thereof she has a-keeping;
She is the girl whom I admire,
  I wish us both a joyful meeting.

Her cheeks are like the crimson rose,
  Her countenance an admiration;
I could not had a better choice
  If I had searched o'er all the nation.

I wonder much at our young men,
  That change their loves and grow so fickle;
I would not gie my ain true love
  For Crœsus' rents, nor thrice as muckle.

Tho' I had a' King Crœsus' rents,
  And all possessed by Alexander;
I'd gie it all, and ten times mair,
  For ae poor nicht to be beside her.

Ye'll bring me here a pint o' wine,
  A server and a silver tassie,
That I may drink before I gang
  A health to my ain bonnie lassie.

Ye powers above, increase her love,
  That such a prize I may inherit;
To gain her love is all I crave,
  And after that we shall be married.

The above song was written in 1636 by Alexander Lesley, of Eden, Deveronside, Aberdeenshire. The lady immortalised in the song was a Miss Helen Christie.

It is interesting to note that Burns copied the tenth verse of Lesley's song for the opening lines of his well-known song:—

  Go bring to me a pint of wine,
    And fill it in a silver tassie.

I have succeeded in recovering the original air to which the song was sung, and Mr. J. B. Allan, A.L.C.M., Glasgow, has kindly arranged it for me.

THE RIGS O' RYE.

'TWAS in the month o' sweet July,
Before the sun had pierced the sky;
'Twas in between twa rigs o' rye
    That I heard twa lovers talking.

The lad said, " Love, I must away,
I've got no longer time to stay;
But I've got a word or two to say,
    If ye've got time to tarry.

" Your father of you takes great care,
Your mother combs down your yellow hair;
And your sisters say ye will get nae share,
    Gin ye gang wi' me, a stranger."

" Let my father fret and my mother frown,
My sisters' words I do disown;
Though they a' were deid and below the groun',
    I'd gang wi' you, a stranger."

" Oh, lassie, lassie, your fortune's sma',
And maybe it will be nane ata';
Yer nae a match for me ava',
    Lay ye yer love on some ither."

The lassie's courage began to fail,
Her red, rosy cheeks grew wan and pale,
And her tears cam' trickling down like hail,
    Or a heavy shower in summer.

He took his handkerchief, linen fine,
He dried her tears, and he kissed her syne;
Says, " Dry up your tears, love, ye shall be mine,
    I said it a' to try you."

He, being a boy of courage bold,
A boy that scarce was nineteen years old;
He made the hills and the valleys roar,
   And he's ta'en his bonnie lassie wi' him.

This couple they've got married noo,
And they've got bairnies one or two;
And they live in Brechin the winter thro',
   And in Montrose in summer.

    This fine old country song appears to have been missed by all the well-known collectors. I sent a copy of it to the late Robert Ford, but by the time it reached him his *Vagabond Songs* were in the press, so that he could not include it. The music is by Mr. J. B. Allan, organist, Glasgow, who noted it down from the singing of an ex-Aberdeenshire ploughman.

YTHANSIDE.

Music by Mr. Jas. B. Allan, A.L.C.M., Glasgow.

KEY A.   Lah is F♯.

As I cam' in by Ythanside,
Where swiftly flows the rolling tide,
A fair young maid passed by my side,
   She looked at me and smiled.
She was a maid of beauty bricht,
As ever trod the braes o' Gight;
I could hae spent the lee-lang nicht
   Wi' her on Ythanside.

I turned by back on Fyvie's bells,
And my poor heart gave many a knell,
I speirt the road to St. John's Wells
   Wi' courage stout and bold.
The maid she turned without delay,
And thus to me began to say—
"I scarcely go two miles this way,
   Young man, I'll tell ye plain.

"But gin ye gang the gate ye came,
I'll get a man to show ye hame,
Out owre yon bonnie flowery glen
   And down by Ythanside."
I thanked the maid and turned richt bold,
The flocks were driving to the fold,
And many a lively tale she told
   Just as we passed along,

Till at length we reached her father's hame;
Sae bashfully as I gaed ben,
Thinks I mysel', "I'm far frae hame,
   Although on Ythanside."
But the people a' they seemed discreet,
And ilka ane about did creep;
The auld guidwife brought ben a seat,
   And bad me to sit down.

I sat me there richt weel content,
The auld guidman for news was bent,
To court the maid was my intent,
   The truth I'll tell you plain.
While I sat there now at my ease,
They treated me to bread and cheese,
The bairnies they played roun' my knees—
   Wasn't that a blythesome sight?

But the servant lads began to spit,
And gather a' up to their fit,
Thinks I, "My lads, ye're gaun to flit,
   And a' bound for your beds."
Then up I started straight outricht,
And bade them a' a blythe guidnicht,
And speirt the road to Mains of Gight,
   To which the maid replied—

"I'll show ye by the barn door."
Judge ye gin our twa hearts were sore
To think we'd part to meet no more
    On bonnie Ythanside.
I held the fair maid by the hand,
The time was short we had to stand;
I got a kiss upon demand,
    These words to me she said—

"When you come back this road again,
It's wi' you then I will be gaun."
And I gaed whistling through the glen,
    And hame by Ythanside.
When he cam' back, 'twas in the spring,
He on her finger put a ring,
And from her hame he has her ta'en
    On bonnie Ythanside.

This couple they've got married now,
    And they've got bairnies one or two,
And as much land as keeps a cow,
    On bonnie Ythanside.

DRUMMALLOCHIE.

KEY D. *Dorian Mode.*

'Twas on a chill November night,
  When fruit and flowers were gone,
One evening as I wandered forth
  Along the banks of Don,
I overheard a fair maid,
  And sweetly thus sang she—
"My love is far frae Sinnahard
  And fair Drummallochie,"

Queen Mary on her Scottish throne
  Was never half so fair,
As round her brow hung many a curl
  And lock o' raven hair.
Her cheeks were like the roses,
  Below her rolling e'e,
And aye she sighed for Sinnahard
  And fair Drummallochie.

Says I—"My pretty, fair maid,
  Why walk ye here alone?
Lamenting for some absent one
  Upon the banks o' Don?
Come, tell the reason o' your grief,
  Come, tell it a' to me,
And why you sigh for Sinnahard
  And fair Drummallochie?"

"Young Peter was my true love's name,
  He lived on the banks o' Don;
He was as fair a young man
  As e'er the sun shone on.
But the cruel wars of Scotland
  Has ta'en my love frae me;
Nae mair we'll meet at Sinnahard
  Nor fair Drummallochie.

"Cursed be the wars o' Scotland,
  Sae cruel and severe;
They ha'e caused mony a fair maid
  To shed mony a silent tear.
They've ta'en frae them their sweethearts,
  As they hae done to me,
Nae mair to meet at Sinnahard
  Nor fair Drummallochie.

" King David had a faithful friend
  In days o' ancient strife;
He loved him as he loved his soul,
  Or as he loved his life;
Their souls were knit together
  In perfect harmony,
And sae is mine to my true love
  Though he be far frae me.

" When Jacob saw his long-lost son,
  He could describe his love;
He prayed for him a blessing
  Down from the Heavens above;
And down before my Maker's throne
  I'll ever bend my knee
For him that's far frae Sinnahard
  And fair Drummallochie.

" Amidst some gentle hopes and fears,
  Among companions gay,
May the powers above protect my love,
  And guard him night and day;
And sometimes in his manly breast
  A sob and sigh may be,
For them who sigh for Sinnahard
  And fair Drummallochie."

Says I—" My pretty, fair maid,
  If ye'll gi'e me your hand,
Upon the bonnie banks o' Don
  I hae baith house and land;
To you alone I'll gi'e them a'
  If you will be my bride,
And forsake yon bonnie laddie
  That lived upon Donside."

Says she—" Young man, your offer's fair,
  But you I must deny,
For the sake o' one young man
  I am to live and die;
And in the space of seven years
  Black shall cover me
For him that's far from Sinnahard
  And fair Drummallochie."

I turned myself right round about,
   And meant to go away,
When looking round behind me
   I heard her sob and say—
" If my true love were in this place
   I'd sworn that that was he,
But he is far frae Sinnahard
   And frae Drummallochie."

When I saw my true love weeping
   Nae langer could I stan',
But flew into her arms twa,
   Says—" Jeannie, I'm the man;
Now, for your constant true love,
   You're free from every care,
And on the bonnie banks o' Don
   We meet to part nae mair."

COURTING AMONG THE KYE.

KEY D. { :s | l :l | s :d'.t | l :- | r :m | s :s.s | m :r | d :- | }

{ :r .m | f :f | m :r | d :r | :m | l :l | s :m | r :- |- ||

ONCE on a fine summer evening
   A gay couple I did spy,
'Twas a young man and a maiden
   A-courting at the kye.

Doon by yon narrow streamlet,
   At the foot of yon excellin' brae,
Desiring that no one should hear them,
   To carry the tidings away.

They being but lately acquainted,
   And I being willing to stay,
I set myself down pretty near them
   To hear what they would say.

He spoke on courtship with courage,
    The features of love would adore,
And he spoke of the terms of marriage—
    A thing he had ne'er done before.

Ay, he kissed and caressed her,
    And ay as he bade her comply,
" Bonnie lassie, think of your sweetheart,
    And leave off keepin' the kye."

" To leave off keeping the kye, lad,
    It's a thing I'm no willin' to do;
Besides, I'm ower young a girlie
    As yet for to marry wi' you.

" I'm nae oot eighteen, lad,
    Till the twenty-seventh o' June,
And I think I'll be soon enough married
    When I am twenty-one.

" My father he is a poor man,
    He is come o' low degree,
And I canna just very well tell you
    Gin a' that he has be free.

" He hasna a cow to spare, lad,
    He's got more to serve than I,
And yet I'm a high-minded girlie,
    Although I am keepin' the kye.

But I'll moin[1] you to anither,
    She's far mair suitin' than I,
She has plenty o' bright yellow guineas,
    And plenty o' cauries[2] and kye.

" She has plenty o' gold-yellow guineas,
    But few do her envy,
And she's almost oot o' hopes noo
    O' seeing her wedding day."

---

[1] Introduce and recommend.   [2] Calves.

" Claes are a mochy posie,
And sheep might go far astray,
And the laddie that marries for siller
Weds a' his pleasures away.

" The ox may hang in the plough, love,
The cow may drown in the mire;
But the laddie will ne'er want his riches
That marries his heart's desire."

So now this couple's got married,
Married in all good array,
And she lives in a cottage wi' her laddie,
And never wants cauries nor kye.

O, GIN THAT I WERE MAIRRIT.

I'M now a lass of thirty-three,
As clever a hizzie as ye'll see,
And feint a ane e'er courtit me,
To tak' me for his ain, O!

Chorus.

O, gin that I were mairrit, mairrit, mairrit,
O, gin that I were mairrit, I raley would do weel, O.

C

I hae two gouns o' my ain mak'—
A bocht ane's seldom on my back—
And plenty trunchets[1] on a rack,
    And bowls eneugh I'm shair, O!

Chorus—O, gin that I were mairrit, etc.

Besides a' this which I have said,
Some siller in my kist[2] I've laid,
And a' my handsome spinnin' made,
    Sae nimbly at the wheel, O!

Chorus—O, gin that I were mairrit, etc.

[1] Breadplates.   [2] Chest or trunk.

THE COLLIER LADDIE.

Quick, a la Marcia.

I'VE been east and I've been west,
    And I've been in Kirkcaldy;
But the bonniest lassie that ever I saw,
    She was following a collier laddie.

She'd silken slippers on her feet,
    Her body neat and handsome;
She'd a sky-blue ribbon in her hair,
    And her eyes like gowd were glancin'.

" Oh, where live ye, my bonnie lass?
    And tell me what they ca' ye?"
" Bonnie Jeanie Gordon is my name,
    And I'm following my collier laddie."

" Oh, see ye not yon hills and dales
    The sun shines on sae brawly—
They a' are mine, and they'll be thine,
    Gin ye'll leave your collier laddie.

And ye shall busk in gay attire,
    Weel busket up sae gaudy,
And ane to wait on every hand,
    Gin ye'll leave your collier laddie."

" Though ye had a' the sun shines on,
    And the earth conceals sae lowly,
I would turn my back on you and it a',
    And embrace my collier laddie."

But he has to her father gane,
    To her father gane so brawly—
Says, " Ye'll make your daughter wed wi' me,
    And forsake her collier laddie.

" I'll gie her lands, and I'll gie her rents,
    And I'll make her a lady,
I'll make her one of a higher degree,
    Than to follow a collier laddie."

Then he has to his daughter gane,
    To his daughter gane sae brawly,
Says, " Ye'll gae wi' this braw gentleman,
    And forsake your collier laddie.

" He'll gie ye lands, and he'll gie ye rents,
    And he'll make you a lady;
He'll make you one of a higher degree
    Than to follow a collier laddie."

"I winna hae his lands nor I winna hae his rents,
    I winna be his lady;
I'll make my bed in the collier's neuk,
    And lie doon wi' my collier laddie."

Gin twenty years had come and gane,
    Twenty years sae brawly,
The same silly gentleman came begging his bread,
    Frae Jean and her collier laddie.

"Faur's a' the lands and faur's a' the rents,
    That was to make me a lady?
I've got gold and gear enough
    And I'm aye wi' my collier laddie."

Now she has to her father gane,
    To her father gane sae brawlie,
Says, "What ye's to gie to yon braw gentleman,
    Ye'll gie me to my collier laddie."

He's counted down five hundred pounds,
    Five hundred pounds sae brawlie,
Says, "Tak' ye that my daughter Jean,
    And gie that to your collier laddie."

"Love for love is the bargain for me,
    Though the wee cot house should haud me;
And the world before me to win my bread,
    And share wi' my collier laddie."

When sending the third, fourth, fifth, sixth, and last verses of this fine old song to Johnson's *Museum*, Burns said, "I do not know a blyther old song than this." Whether the additional verses were known in Burns' time or have been added to the song since I have been unable to ascertain, but probably he missed them. I think my readers will agree with me that without the first, second, twelfth, and thirteenth verses the story would not be complete. The air to which it is now set was noted down by Mr. J. B. Allan, organist, Glasgow, from the singing of a gentleman who heard it sung at a social gathering in Aberdeenshire about thirty years ago.

In the North-eastern Counties "Ploughman Laddie" is substituted for "Collier Laddie," and the opening verse is generally sung as follows:—

I've been east, and I've been west,
    And I've been in St. Johnstone:
But the bonniest laddie that ever I saw
    Was a ploughman laddie dancing.

LOVE'S ADIEU.

Music by the late Wm. G. Jarvis, Bandmaster, Glasgow Police.

THE e'e o' the dawn, Eliza,
　　Blinks over the dark, green sea,
An' the moon's creepin' doon to the hill tap
　　Richt dim an' drowsilie;
An' the music o' the mornin'
　　Is murmurin' alang the air,
Yet still my dowie heart lingers
　　To catch one sweet throb mair.

We've been as blest, Eliza,
　　As children o' earth can be;
Though my fondest wish has been nipt by
　　The bonds o' povertie;
An' through life's misty sojourn
　　That still may be our fa',
But hearts that are linked for ever
　　Hae strength to bear it a'.

The cot by the mutterin' burnie,
　　Its wee bit garden an' field,
May hae mair o' the blessin's o' Heaven
　　Than lichts o' the lordliest bield;
There's mony a young brow braided
　　Wi' jewels o' far-aff isles,
But woe may be drinkin' the heart-springs,
　　While we see nought but smiles.

But adieu, my ain Eliza,
　　Where'er my wanderin's be,
Undyin' remembrance will mak ye
　　The star o' my destinie.
An' well I ken, thou loved one,
　　That aye till I return
Thou'lt treasure pure faith in thy bosom,
　　Like a gem in a golden urn.

This song, which equals some of Burns' and Tannahill's finest lyric pieces, was written about eighty years ago by Joseph Grant, a Kincardineshire farm servant, who, amid toil and poverty, devoted his leisure hours to reading and the cultivation of his mind. He is the author of two books, entitled *Juvenile Lays* and *Kincardineshire Traditions*. While engaged preparing a volume of his tales for the press he was seized with a cold, which settled in his lungs, and he died at Affrusk, in April, 1835, in the thirtieth year of his age.

I'LL NE'ER FORGET THE PARTING.

KEY C.

My parents reared me tenderly,
    They had no child but me,
But I, being fond of rambling,
    With them I could not 'gree.
Till I became a courter,
    Which grieved their hearts full sore,
So I left my aged parents,
    Never to see them more.

There was a wealthy farmer
    In the country not far by
Who had a lovely daughter,
    On her I cast an eye.
He had an only daughter,
    Most beautiful and fair,
And there's none in all this world
    With her that I could compare.

I asked her if she would be satisfied
    Were I to cross the main,
Or if she would prove true to me
    Till I returned again.

She swore she would prove true to me
  Till death would prove unkind,
So we kissed, shook hands, and parted
  And I left my girl behind.

As soon as I left England,
  For Scotland I sailed on;
I steered my course for Glasgow
  To view that famous town.
Trade and money being plenty,
  The girls to me proved kind;
But I ne'er forgot on the parting vows
  Of the girl I left behind.

One night as I had stopped my work,
  Went up St. George's Square,
The mail coach new arrived,
  The post boy met me there.
He handed me a letter,
  Made me to understand
That the girl I left behind me
  Was wed to another man.

If a' be true that's tell't to me
  I'll ne'er believe one more,
For the last time that we parted
  A solemn vow she swore.
The last time that we parted
  A solemn vow she swore
That she'd wed wi' I and none but I,
  And she swore it o'er and o'er.

I walked a little further on,
  Still thinking on the news too true,
And gazing all around me,
  Not knowing what to do.
Thinks I all labours I'll gae o'er,
  All company resign,
And I'll rove about from town to town
  For the girl that I left behind.

I steered my course to London,
  Strange faces for to see,
And bonnie Peggy Walker,
  She's fa'en in love wi' me.

Bonnie Peggy Walker,
  She's lovely and divine,
But I'll never forget on the parting vows
  Of the girl I left behind.

One night as I sat lamenting,
  She said, " Don't grieve, my boy,
For I've got money plenty
  To serve both you and I."
She says, " Your pockets will be filled,
  All labours ye'll gie o'er,
If ye would consent to marry me,
  And say ye would rove no more."

" If I would consent to marry you
  I would be doing much wrong;
Besides, all my companions
  On me they would look down.
But I'll go and see my parents dear,
  Before that I resign,
And there I'll take a last farewell
  Of the girl that I left behind."

" If a' be true ye tell to me
  Ye are the worst of men,
For ever since you came to town
  To you I've proved a friend.
You've had my money at your command
  While fortune seemed to frown,
And many's the time I have ta'en your part
  When others would have run you down."

When I related in my heart,
  All she had said was true,
I promised for to marry her—
  What other could I do?
Now Peggy's mistress of my house,
  She's lovely and divine,
So I'll mind nae mair on the parting vows
  Of the girl that I left behind.

THE HEDGER.

As I was a-walking one morning in May,
I met a jolly hedger upon the King's highway;
With his spade upon his shoulder and his bottle o' sma' beer,
He's as happy as the laird with ten thousand pounds a year.

This hedger was met by a gentleman one day;
"Come here, my honest fellow, come, tell to me I pray,
You have a large family, I know it to be true,
And how do you maintain them so well as you do?"

"Sometimes I reap, sir, and sometimes I sow,
Sometimes a-hedging and a-ditching I do go;
There's nothing comes amiss to me from the harrows to the
          plough,
And I aye mak' my living by the sweat o' my brow.

"When I come home at even, wet and weary though I be,
I take my youngest bairnie and dandles it on my knee,
While the others they come round me with all their prattling
          noise,
That's all the pleasure that a poor man enjoys.

" My wife and I together are joined in one yoke,
We live like two turtle doves that nothing can provoke;
Although the times are hard, sir, and we are very poor,
We banish all the ravenous wolves away from our door."

" Well done, my honest fellow, ye speak well o' your wife,
You'll have a good living all the days o' your life;
For fifty good acres of land I'll give to thee,
For to maintain your wife and your small family."

OOR DOCHTER JEAN.

Oor dochter Jean cam hame yestreen,
Wi' rosy cheeks an' lauchin' e'en,
An' when I speir'd her whaur she'd been
She blush'd an' said a-roamin'.

Wi' Fermer Joe o' Auchinglen,
Aroun' the wuds and doon the den,
An' what he said I fa'en wad ken,
Sin' oor Jean gaed a-roamin'.

An' when her mither spies the ring,
She winks her e'e, and starts to sing,
An' as we listen to its swing,
We catch the words a-roamin'.

> Wi' Fermer Joe, etc.

Weel, Fermer Joe stapp'd yont a'e day,
An' stood, but kent na what to say,
Jist mummell'd something, by the way—
D'ye ken your Jean's been roamin'?

> Wi' Fermer Joe, etc.

We've ha'en an' inklin' that oor Jean's
Been trailin' roun' the wuds at e'en;
Why stan' an' gape? Ye've nocht to screen
He blush'd, said aye, Jean's roamin'.

> Wi' Fermer Joe, etc.

Weel, there's my han', I wish ye weel,
Aff decent folk a couthie chiel',
An' lang may Jean as cantie feel
When she comes hame frae roamin'.

> Wi' Fermer Joe, etc.

I'm prood oor lass yer hert has won:
She couldna wiled a brawer son;
An' noo, when a' thing's said an' done
May she gang lang a-roamin'.

> Wi' Fermer Joe, etc.

A couthie wife I'll mak o' Jean,
She'll keep my house fu' trig an' clean,
An' ne'er regret the day, I ween,
When she gaed first a-roamin'.

> Wi' Fermer Joe, etc.

This song was sent to me by Mr. Thos. M'Rorie, 4 James Nisbet Street, Glasgow.

Mr. James B. Allan, A.L.C.M., Glasgow, has kindly arranged the music for me.

I'M A WORKIN' CHAP.

KEY C. {:d¹.t | l :- :l | r :- :r | f :- :f | s :- :s | l :- :l | r :- :f | m :- :r | d :- }

{ :d¹.t | l :- :l | r :- :r | f :- :f | s :- :s | l :- :l | r :- :f | m :- :r | d :- }

{ :l | r¹ :- :r¹| l :- :l | r¹ :- :r¹| l :- :t | d¹ :- :d¹| s :- :s | d¹ :- :t | l :- }

{ :l | r¹ :- :t | d¹ :- :s | d¹ :- :t | l :- :l | s :s :s | d¹ :- :t | l :- :r | r :- ||

CHORUS.
{ :d¹.t | l :- :l | r :- :r | f :- :f | s :- :s | l :- :l | d :- :d | m :- :f | s :- }

{ :l | r¹ :- :t | d¹ :- :s | d¹ :- :t | l :- :l | s :s :s | d¹ :- :t | l :- :r | r :- ||

I'M a workin' chap, as you may see,
You'll find an honest lad in me;
I'm neither haughty, mean, nor proud,
Nor ever tak's the thing too rude.
I never gang abune my means,
Nor seek assistance frae my frien's,
But day and nicht through thick and thin,
I'm workin' life out to keep life in.

Chorus.

Nae maitter, frien's, whate'er befa',
The puir folks they maun work awa',
Through frost and snaw and rain and wind,
They're working life out to keep life in.

The puir needle-woman that we saw
In reality and on the wa',
A picture sorrowful to see,
I'm sure wi' me you'll a' agree
Her pay's scarce able to feed a mouse.
Far less to keep hersel' and house;
She's naked, hungry, pale, and thin,
Workin' life out to keep life in.

    Chorus—Nae maitter frien's, etc.

Don't ca' a man a drunken sot
Because he wears a ragged coat;
It's better far, mind, don't forget,
To rin in rags than rin in debt.
He may look seedy, very true,
But still his creditors are few;
And he toddles on, devoid o' sin,
Workin' life out to keep life in.

    Chorus—Nae maitter frien's, etc.

But maybe, frien's, I've stayed ower lang,
But I hope I hae said naething wrang,
I only merely want to show
The way the puir folk hae to go.
Just look at a man wi' a housefu' o' bairns,
To rear them up it tak's a' he earns,
Wi' a willin' heart and a coat gey thin,
He's workin' life out to keep life in.

    Chorus—Nae maitter, frien's, etc.

MY NAME IS DONALD BLUE.

My name is Donald Blue, an' ye ken me fu' weel,
Straik me canny by the hair, I'm a quiet, simple chiel;
But gin ye rouse the bear, I'm as rouche as the deil,
    Gin 1 get a claucht o' yer noddle.

But I'll tell ye o' a trick, man, that happened in the South;
A smith got a wife, an' she had an unco drouth;
She liket it sae weel, put sae muckle in her mouth,
    She was aften helpet hame in the mornin'.

So it happen'd ae day, the smith he was thrang,
They brocht a wife till him—a wife that couldna gang;
He took her on his back, an' up the stair he ran,
    An' flang her on the bed wi' a fury.

He lockit the door, brocht the key in his han',
And cam' doon the stairs, cryin', "Oh, bewitched man!
This conduct o' her's I'm no' fit to stan';
    I'll enlist for a sodger in the mornin'."

He fell to his work—he was shoein' a horse;
They cried, "Tak' in your wife, smith, she's lyin' at the cross,"
He lifted up his hammer, and he strack wi' siccan force,
    He knockit doon the studdy in his fury.

"The deil's in the folk. What do they mean ava?
Gin I've ae drucken wife, L'od, I'm no' needin' twa."
But they cried a' the louder—"Tak her in frae the snaw,
    Or surely she will perish ere the mornin'."

So the smith he gaed oot, an' viewed her a' roun',
"By my sooth! an' it's her; but hoo did she win doon?"
He hoisted her awa' on his back up to the room,
    Whaur the ither wife was lyin' soondly snorin'.

The smith, to his surprise, couldna tell which was his,
Frae the tap to the tae they were dressed in a piece,
An' sae closely they resembled each ither in the face,
    He couldna tell which was his Jeanie.

"Deil ma' care!" says the smith; "let them baith lie still,
When ance she's sober she'll surely ken hersel'."
Noo frae that day to this Jeanie never buys a gill,
    Nor will she wet her mou' in the mornin'.

This has been a favourite bothy song all over the country for the past
fifty years, but with the exception of a version which appears in Ford's
Vagabond Songs and Ballads, it has not been printed hitherto. Ford states
that in the counties of Perth, Fife, and Forfar, it was sung to the air of
"Johnnie Cope," but the tune it is here set to is the one it is sung to in
the North of Scotland, to which the song apparently belongs

TAK IT, MAN, TAK IT.

LANGSYNE, fine I mind, little mair than a lad,
   I wrocht wi' John Jackson at Inkaboot Mill;
His ae bonnie dochter a hillockit jaud,
   Aye likeit to tease me to show aff her skill.

Her two een I wiss, they demanded a kiss,
But her taunting tongue ever said, " Nay, my lad, nay,"
Whilst the happer's loud clapper cried, " Tut, end the matter,"
And kept at it constantly singing all day.

Chorus.

Tak' it, man, tak' it, man,
Tak' it, man, tak' it, man,
Tak' it, man, tak' it. Oh, come, come away!
Be brave-hearted, Colin,
A kiss that is stolen
Is worth twenty ithers, sae dinna delay.

If this be the way o't, thinks I to mysel',
Weel-a-weel, then, the least I can do is to try;
Sae the neist time we met I said to her, " Bell,
Ae kiss ere I bid you a loving goodbye?"
" Awa to the deil! what is wrang wi' the chiel?"
She cried, whilst she slapped me, and kept me at bay.
Losh, I felt quite down-hearted, downcast, and deserted,
Still the happer kept busily singing all day.

Tak' it, man, etc.

Three lang dreary months she kept out o' my gate,
Till ae day she met me, she said just by chance,
For the cauldness between us, Bell gied me the wyte
Wi' hauf smothered laugh and a real pawkie glance.
Wi' arm round her waist, faith I kissed her in haste,
Although she declared it was mean and foul play;
I could see by her manner I wasna a sinner,
And the happer kept steadily singing all day.

Tak' it, man, etc.

Although we met often it couldna be said
We ever felt happy aye living apart;
A bachelor I was, and she was a maid,
Sae as husband and wife we agreed on a start.
Without muckle din soon the cries were gi'en in,
And the waddin', believe me, made a' our freens gay;
Bell voted a blessing on my way o' kissing,
And the happer kept merrily singing all day.

Tak' it, man, etc.

Now I am a gutcher,[1] and growing gey bauld,
  But Bell's bonnie ringlets her brow still adorn;
And somehow or ither we never feel auld,
  Although no sae souple at e'ening and morn;
Our hearts are content, we juist tak' what is sent,
  We ken we are nearin' the fit o' life's brae,
But we'll aye be cheery, for wha would grow weary
  Whilst the happer keeps joyfully singing all day.

       Tak' it, man, etc.

            [1] Grandfather.

This song, together with the music, was sent to me by Mr. Walter Towers, Bonnybridge, Stirlingshire.

I'LL HANG MY HARP.

I'LL hang my harp on a willow tree,
  And I'll off to the wars again;
My peaceful home has no charms for me,
  The battlefield no pain.

For the lady I love will soon be a bride,
  With a diadem on her brow,
Oh! why did she flatter my boyish pride?
  She's going to leave me now.

She took me away from my war-like lord,
  And she gave me a silken suit;
I thought no more of my master's sword
  When I played on my lady's lute.
She seemed to think me a boy above
  Her pages of low degree,
Oh! had I but loved with a boyish love
  It would have been better for me.

Then I'll hide in my breast every selfish care,
  And I'll flush my pale cheek with wine,
When smiles awaken the bridal pair
  I'll hasten to give them mine.
I'll laugh and I'll sing though my heart may bleed,
  And I'll walk in the festive train,
And if I survive it I'll mount my steed
  And I'll off to the wars again.

But one golden tress of her hair I'll twine
  In my helmet's sable plume,
And then on the field of Palestine
  I'll seek an early doom.
And if by the Saracen's hand I fall,
  'Mid the noble and the brave,
A tear from my lady-love is all
  I seek for the warrior's grave.

Both words and music of this song were sent me by Mr. James B. Allan,
A.L.C.M., music teacher, Glasgow, who noted them down from the singing
of his mother, Mrs. D. S. Allan. Mr. Allan states that the hero of the song
was a pageboy in the service of Queen Victoria, who had fallen in love with
her before she came to the throne.

From another source I learn that when Queen Victoria was about seventeen
years of age Lord Elphinstone was a handsome young Guardsman, and it
was currently reported and believed that the youthful pair had formed a
mutual attachment. He was soon thereafter appointed Governor of Madras,
and, rumour had it, was thus sent away from the country. This song was,
according to rumour, composed to express his feelings; indeed, report said
that he was the poet himself.

When singing the song, the last two lines of each verse are sometimes
repeated according to the taste of the singer.

I AM GAUN TO THE GARRET.

My mither has three butter platies,
Platies? " Ay, platies,"
My mither has three butter platies
    And she's nae ither dochters but me.

        But I maun gang to the garret,
        The garret? " Ay, the garret," ·
        But I maun gang to the garret,
            Since there's nae bonnie laddie for me.

My father's a wee white horsie,
A horsie? " Ay, a horsie,"
My father's a wee white horsie
    And he's nae ither dochters but me.

        But I maun gang to the garret, etc.

My mither has forty white shillin's,
White shillin's? " Ay, white shillin's,"
My mither has forty white shillin's
    And she's nae ither dochters but me.

        But I maun gang to the garret, etc.

But down in yon howe there's a miller,
A miller? " Ay a miller,"
But down in yon howe there's a miller
    And he sometimes comes and sees me.

        So noo I'm gaun to be marrit,
        Marrit? " Ay, marrit,"
        So noo I'm gaun to be marrit
            Before that my beauty decay.

CATHIE AND ME.

THE sun kissed the brow of the lovely Ben Ledi,
   And wrapt it in raiment of rainbowlike hue;
As round by the Borland, secure in my plaidie,
   I wandered with Cathie, sweet, loving, and true.

Among the fair woods of the far-winding Carron,
   The dear feathered songsters in rapturous glee
Sang softly and sweetly, until a wee star shone,
   Afar from the east on my Cathie and me.

    Cathie, Cathie, my lovely Cathie,
    The wide world's kingdom for Cathie and me.

Away with the gay, gaudie sights of the city,
   Their grandeur is meaningless, cheerless, and cold;
The greed for riches drowns both love and pity
   Within the proud hearts of the grovellers for gold.
Give me, in my musings, the high vault of heaven,
   Whatever my lot and wherever I be;
The greatest of blessings to me has been given,
   When fate kindly gifted my Cathie to me.

    Cathie, Cathie, my lovely Cathie,
    Heaven never saw happier than Cathie and me.

This sweet little love song was written specially for this series by
Mr. Walter Towers, Bonnybridge. Mr. Towers, who is one of Stirlingshire's
grand old men, is a native of Carronshore, and his ancestors were farmers
in that part of the country for upwards of three hundred years. He
published at Glasgow in 1885 a volume of poems, songs, and ballads, and
he is the author of " Tak' It, Man, Tak' It."

The music is by Dr. Mitchell, Falkirk.

BLYTHE MORMOND BRAES.

Key F. { .1₁ | 1₁ .,t₁ :d .,r | m .l :l .s | m .,r :d .m | s₁ : . }

{ .d ,t₁ | 1₁ .,t₁ :d .,r | m .l :l .s | m .r :m .s | 1 :- . ||

    Oh, wat ye wha's in yon wee hoose
      Beneath blythe Mormond Braes?
    Bonnie Nelly, where the hawthorn grows,
      Sings bleachin' at her claes.

Oh, Nelly she's a bonnie, bonnie lass,
  She's the flower oot owre them a',
She's a' my thocht, she's a' my care,
  And comfort owre them a'.

O, Nelly dear, blink owre the burn,
  Wi' the pearlin's busk ye braw,
And I'll convey ye through the howe,
  As far's your daddy's ha'.

And gin your mammy on ye frown,
  For bein' sae lang wi' me,
My dear, I'll tak' ye to mysel',
  And love ye till I dee.

The wanton lads in Crimon' lan's
  Gang trig to kirk and fair,
They woo their loves wi' a' their snacks,
  But I've got nane to spare.

But I love her, and she loves me,
  And wha daur say us na?
My he'rt will no be free frae care,
  Till Nelly be my a'.

'Mang a' the nichts that e'er I spent,
  Was twal months sax and twa,
But the ither nichts amang the bents
  I'm sure 'twas worth them a'.

Come portion dark, come portion fair,
  Come bitter frosts and snaw,
My he'rt will never be my ain
  Till Nelly be my a'.

O, Nelly dear, ne'er fash your heid,
  Tho' we be scant o' gear,
For tocher I will never grudge,
  My ain's but sma I fear.

But if health attend, and han's keep hale,
  We'll drive dull care awa',
And win our breid wi' eident toil,
  Ne'er live to use it a'.

MORMOND BRAES.

As I gaed doon by Strichen toon,
I heard a fair maid mourin',
And she was makin' sair complaint
For her true love ne'er returnin'.
It's Mormand Braes where heather grows,
Where aft times I.have been cheery,
It's Mormand Braes where heather grows,
And it's there I've lost my dearie.

Refrain.

Sae fare ye weel, ye Mormand Braes,
Where aftimes I've been cheery,
Fare ye weel, ye Mormand Braes,
For it's there I've lost my dearie.

Oh, I'll put on my goon o' green,
It's a forsaken token,
And that will let the young men know
That the bands o' love are broken.
There's mony a horse has snappert and fa'en,
And risen and gane fu' rarely,
There's mony a lass has lost her lad,
And gotten anither richt early.

There's as guid fish into the sea
  As ever yet was taken,
I'll cast my line and try again,
  I'm only ance forsaken.
Sae I'll gae doon to Strichen toon
  Where I was bred and born,
And there I'll get anither sweetheart,
  Will mairry me the morn.

    Sae fare ye weel, ye Mormand Braes,
      Where aftimes I've been cheery,
    Fare ye weel, ye Mormand Braes,
      For it's there I've lost my dearie.

THE MERCHANT'S DAUGHTER TURNED SAILOR:

Or THE DRAWING OF THE LOTS.

As I was a-walking in London's fair street,
There with my true love I chanced for to meet.
" Where are ye going, sailor, young sailor?" said she,
" I'm bound for New England, New England," said he.

" If ye're bound for New England right fain would I go,
But how to get over is more than I know,
But amongst all your sailors, if ye want a hand,
I'll work my passage over as well as I can."

Our ship has got rigged, and ready to sail,
And we all went away with a fine flowing gale,
We sailed along with a favouring wind,
Till our ship split asunder, to the bottom she went.

Twenty-five of us sailors got into a boat,
Across the wide ocean away we did float;
Provisions running short, grim death drawing nigh,
The lots were passed round to see which of us should die.

The lots were passed round all in a black shoe,
And each young sailor his lot out he drew;
And among all the sailors the lots fell on she,
So she had to be slain their provisions to be.

The lots were passed round all in a black shoe,
To see which young sailor her butcher would be;
And among all the sailors the lot fell on she,
So she has to be slain by the young man, her dear.

" Oh, hold your hands, butcher!" this fair maid she said.
" Are ye going to murder an innocent maid?
I'm a rich merchant's daughter in London," said she;
" So ye see what I've come to by the loving of thee."

Like a flash of lightning this changed his face.
He pitied himself, and with many's the kiss,
Says, " Oh, my dearest jewel, since I've found you so just,
In the hope of your long life, love, I will die first."

The lots were passed round all in a black shoe,
To see which young sailor his butcher would be;
And be quick in your motions, for the last bite is done,
But ere that fatal blow they all heard a gun.

" Oh, hold your hands, butcher," the captain he cries;
" For we're near some harbour!" A vessel he spies.
We sailed along with a fine flowing tide,
And we all reached a harbour near by a townside.

Now this couple have got married, as we now do hear,
And the King's settled on them five hundred a year;
And now he does love her as dear as his life,
And by all accounts she is a loving sweet wife.

I picked up this old ballad, both words and music, from the singing of a
farm servant at the farm of Luncarty, in the parish of King Edward,
Aberdeenshire, about forty-five years ago.

DONALD'S RETURN TO GLENCOE.

Air—Same as preceding song.

As I was a-walking one evening of late
Where Flora's gay mantle the fields decorate,
I carelessly wandered, where I did not know,
On the banks of a fountain that lies in Glencoe.

Like her whom the prize of Mount Ida had won,
There approached me a lassie as bright as the sun,
The ribbons and tartans all around her did flow,
That once graced Macdonald, the pride o' Glencoe.

With courage undaunted I to her drew near,
While the red rose and the lily on her cheek did appear;
I asked her name, and how far she'd to go,
" Young man," she made answer, " I'm bound for Glencoe."

I said, " My dear lassie, your enchanting smile
And comely fair features does my heart beguile;
And if your affections on me you'll bestow,
You'll bless the happy hour that we met in Glencoe."

" Young man," she made answer, " your love I disdain,
I once had a sweetheart, young Donald by name,
He went to the wars nearly ten years ago,
And a maid I'll remain till he returns to Glencoe."

" The power of the French, it is hard to pull down,
They have beat many heroes of fame and renoun;
And like them, young Donald, as it may happen so—
The man you love dearly perchance is laid low."

" My Donald's true valour when tried in the field,
Like his gallant ancestors, disdaining to yield,
And French and the Spaniards he'll soon overthrow,
And in splendour return to my arms in Glencoe."

" Perhaps your young Donald regards not your name,
But has placed his affections on some foreign dame;
He may have forgotten you for aught that you know,
The bonnie young lassie he left in Glencoe."

"My Donald from his promise can never depart,
For love, truth, and honour abound in his heart;
And should he ne'er return aye single I'll go,
And mourn for my Donald, the pride o' Glencoe."

Now proving her constant, I pulled out a glove,
Which in parting she gave me as a token of love;
She flew to my breast, while the tears down did flow,
Crying, "You're my dear Donald, returned to Glencoe."

"Cheer up, my dear Flora, your sorrows are o'er,
While life does remain, we will never part more;
The rude blasts of war at a distance may blow,
But in peace and content we'll abide in Glencoe."

'NEATH THE GLOAMIN' STAR AT E'EN.

Air—"When the Kye Comes Hame."

THE parting rays of Phoebus
　　Are ling'ring in the sky,
And mute is ilka songster,
　　And hushed its hymn of joy;
But I maun haste awa',
　　Where the tryst was set yestreen,
To meet my bonnie lassie
　　'Neath the gloamin' star at e'en.

Refrain.

When the gloamin' star is seen,
When the gloamin' star is seen;
　　To meet my bonnie lassie
　　'Neath the gloamin' star at e'en.

Since e'er I was a laddie,
　　And toilin' at the plough,
I've wrestled sair wi' fortune
　　This weary warld through;

But what lightens a' my toil
  Is that happy hour at e'en,
The hour I meet my lassie,
  When the gloamin' star is seen.

    When the gloamin' star is seen, etc.

Awa' ye haughty nobles,
  Wha' deem sic pleasures sma',
There's joy that never enters
  Your lordly hame or ha';
For the joy of joys to me
  Is that happy hour at e'en,
The hour I meet my lassie,
  When the gloamin' star is seen.

    'Neath the gloamin' star at e'en, etc.

Why should I seek for riches
  When toilin' at the plough?
There's flowers into the peasant's path
  That kings might stoop to pu';
But the hallowed lowe o' love
  In its purest form is seen,
Where the ploughboy meets his lassie
  'Neath the gloamin' star at e'en.

    'Neath the gloamin' star at e'en, etc.

Shine on thou twinklin' starrie,
  I love thy charming ray,
Thou tell'st to me a tale of joy
  Nae ither tongue can say;
For yonder comes my lassie,
  In beauty like a queen,
And I'll clasp her to my bosom
  'Neath the gloamin' star at e'en.

      'Neath the gloamin' star at e'en,
      'Neath the gloamin' star at e'en;
        And I'll clasp her to my bosom
      'Neath the gloamin' star at e'en.

RURAL COURTSHIP.

As I cam' in by Monymusk,
  And doun by Alford's dale,
A sad misfortune happened to me,
  And I think nae shame to tell.
    Lal ti' doo, a riddle o'o,
    Lal ti' dooral la.

As I gaed in by Monymusk
  The moon was shinin' clear;
And I held on to Lethendy
  To see my Maggie dear.

I did gang, when I did think
  That a' were sleepin' soun';
But plague upon yon auld wife,
  For she cam' slinkin' doun.

Sae cannily she slipt the lock,
  And set the door agee;
Then crawled upon her han's an' knees
  To see wha it could be.

Then to the bells, wi' a' her micht,
  Sae loud she made them ring,
Till faith I thocht about my lugs
  The biggin' she wad bring.

And when she saw I wadna slip,
   She ran to the guidman,
Says:—"There's a lad into the house,
   An' that I winna stan'."

For it is a most disgraceful thing,
   It wad provoke a saunt,
To see a' the servant girls wi' lads
   When the gentle anes maun want.

Providence has acted wrang
   Sic pleasures for to gie
To ony servant lad or lass
   Just workin' for a fee.

The auld man cam' ben himsel',
   An' he push'd ben his heid;
Guidfaith I thocht it was a ghost
   Just risen frae the deid.

He'd duddy drawers upon his legs,
   He'd on a cap o' white,
An' he'd a face as lang's my leg,
   An' in his hand a light.

He's ta'en me by the shoulders broad,
   An' push'd me out o' doors;
Think's I, my auld lad, I'll come back
   When sleepin' gars ye snore.

The refrain is sung at the end of each verse.

THE STAR O' BANCHORY'S LAND.

Air—"Drumdelgie" (see music in Part II.).

BANCHORY's lan's are bonnie,
   When spring rolls in the year,
Wi' lasses sweet and mony,
   But nane sae sweet's my dear.
There's nane sae sweet's my only dear,
   To lee 'twould be a sin;
And I do think she should be styled
   The star o' Banchory's lan'.

She is a handsome creature,
  Her humour's frank and free,
And mony's the nicht she's ga'en consent
  To tak a walk wi' me.
Oh! mony's the nicht she's ga'en consent
  To walk down by the Lynn;
May Heaven bless you, bonnie lass,
  That lives at Cairney Whing.[1]

I'm deep in love, and sare oppressed,
  And troubled in my mind;
My restless heart within my breast
  Nae comfort e'er can find.
My restless heart within my breast
  Nae comfort finds at a',
It's a' for Bet o' Cairney Whing,
  She's stown my heart awa'.

'Twas on a simmer's evening,
  As I cam frae the fair,
While standing gazing round and round
  I spied my loved one there.
Oh! standing gazing round and round,
  My loved one met my view;
But I could not get a word with her
  For all that I could do.

'Twas on a simmer's evening,
  When Phœbus left the sky,
That I did sing with all my might,
  And my loved one passing by.
Oh! I did sing with all my might,
  And my loved one passing on,
And many an anxious eye I cast
  To see if she would come.

Oh! cursed be fickle fortune,
  That does our lives all try,
That in a moment lifts our hopes
  And wafts them to the sky.
But the next moment buries our hopes,
  And sinks them in the deep,
That disappoints the gallant squire
  And leaves the maid to weep.

<hr />

[1] Pronounced " Karnie Whin."

Remember, Bonnie Betsy,
    When you and I did part;
Oh! don't you mind yon awful nicht,
    Alas! it grieves my heart;
Oh, don't you mind yon awful nicht,
    Alas! it gives me pain,
For I ne'er had it in my power
    To meet with you again.

But He who rules the universe,
    And fixed the stars on high,
To whom creation all doth bow,
    In nations low or high;
To whom creation all doth bow,
    Submissive to His plan;
Give me the lass that I lo'e best,
    The star o' Banchory's lan'.

This is another bothy song regarding which no information can be got.
I am informed that it has been a great favourite in the North off Scotland
for upwards of half-a-century. It was missed by the late Dean Christie
and Robert Ford, and has not as yet been printed in any collection.

HALF-PAST TEN.

I MIND when I courted my ain wifie Jean,
Though aften I gaed, she little was seen;
For her father, the elder, like a' godly men,
Aye steekit his door about half-past ten.

Ae Sacrament Sabbath I saw Jeanie hame,
Ony lad wi' his lassie wad hae dune the same;
We crackit sae lang at the cosy fire-en'
That the time slipt awa' till near half-past ten.

The worthy man read, syne fervently pray'd,
And when he was dune he solemnly said—
" It has aye been a rule—but 'tis likely ye ken—
That we steek a' our doors about half-past ten."

The hint was eneuch for a blate lad like me,
But I catch'd a bit blink o' Jeanie's black e'e,
As much as to say—Come ye back to the glen,
An' ye'll maybe stay langer than half-past ten.

Ae nicht twa-three lads an' mysel' did agree
To gang some place near, just to hae a bit spree;
Quo' I—" What d'ye think o' gaun doon to the glen,
For we're sure to be hame about half-past ten?"

We a' were received wi' hearty gudewill,
An' the elder, nae less, broached a cask of his yill;
Syne gaed aff to his bed, and says, " Jean, ye'll atten'
That the doors are a' lockit by half-past ten."

" Oy, ay," says Jean, but the best o' the joke
Was her slippin' ben an' stoppin' the clock.
I'm no' gaun to tell the hoo or the when,
But the hands werena pointin' to half-past ten.

About four i' the mornin' the auld man arose,
An' lichtin' a spunk, to the clock straught he goes;
" Gude sauf us, gudewife! did ye hear me gae ben?
Lod, the lads are awa' before half-past ten."

But the cat very soon was let oot o' the poke,
By the kecklin' o' hens an' the craw o' the cock;
An' opening the shutters, he clearly saw then
We wad a' hae our breakfasts ere half-past ten.

Ye ne'er heard sic lauchin' a' the days o' yer life,
An' nane were sae hearty's the auld man an' wife;
Quo' he, " What'll lassies no' do for the men?
Even cheat their auld faithers wi' half-past ten."

It was a' settled then that Jean should be mine,
The waddin' sune followed; an' we've aye sin syne
Lived happy thegither, an' hope to the en'
We'll aye mind that nicht an' its half-past ten.

An' noo a wee bit advice I wad gie,
Ne'er stint young folks' time when they gang to a spree;
I'm a faither mysel', but brawly I ken
That the fun juist begins aboot half-past ten.

This highly humourous song has been a great favourite among country
people all over Scotland for many years past, although it has seldom
appeared in print. I heard it sung for the first time in Alvah, Banffshire,
forty years ago. It was written by a lady named Mrs. Bacon, residing at
Bainsford, Falkirk.

THE BONNIE LASSIE'S ANSWER WAS AYE "OH, NO."

Fare-ye-well to Glasgow, and adieu to Lanrickshire,
And fare-ye-well, my parents dear, I'll never see you mair,
For I am bound to go, my love, where no one shall me know,
But the bonnie lassie's answer was aye "Oh, no."

'Twas aye "Oh, no, my love"; 'twas aye "Oh, no."
The bonnie lassie's answer was aye "Oh, no."

It's for the want o' pocket money and for the want o' cash
Makes mony a bonnie laddie to leave his bonnie lass;
So I am bound to go, my love, where no one shall me know,
But the bonne lassie's answer was aye " Oh, no."

  'Twas aye " Oh, no, my love "; 'twas aye " Oh, no."
  The bonnie lassie's answer was aye " Oh, no."

The King is wanting men, they say, and I for one maun go,
And it's for my very life, my dear; I dare not answer no;
So I am bound to go, my love, where no one shall me know,
But the bonnie lassie's answer was aye " Oh, no."

  'Twas aye " Oh, no, my love "; 'twas aye " Oh, no."
  The bonnie lassie's answer was aye " Oh, no."

Oh, stay at hame, my bonnie lad, and dinna gang afar,
For little, little do you know the dangers o' the war;
O, I am bound to go, my love, where no one shall me know,
But the bonnie lassie's answer was aye " Oh, no."

  'Twas aye " Oh, no, my love "; 'twas aye " Oh, no."
  And the bonnie lassie's answer was aye " Oh, no."

'Tis I'll cut off my yellow hair, and gang alang wi' thee,
And be your faithful comrade in ilk' foreign countrie,
Since ye are bound to go, my love, where no one shall you know,
But the bonnie laddie's answer was aye " Oh, no."

  'Twas aye " Oh, no, my love "; 'twas aye " Oh, no."
  And the bonnie laddie's answer was aye " Oh, no."

O stay at hame, my bonnie lass, and dinna gang wi' me,
For little, little do you know the dangers o' the sea;
But I am bound to go, my love, where no one shall me know,
And the bonnie lassie's answer was aye " Oh, no."

  'Twas aye " Oh, no, my love "; 'twas aye " Oh, no."
  And the bonnie lassie's answer was aye " Oh, no."

The fervent love I bear to you is constant, true, and kind,
You're always present to my view, and never from my mind;
But I am bound to go, my love, where no one shall me know,
And the bonnie lassie's answer was aye " Oh, no."

  'Twas aye " Oh, no, my love "; 'twas aye " Oh, no."
  And the bonnie lassie's answer was aye " Oh, no."

Farewell to Cathkin's sunny braes, where oft-times we have
    been,
And fare-ye-well to the banks o' Clyde and bonnie Glasgow
    Green;
For I am bound to go, my love, where no one shall me know,
But the bonnie lassie's answer was aye " Oh, no."
    'Twas aye " Oh, no, my love "; 'twas aye " Oh, no."
    And the bonnie lassie's answer was aye " Oh, no."

Fare-ye-well, my comrades dear, I own my heart is sore,
Farewell for aye, my bonnie Jean, I'll never see you more;
For I am bound to go, my love, where no one shall me know,
And the bonnie lassie's answer was aye " Oh, no."
    'Twas aye " Oh, no, my love "; 'twas aye " Oh, no."
    And the bonnie lassie's answer was aye " Oh, no."

THE LASS O' GLENSHEE.

Air—" The Road and the Miles to Dundee."

Ae braw summer day, when the heather was blooming,
    And the silent hills hummed wi' the honey-lade bee,
I met a fair maid as I homeward was roaming,
    A-herding her sheep on the hills o' Glenshee.

The rose on her cheek it was gem'd wi' a dimple,
    And blythe was the blink o' her bonnie blue e'e;
Her face was enchantin', sae sweet an' sae simple,
    My heart sune belanged to the lass o' Glenshee.

I kiss'd and caress'd her, and said, " My dear lassie,
    If you will but gang to St. Johnston wi' me,
There's nane o' the fair shall set foot on the causeway
    Wi' clothing sae fine as the lass o' Glenshee.

" A carriage o' pleasure ye shall hae to ride in,
    An' folk shall say ' Madam ' when they speak to thee,
An' servants ye'll hae to beck at your biddin'—
    I'll mak' you my lady, sweet lass o' Glenshee."

" Oh, mock nae me, sir, wi' your carriage to ride in,
    Nor think that your grandeur I value a flee;
I would think mysel' blessed in a coatie o' plaidin'
    Wi' an innocent herd on the hills o' Glenshee."

" Believe me, dear lassie, Caledonia's clear waters
 May alter their course and run back frae the sea;
Her brave, hardy sons may submit to the fetters,
 But alter what will I'll be constant to thee.

" The lark may forget his sweet sang in the mornin',
 The spring may forget to revive on the lea;
But never will I, while my senses do govern,
 Forget to be kind to the lass o' Glenshee."

" Oh, leave me, sweet lad, for I am sure I would blunder,
 An' set a' the gentry a-laughin' at me;
They are book-taught in manners, baith auld an' young yonder,
 A thing we ken nocht o' up here in Glenshee.

" They would say, ' Look at him, wi' his dull Hieland lady,
 Set up for a show in a window sae hie,
Roll'd up like a witch in a hameit-spun plaidie',
 An', pointin', they'd jeer at the lass o' Glenshee."

" Dinna think o' sic stories, but come up behind me,
 Ere Phœbus goes round my sweet bride you shall be;
This night in my arms I'll dote on you kindly."
 She smiled, she consented; I took her wi' me.

Now years hae gane by since we buskit thegither,
 An' seasons hae changed, but nae change is wi' me;
She's ever as gay as the fine summer weather
 When the sun's at its height on the hills o' Glenshee.

To meet wi' my Jenny my life I would venture,
 She's sweet as the echo that rings on the lea;
She's spotless an' pure as the snaw-robe o' winter
 When laid oot to bleach on the hills o' Glenshee.

I do not know a more popular song than this. It has been sung in
nearly every farmhouse, cottage, and bothy in Scotland for the past seventy
or eighty years. The author of it was a shoemaker named Andrew Sharpe,
a native of Perth, who died there on 5th February, 1817.

THE BLEACHER LASSIE O' KELVINHAUGH.

Air—"My Faithful Fond One."

As I went out on a summer's evening
　To view the fields in sweet Kelvinhaugh,
'Twas there I met a well-faur'd lassie,
　Wi' cheeks like roses and skin like snaw.

Says I, " My lassie, where are you going?
　What do you do by the Broomielaw?"
Says she, " Kind sir, I'm a bleacher lassie
　In Cochrane's Bleachfields in Kelvinhaugh."

Says I, " My lassie, will ye go wi' me?
　I'll buy you gowns and diamonds braw."
" Oh, no, kind sir, I may plainly tell you
　I've a lad o' my ain, but he's far awa'."

Says I, " My lassie, you are hard-hearted;
　I wish your fair face I never saw,
For my heart is bleeding baith late and early
　For the bleacher lassie o' Kelvinhaugh."

" It's seven years since he's gane and left me,
　Seven lang years since he's gane awa',
But other seven I'll wait upon him,
　I'll bleach a while on sweet Kelvinhaugh."

" Oh, lassie, lassie, ye hae been faithful,
　And thocht on me when far awa';
True love will surely be rewarded,
　We'll part nae mair on sweet Kelvinhaugh."

Now, this couple they have got married,
　And they keep an ale house between them twa.
And the sailor laddies they gang a-drinking
　To the bleacher lassies o' Kelvinhaugh.

　　The bleacher lassie appears to have been originally a Glasgow street song,
but it soon became a favourite all over the country. A matter of thirty
years ago it was sung at harvest homes and merry meetings, and was about
as well known as " The Collier Laddie " and " The Bonnie Parks o' Kilty.'
It seems to have been missed by collectors such as the late Robert Ford and
others

TO PAD THE ROAD WI' ME.

SAYS I, "My dearest Mollie,
  Come let us fix the time
When you and I will married be,
  And wedlock us combine.
When you and I get married, love,
  Right happy we will be,
For ye are the bonnie lassie
  That's to pad the road wi' me."

" To pad the road wi' you, kind sir;
  Cauld winter's coming on,
Besides my aged parents
  Have ne'er a girl but one;
Besides, my aged parents
  Have ne'er a girl but me,
So I'm no the bonnie lassie
  That's to pad the road wi' thee."

" Oh, never mind cauld winter, love,
  The spring will follow soon;
Come sit ye down beside me,
  And I'll sing you a nice song.

I'll sing you a nice song,
  While I diddle you on my knee,
For ye are the bonnie lassie
  That's to pad the road wi' me."

Sae she has donned her hose and shoon,
  And to the kirk they've gaen,
And lang, ay lang ere morning
  That couple were made ane.
And lang, lang ere the morning
  Her troubles were set free,
For she's the bonnie lassie
  That's to pad the road wi' me.

This song was sent to me by Mr. W. Malcolm, Arbroath.

FORGLEN YOU KNOW.

ALL ye that's young and gay,
  To me ye will draw nigh,
And a story to you I will tell;
  It's at Forglen you know,
  Pretty plantins doth grow,
And it's there where two lovers do dwell.

The house is to be seen
  In the middle of the green,
Most beautiful buildings appear;
  Likewise the fishing pond,
  Where the small fish abound,
Makes the hearts of young lovers to cheer.

One evening fresh and fair
  I went out to take the air,
Myself to amuse for a while;
  And there I did hear
  Something tingling in my ear
Which made me in silence to smile.

I slowly stepped on
  To the place where it came from
With the softest of footsteps I could move;
  And 'twas there that I did see,
  At the foot of a tree,
A young man embracing his love.

All in his arms twain,
It was there she did remain,'
While these words unto her he did say—
My dearest of all,
I've got bad news to tell,
For from you, lovey, I must away.

But oh, he said again,
I wish I could remain
Some longer in your company, my dear;
For you're sweeter unto me
Than the honey to the bee,
Or the lark in the morning to cheer.

Your cheek is like the rose
That in yonder garden grows,
And your teeth's like the ivory or snow;
Your skin is white as milk,
And as soft as any silk,
Or the wool that on young lambs doth grow.

Your love is like the moon
That wanders up and down,
And at every month's end it is new;
But mine is like the sun
In the firmament goes round,
And for ever proves constant and true.

Like David and his clan
Banished from his native land,
Like Lazarus was slighted also;
Which causes me to weep
Many a night when I should sleep,
My darling for thinking of you.

But here is your health,
And I wish it were myself,
And to those who are constant and true;
Keeping constant and kind,
Never altering in mind,
Unto those who are constant to you.

THE BONNIE LAD THAT HANDLES THE PLOUGH.

Success and flourish to a' barley rigs,
Here's a health unto the farmer, likewise unto his lads,
Wishin' them to prosper by the handlin' o' the plough,
An' the kissin' o' a bonnie lass when there's nothing else to do.

The tailor he's a laddie that sews at a cloot,
He'll tak' an aul' coat an' he'll turn't inside oot,
He'll turn't inside oot an' he'll mak' it look like new,
But he's far frae like the bonnie lad that handles the plough.

The mason he's a laddie that's prood o' his post,
Gin it werena for the mason we wad a' dee wi' frost;
But the mason's like the rest he'd hae little for to do,
Gin it werena for the bonnie lad that handles the plough.

The smith he's a laddie that's a' owre wi' brook,
But when he sees a bonnie lass sae blythesome he does look,
He kisses her an' claps her an' ca's her his doo;
But he's far frae like the bonnie lad that handles the plough.

The souter he's a laddie that works wi' his awl,
Gin it werena for the souter we wad a' dee wi' caul';
But the souter's like the rest, he'd hae little for to do,
Gin it werena for the bonnie lad that handles the plough.

The wricht he's a laddie that handles the plane,
Gin it werena for the wright we wad a' dee wi' rain;
But he like a' the rest wad get little for to do,
Gin it werena for the bonnie lad that handles the plough.

Note.—The first four lines are always repeated at the end of each verse
as a chorus.

THE FEEING TIME.

A FRIEN' and I struck frae Mulguy,
  For Glasgow town we took our way,
When all along the road was strung
  Wi' lads and bonnie lasses gay.
When drawing nigh one I did spy,
  Was walking slowly by hersel';
For fear the rain her claes might stain,
  I did display my umbrell'.

" Where are you gaun, by bonnie lass?
  How far now are you gaun this way?"
" To Glasgow town, sir, I am bound,
  For this, you know, is feeing day."
Says I, " The day seems wet to be,
  Although the morning did look fine ";
Smiling, she said, " I am afraid
  I'll no' be in by feeing time."

" Cheer up your heart, my bonnie lass,
  We'll hae gude weather by and by;
And don't be sad when wi' a lad—
  A rovin' baker frae Mulguy.
And if you will accept a glass
  O' brandy, whisky, rum, or wine,
We'll hae a gill, and then we will
  Reach Glasgow Fair by feeing time."

She gave consent, and in we went
  Into an ale-house by the way;
Glass after glass around did pass,
  Till we baith forgot it was feeing day.
The clock struck three, she smiled on me;
  " Young man," says she, " the fault is thine,
The night is on, and I'm far from home—
  Besides, I've lost my feeing time."

" My lass, don't grieve, for while I live
  I ne'er intend to harm you;
The marriage tie, if you will try,
  Your baker lad will aye prove true."

" I am too young to wed a man;
  Besides, my mither's nane but me,
But I'll comply, and ne'er deny,
  I'd wed before I'd tak' a fee."

We spent the nicht in merriment,
  And we got wedded the next day;
And aye since then she smiles and says —
  " I'm glad I lost my feeing day."
My love and I do well agree,
  I'm sure she never will repine;
But every day will smile and say—
  " I'm glad I lost my feeing time."

THE TARDY WOOER.

Down in yon valley a young couple tarried,
  A man and a maid both gallant and gay,
Lang, lang had they courted, but ne'er spoke o' marriage,
  Till ae summer's evening the lassie did say—

" A-wooing, a-wooing, I'm wearied a-wooing,
  Ye'll marry, my laddie, or else stand aside;
Although I confess that I lo'e ye most dearly,
  Because you're the flooer o' the hale waterside."

" When a man's married his joys are ended,
  And when a man's married his pleasures are gone;
He's ta'en from a' liberty, tied to a' slavery,
  So fare ye weel, lassie, I'll marry wi' none.

" But if ye be first married call me to your wedding,
  And if I be first married then I'll call on thee,
And should I hear of it I'll come without bidding,
  If e'er such a thing as your marriage should be."

These two lovers parted, awa' went the lassie,
  But she had not gone very far on her way home
When she met with another who proved a true lover,
  And very soon after her favour did gain.

She sent her old lover a fine charming letter,
  To come to her wedding on the ninth day o' June,
As she would prefer him instead of a better
  To stand at her table and serve her bridegroom.

He saddled his steed and rode on to her station,
  Saying, " Oh, had I known you'd have been so soon gone,
I would have married, and no longer tarried,
  So mount on behind me and leave your bridegroom."

" You said, ' When a man's married his joy was ended,
  And when a man's married his pleasure was gone;
He was ta'en from a' liberty, tied to a' slavery,'
  So fare ye weel, young man, I wish you well home.

" Ye may come to my wedding, though no' to my bedding,
  Ye may come to my wedding on the ninth day o' June;
And I will prefer you instead o' a better
  To stand by my table and serve my bridegroom.

" Many's the night that we spent in courting,
  And many's the lang night that we spent in vain;
But though I should live to be a hundred years older,
  I never would spend them so foolish again."

This is a real bothy song, and a matter of thirty years ago it was a great favourite in the North of Scotland, and as it has been frequently asked for recently in the weekly newspapers it must be a favourite among a section of the community.

ALFORD VALE.

Air—" The Shearin's No For You," or " Kelvingrove."

WILL ye come to Alford Vale,
  Bonnie lassie, O?
Where 'tis sunny as thysel',
  Bonnie lassie, O;
Where the Haughton woods are ringin'
With the merlin's merry singin',
To one's bosom solace bringin',
  Bonnie lassie, O.

Wouldst thou leave the city's din,
  Bonnie lassie, O,
For the braiken, broom, and whin,
  Bonnie lassie, O?

And alone—yet not alone—
Wander by the winding Don,
Gliding, gurgling, gambolling on,
  Bonnie lassie, O.

There the sunbeams brightest gleam,
  Bonnie lassie, O,
O'er the woodland, lawn, and stream,
  Bonnie lassie, O.
Where softest falls the dew,
On the lands of rarest hue,
All as beautiful as you,
  Bonnie lassie, O.

There the minstrels sweetest sing,
  Bonnie lassie, O,
Proclaiming earliest spring,
  Bonnie lassie, O.
Where summer in her pride,
As she spreads rich blossoms wide,
Loves the longest to abide,
  Bonnie lassie, O.

'Tis the gem of Scottish vales,
  Bonnie lassie, O,
'Tis the spot for moonlight tales,
  Bonnie lassie, O,
Which young love delights to hear
Pour'd so sweetly in the ear,
From the lips it deems most dear,
  Bonnie lassie, O.

To the dusty town's turmoil,
  Bonnie lassie, O,
Bid a farewell for a while,
  Bonnie lassie, O,
And come to Alford's vale,
To a heart I daurna tell—
That adores thee for thysel',
  Bonnie lassie, O.

Words by La Teste, the Elgin poet, as altered by the editor to suit the melody to which the song is commonly sung.

Printed by permission of the proprietors of the *Elgin Courant and Courier*.

THE CONSTANT LOVER.

ALTHOUGH my parents me disdain,
  For loving of my own dear honey,
It's not my thoughts my mind to change,
  Either for gold or yet for money.

Could I give my love such a slight,
  My friends to please, myself to anger?
O, no, I never will do that,
  I'll prove as true as did Leander.

What hardships for her could I endure!
  To swim the seas for her I'm able;
And joy and pleasure it would be,
  To me to wait upon her table.

And had I all King Cæsar's rents,
  Or all the lands o' Allanbuie,
O, I wad give it all to you,
  If ye wad only let me woo ye.

For I have long a prisoner been,
  And strongly fettered with your beauty;
But bond or free's all one to me,
  I find true love can serve no duty.

The frost and snow kill flowers, you know,
  But in their roots they never sever;
But love's a thing, just like the spring,
  That never dies but rises ever.

If you will die, love, so will I,
  And if you live we'll live together,
That all my friends may plainly see
  Us never part till death us sever.

The honeycomb was ne'er so sweet,
  It never was so sweet unto me,
The honeycomb was ne'er so sweet
  As you are sweet to me, my honey.

This is a curious ballad. It savours of both the old and the new styles. While contrasting the lands of Allanbuie, near Keith, Banffshire, with the rents of Cæsar savours of the ridiculous, the author must have had some knowledge of the Latin poets from his reference to Leander.

BONNIE LASSIE, COME TO THE NORTH HIELANDS.

Down in yon meadow, I chanced for to spy
A bonnie young lassie that pleased my eye;
She had a hat on her head set agee—
Bonnie lassie, come to the North Hielands wi' me.

It's to the North Hielands, lad, I daurna gang,
For dark is the night and the road it is lang,
For dark is the night, and that's nae for me,
So I daurna gang to the North Hielands wi' thee.

It's in the North Hielands I hae a bit land,
And ye will get a'thing just at your command,
And ye will get everything fitting for thee,
Bonnie lassie, come to the North Hielands wi' me.

It's to the North Hielands, lad, I daurna gang,
My mammie and daddie for me wad think lang,
And for their ain lassie I'm sure they wad dee,
Sae I daurna gang to the North Hielands wi' thee.

It's in the North Hielands I hae a green wood,
And ye will get plenty o' sweet milk and crud (curd),
And ye will got plenty o' sugar and tea,
Bonnie lassie, come to the North Hielands wi' me.

It's to the North Hielands, lad, I daurna gang,
For it's for his lassie my lad wad think lang,
It's for his dearie I'm sure he wad dee,
Sae I daurna gang to the North Hielands wi' thee.

It's fare-ye-weel, lassie, and since it is so,
My blessing gang wi' thee where ever ye go,
My blessing gang wi' ye by land or by sea,
Since ye winna gang to the North Hielands wi' me.

It's wait a wee, laddie, O, what's a' your haste?
What I said to you it was but a jest,
Though my mammie and daddie and my frien's a' should dee,
Braw lad, I'll gang to the North Hielands wi' thee.

BOYNDLIE'S BRAES.

Air—" Drumdelgie."

BOYNDLIE's banks and braes are steep,
　And decked wi' flo'ers o' mony a hue,
There the birdies sing sae sweet,
　And burnies wimple down the howe.

　　　　Liltin adie, toorin adie,
　　　　Liltin adie, toorin oo.

There does dwell my bonnie Nell,
　Wi' gowden locks and face sae fair;
And I cam' ower frae Aberdour
　To lat her taste my fruits sae rare.

　　　　Liltin adie, etc.

The lasses about Boyndlie's braes
　They dress themselves wi' care and skill;
But when they a' hae done their best,
　They are but nought unto my Nell.

　　　　Liltin adie, etc.

Her eyes they shine like diamonds fine,
　Her cheeks ye micht bleed wi' a strae;
The blythesome blink o' Nellie's e'e
　Has fairly stown my heart away.

　　　　Liltin adie, etc.

I'm but a 'prentice laddie, yet,
　Jist workin' for my penny fee;
But were I laird o' Boyndlie's lands,
　I wad them a' to Nellie gie.

　　　　Liltin adie, etc.

But we are young and hae nae wit
　O' hoose-haddin' to hae the care;
And we will wait a whilie yet,
　And we will aye be gatherin' mair.

　　　　Liltin adie, etc.

HEARKEN, LADIES, AND I WILL TELL YOU.
Or, THE CONSTANT LOVERS.

HEARKEN, ladies, and I will tell you
  Of a lad and a country lass,
Seven long years they've been a-courting,
  Many a jovial hour 'tween them has passed.

I must away, I can stay no longer,
  The storm and tempest I mean to cross;
But over this mountain I go with pleasure,
  This very night I'll be with my lass.

When he came to his true love's window,
  He kneeled low down upon a stone,
And thro' the pane he whispered low,
  Saying, "Is my true love now within?"

She lifted her head from the soft down pillow,
  And slowly raised her milk-white breast,
Says, "Who is this that's at my window,
  Disturbing me at my night's rest?"

Arise, arise, it's your own true lover,
  Arise, and open and let me in;
For I am weary of my long journey,
  Besides I'm wet, love, unto the skin.

It's up she got with the greatest pleasure
  For to let her true love in;
They kissed, shook hands, and embraced each other,
  And then the long night was at an end.

THE TEEM WA'S.

COME, hark a while, and I will speak,
Yonder's a house where I never saw reek,
It's a' enclosèd but the lum,
But surely the wa's belangs to some.

"Indeed, kind sir, I canna weel tell;
But here's the young man comin' himsel',
And he will tell you a' the cause
Hoo naebody lives in yon teem wa's."

Come, hark a while, and I will speir,
What frightens folk frae bidin' here?
Gin ghost or boodies mak' a din
At yon house back or yet within?

"Come hither by and tak' a lean
At this dykeside, it's dry and clean,
And I'll tell you the very cause
Why naebody lives within yon wa's."

"Indeed, kind sir, I will speak free—
I want a wife to bide wi' me;
But the lasses they're so very scant,
And I dinna like to be in want."

Ye are a fool for sayin' so,
Ye micht hae twa when ane wad do;
The lasses they're nae sae very scant,
For there's mony a bonnie lassie a man does want.

"But, what way will I come to know
Gin the lassie she likes me or no?"
Look to her face and behold her eyes,
And you'll shortly know where her love lies.

It's sometimes aye, and sometimes no,
And by other tokens you'll come to know;
For the lasses mony a time say no,
When it's just the road they want to go.

But dinna court ane that is owre auld,
Or than wi' her ye may catch cauld;
And dinna court ane that is owre young,
Or she may deave ye wi' her tongue.

Dinna tak' ane for the sake o' her siller,
Gin that be the thing that's drawin' ye to her:
And dinna tak' ane that's fond o' braws,
She'll ne'er dae weel in yon teem wa's.

For siller's but a blindin' bribe,
Haps mony a faut and a failin' side;
And afterwards it will appear
When folks begin to lose the gear.

And beauty it is but a cheat,
Leads mony a young man aff o's feet;
And afterwards he'll come to know
That beauty's naething but a show.

But if ye wish to get aff the stage,
Try and get ane about middle age;
Try and get ane that's baith modest and douce,
And then tak' her hame to yon teem house.

" The very next time that ye come by,
Ye'll see my lum, it will reek to the sky;
And ye'll get a supper o' a gude fat hen,
And ye'll get a nicht o' a bed in the ben."

ROSEY ANDERSON.

HAY MARSHALL was a gentleman as ever lived on earth,
He courted Rosey Anderson, a lady into Perth;
He courted her, and married her, made her his wedded wife.
And at that day, I dare to say, he loved her as his life.

There was an Assembly into Perth, and Rosey she was there;
Lord Elgin danced with her that night, and did her heart
ensnare,
Lord Elgin danced with her that night, and then conveyed her
home;
Hay Marshall he came rushing in before he left the room.

" I'm all into surprised," he says, " I'm all into surprise,
To see you kiss my wedded wife before my very eyes."
" Do not be in surprise," he says, " nor do not think it odd.
Though I've conveyed your lady home from the dangers on the
road.

" I did not kiss your wedded wife, nor did I with her stay,
I only brought her safely home from the dangers on the way."
" Oh, had she not a maid," he says, " or had she not a guide?
Or had she not a candle-light, or why was she afraid?"

Betty she was called upon the quarrel for to face—
" I would have brought my lady home but Lord Elgin took
    my place."
" Although you be a Lord," he said, " and I but a provost's son,
I'll make you smart for this, my Lord, although you think it's
    fun."

He took his Rosey by the hand, and led her through the room,
Saying, " I'll send you up to fair London till a' this clash goes
    down;
I'll send you up till fair London, your mother to be your guide,
And let them all say what they will, I'll still be on your side."

Weeks barely nine she had not been into fair London toun
Till word came back to Hay Marshall that Rosey play'd the
    loun:
" Oh, woe be to your roses red that ever I loved you,
For to forsake your own husband amongst the beds o' rue."

A lady from her window high was spying with her glass,
And what did she spy but a light grey gown rolling amongst the
    grass;
Hay Marshall had twenty witnesses, and Rosey had but two:
" Waes me!" cries Rosey Anderson. " Alas! what shall I do?

" My very meat I cannot take, my clothes I wear them worse:
Waes me!" cries Rosey Anderson, " my life to me's a curse;
If it was to do what's done," she says, " if it was to do what's
    done,
Hay Marshall's face I would embrace, Lord Elgin's I would
    shun.

" The springtime is coming on, some regiments will be here,
I'll maybe get an officer my broken heart to cheer."
Now she has got an officer her broken heart to bind,
Now she has got an officer, but he has proved unkind.

He's left her for to lie her lane, which causes her to cry:
" In Bedlam I must lie my lane, in Bedlam I must die!
Ye ladies all, both far and near, a warning take by me,
And don't forsake your own husbands for any Lords you see."

Thomas Hay Marshall, the husband of Rosey Anderson, was for a time
Provost of Perth himself, and Lord Elgin who figures in the ballad was
subsequently British Ambassador at Constantinople, and it was he who
brought what is known as the " Elgin marbles " from that city to the British
Museum.

JOHNNY SANDS.

A MAN whose name was Johnny Sands
　　Had married Betty Haig,
And though she brought him gold and lands,
　　She proved a terrible plague.
For, oh, she was a scolding wife,
　　Full of caprice and whim;
He said that he was tired of life,
　　And she was tired of him,
　　And she was tired of him.

Says he, Then I wall drown myself;
　　The river runs below.
Says she, Pray do, you silly elf,
　　I wished it long ago.
Says he, Upon the brink I'll stand,
　　Do you run down the hill
And push me in with all your might.
　　Says she, My love, I will,
　　Says she, My love, I will.

For fear that I should courage lack,
　　And try to save my life,
Pray, tie my hands behind my back.
　　I will, replied his wife.
She tied them fast as you may think,
　　And when securely done;
Now stand, she says, upon the brink
　　And I'll prepare to run,
　　And I'll prepare to run.

All down the hill his loving bride
　　Now ran with all her force
To push him in, he stepped aside,
　　And she fell in, of course.
Now splashing, dashing like a fish;
　　Oh, save me, Johnny Sands.
I can't, my dear, though much I wish,
　　For you have tied my hands,
　　For you have tied my hands.

THE GAIRDNER AND THE PLOUGHMAN.

A GAIRDNER lad that lives near by,
  Lang he has wooed me;
And he's gi'en me his hert to keep,
  A pledge o' love to be-be,
  A pledge o' love to be.

Sae lang's I keep't my gairdner's hert,
  I lat my ain gang free;
But the blithe blink o' the plooman lad
  Has stown my hert frae me-me,
  Has stown my hert frae me.

The first time that I saw my love,
  I was ploughin' on yon brae broo,
And I could neither haud nor ca',
  It was a' for the love o' you-you,
  It was a' for the love o' you.

The next time that I did you see,
  You were under a bush o' rue;
And aye the sweeter that ye sang
  The nearer the bush I drew-drew,
  The nearer the bush I drew.

Mak' up your goon my bonnie lass,
  And mak' it neat and fine;
And ye shall be the plooman's wife,
  For the gairdner's changed his min'-min',
  For the gairdner's changed his min'.

The plooman lad he hearin' this,
  Just in a bush near by;
Says, "Say nae mair, my bonnie lassie,
  O, ye ken better why-why,
  O, ye ken better why.

The last time that I did you see,
  You were under a bush o' rue;
And aye the sweeter that ye sang
  The nearer the bush I drew-drew,
  The nearer the bush I drew.

BLOW THE CANDLE OUT.

'Twas a young apprentice boy
    Came courting his dear,
The moon was shining bright
    And the stars were twinkling clear;
He went to his love's window
    To ease her of her pain:
His darling rose and let him in,
    Then went to bed again.

It's early next morning,
    Before the break of day;
The laddie rose, put on his clothes,
    A' for to go away;
But when that he was going away,
    His love to him called out—
" Come, take me in your arms, love,
    And blow the candle out."

My father and my mother,
    They taunt me very sore
For keeping o' your company, love,
    But I will keep it more,
For a' the taunts that they can gi'e
    They'll never change my heart;
So, come here, my dear, and I'll meet you here,
    Let the night be ever so dark.

Your father and your mother
    In yonder room do lie,
Embracing one another,
    And so may you and I;
Embracing one another
    Without a fear or doubt,
So take me in your arms, love,
    And blow the candle out.

My bosom is on fire, love,
    The more I gaze on thee,
And as I wander lower
    I am no longer free;
And while I gaze your rosy lips
    Do sweetly seem to pout,
So hasten to my arms, love,
    And blow the candle out.

THE WIND BLEW THE BONNIE LASSIE'S PLAIDIE AWA'.

Air—" The White Cockade."

FRAE a butcher laddie that lived in Crieff,
A bonnie lassie cam' to buy some beef;
He took her in his arms and down she did fa',
And the wind blew the bonnie lassie's plaidie awa'.
   Her plaidie awa', her plaidie awa',
   The wind blew the bonnie lassie's plaidie awa'.

The plaidie was lost and it couldna be found,
The deil's in the plaid, it's awa' wi' the win';
An' what will I say to the auld folks ava?
I daurna say the win' blew the plaidie awa'.
   The plaidie awa', etc.

It wasna lang after the plaidie was lost,
Till the bonnie lassie grew thick about the waist,
And Rab he was blamed for the hale o' it a',
And the win' blawin' the bonnie lassie's plaidie awa'.
   Her plaidie awa', etc.

Then Rab he was summoned to answer the Session,
An' they a' cried out ye maun mak' a confession;
But Rab never answered them ae word ava
But " the win' blew the bonnie lassie's plaidie awa'."
   Her plaidie awa', etc.

The auld wife cam' in poor Rab to accuse,
The minister an' elders began to abuse
Poor Rab for tryin' to mak' ane into twa;
But Rab said, " The win' blew the plaidie awa'."
   The plaidie awa', etc.

The lassie was sent for to come there hersel',
She look'd in his face, says, " Ye ken hoo I fell?
An' ye were the cause o't, ye daurna say na',
For 'twas then that the win' blew my plaidie awa'."
   My plaidie awa', etc.

Rab look'd in her face and he gied a bit smile,
He says, " Bonnie lassie, I winna you beguile,
The minister he's here he'll mak' ane o' us twa,
That will pay for the plaid that the win' blew awa'."
    That the win' blew awa', etc.

The whisky was sent for to mak' a' thing richt,
The minister an' elders they sat a' nicht,
They sat an' they sang till the cock he did craw,
" The win' blew the bonnie lassie's plaidie awa'."
    Her plaidie awa', etc.

Now Rab and his lassie they are han' in han',
An' they live as contented as ony in the lan';
An' when he gets drunk he minds on the fa',
An' he sings," 'Twas the win' blew the plaidie awa'."
    Her plaidie awa', her plaidie awa',
    'Twas the win' blew the bonnie lassie's plaidie awa'.

KISSIN' IN THE DARK.

FOR lang I courted Jeanie,
    And wrocht wi' might and main,
To get a puckle siller
    And a biggin' o' my ain;
Ilka nicht I gaed to see her,
    Be it late or be it mirk,
And when she cam' to meet me,
    I wad kiss her in the dark.

        The dark, the dark,
        The dark, the dark, the dark;
        And when she cam' to meet me,
        I wad kiss her in the dark.

Ae nicht I gaed to see her,
    And my Jeanie bein' frae hame,
I slippit to the window
    And I rattled at the pane;
Oot cam' Jeanie's mither,
    And the nicht it bein' sae dark,
I took her in my airms
    And kissed her in the dark.
        The dark, etc.

She ruggit, and she tuggit,
　　And she tried to get awa';
But I held her aye the closer,
　　And I gae her ither twa';
Then oot she burst a-lauchin',
　　Says, " This is awfa' wark,
To tousle an aul' body
　　And to kiss her in the dark."

　　　　The dark, etc.

Then I made for rinnin',
　　But she held me sure and fast;
Says, " Ye needna' be in a hurry, man,
　　The secret's oot at last;
Jeanie's doon at auntie's,
　　And she'll get an awfa' start,
When I tell her how ye tousled me
　　And kissed me in the dark.

　　　　The dark, etc.

I stopped wi' Jeanie's mither,
　　Till my Jeanie did come hame,
She tell't her a' the story,
　　Which I thocht an awfa' shame;
But noo I've gotten Jeanie
　　Aifter a' the coortin' wark,
And there's few that lands so lucky
　　Wi' their kissin' in the dark.

　　　　The dark, etc.

We hidna lang been marriet
　　When Jeanie's mither grew ill;
She sent for a lawyer,
　　She was gaen to mak' her will,
She has left me a' her siller,
　　And made mony a remark;
For I got the aul' wife's blessin'
　　For the kissin' in the dark.

　　　　　　The dark, the dark,
　　　　　　The dark, the dark, the dark;
　　　　　　For when she cam' to meet me,
　　　　　　I kissed her in the dark.

THE BONNIE WEE WINDOW.

THERE was a young lass, and her name it was Nell,
In a bonnie wee house wi' her grannie did dwell,
The house it was wee, but the windows were less,
It had but four panes and ane wanted gless.

   'Twas a bonnie wee window, a sweet little window,
   The bonniest window that ever ye saw.

For this broken pane they a purpose did fin',
To lat onything out, or tak' onything in;
But to Nelly it served for a purpose maist dear,
For her lovers at nicht cam' a-courting her here

   At this bonnie wee window, etc.

It happened ae nicht grannie gaed to her bed,
That Johnnie, the brawest lad young Nelly had,
Cam' far o'er the hills his dear lassie to see,
And wi' high expectations there planted was he,

   At this bonnie wee window, etc.

But the fond, youthfu' pair hadna got muckle said
When grannie cried, " Nell, come awa to your bed ";
" I'm comin', dear grannie," young Nelly did say;
" So, fare-ye-weel, Johnnie, for I maun away

   Frae this bonnie wee window," etc.

" Oh! Nelly, dear lass, dinna tak' it amiss,
But before ye gae 'wa' ye maun grant me a kiss,"
So aff gaed his bonnet, but gudeness kens hoo
He managed sae quickly to get his head through

   This bonnie wee window, etc.

A kiss Johnnie got, and sweet was the smack,
But for his dear life couldna get his head back,
He ruggit, he tuggit, he bawled, and he cursed,
Till Nell's sides wi' lauchin' were baith like to burst,

   At his head in the window, etc.

Noo when the auld grannie did hear the uproar
She rax'd for the poker, syne ran to the door,
And ower Johnnie's back sic a thump she laid on,
Anither sic like would ha'e crack'd his backbone.

    And his head in the window, etc.

A' burnin' wi' shame, and smarting wi' pain,
He ruggit and tuggit wi' micht and wi' main,
Till the jambs they gaed way and the lintel did break,
Though still the best half o't stuck to his neck.

    'Twas an awfu' wee window, etc.

As soon as the window in ruins did lie,
Auld grannie let out such a horrible cry,
It alarmed a' the neighbours—lad, lass, man, and wife,
And caused poor Johnnie to rin for his life

    Frae the bonnie wee window, etc.

O'er hill and o'er dale he pursued his way hame,
Like a bear that was hunted, ne'er lookin' behin';
And the neighbours they followed wi' clamour and squeals,
While some o' them hunted their dogs at his heels,

    As he ran frae the window, etc.

When Johnnie got hame, wi' a hatchet did he
Frae his wooden gravat syne set himsel' free;
But he vow'd that the deil micht tak' him for his ain
If he e'er kissed a lass through a window again,

    Be she ever sae bonnie, or live wi' her grannie,
    Or the bonniest wee lassie that ever he saw.

JOHNNIE'S GOT HIS JEAN, O.

"O, LASS, gin ye wad think it richt,
To gang wi' me this very nicht,
We'll cuddle till the mornin' licht,
    By a' the lave unseen, O;
      And ye shall be my dearie,
      My ain dearest dearie;
      It's ye shall be my dearie
        Gin ye meet me at e'en, O."

" I daurna for my mammie gae,
She locks the door and keeps the key;
And e'en and mornin' charges me,
　　And aye aboot the men, O.
　　　She says they're a' deceivers,
　　　Deceivers, deceivers,
　　　She says they're a' deceivers,
　　　　We canna trust to ane, O."

" O, never mind your mammie's yell,
Nae doubt she met your dad hersel';
And should she flyte ye may her tell
　　She's aften dune the same, O.
　　　Sae, lassie, gie's yer hand on't,
　　　Your bonnie milk-white hand on't,
　　　O, lassie, gie's your hand on't,
　　　　And scorn to lie your lane, O."

" O, lad, my hand I canna gie,
But aiblins I may steal the key,
And meet you at the birken tree
　　That grows down in the glen, O.
　　　But dinna lippen, laddie,
　　　I canna promise, laddie,
　　　O, dinna lippen, laddie,
　　　　In case I canna win, O."

Noo, he's gane to the birken tree,
In hopes his true love there to see;
And wha cam' trippin' owre the lea,
　　But his ain dear, bonnie Jean, O.
　　　And she clink'd doon beside him,
　　　Beside him, beside him,
　　　And she clink'd doon beside him,
　　　　Upon the grass sae green, O.

I'm overjoyed wi' rapture noo,"
Cried he, and pree'd her cherry mou',
And Jean she ne'er had cause to rue
　　That nicht upon the green, O.
　　　For she has got her Johnnie,
　　　Her sweet and loving Johnnie,
　　　For noo she's got her Johnnie,
　　　　And Johnnie's got his Jean, O.

THE GALLANT SHOEMAKER.

THERE lived a maiden down near-by
  And, oh, but she was a charming creature;
Her father he had none but she,
  And her love was a gallant shoemaker.

    Her father he had none but she,
      And her love was a gallant shoemaker.

She was courted by none o' the worst,
  And amang the rest was a rich young farmer,
He swore he would have her for his wife,
  And wi' hooses and lan's he would invest her.

    He swore he would have, etc.

Some delight in the farmin' line,
  But my bonnie love delights in leather;
Him I love and long to see,
  And I'll ne'er forsake my shoemaker.

    Him I love, etc.

" Never mind," her father said,
  " Into a room I will confine her;
And I will make her gie consent
  To marry wi' this rich young farmer."

She has written a broad letter
  And sent it to her shoemaker—
" For your sake I'm keepit close,
  And can see neither win' nor weather.

" Men and horses, lovie, ye'll provide,
  Or else the farmer he will get me;
And at the twalt hour o' the nicht
  Ye'll frae the farmer come and tak' me.

" I often wake, I seldom sleep,
  I'll quickly dress and soon be ready;
And o'er the window to you I'll creep,
  For fear o' wakenin' o' my daddy."

When he had read the letter o'er,
  It put him in an unco swither,
He being but a poor 'prentice lad,
  And had nae way for to do wi' her.

But yet again the letter said—
  "Though we be young we'll gather siller,
The world's wide, and wi' you I'll bide,
  Afore I marry a drudgin' farmer."

As he cam' ridin' up the street,
  She heard the horse's feet clitter, clatter—
"Sleep ye, or wake ye, my bonnie love?
  For here am I your shoemaker."

When she was on his high horse set,
  And on behind her shoemaker,
She bade the minstrels a' play up—
  "My love's a gallant shoemaker";
And aye she bade the minstrels play—
  "Adieu and fareweel to the rich young farmer."

And when she was in her down bed laid,
  And down beside her shoemaker;
She bade them a' do as they liked,
  For she had gotten her shoemaker;
Aye, she bade them please themsel's,
  For she had gotten her shoemaker.

THERE CAM' A LADDIE FRAE THE NORTH.

THERE cam' a laddie frae the north,
  Wi' courage frank and free;
And he's fa'en in love wi' a bonnie lass
  That lived into Dundee.

"What aileth thee, my bonnie lass,
  That the saut tear blin's your e'e?"
"O, haud your tongue, young man," she said,
  "And dinna scorn me.

"Dinna ye mind, young man," she said,
  "When sportin' we hae been,
Ye promised for to marry me,
  And frae shame ye wad me screen?"

" And sae I will, my bonnie lass,
    Ere mony months gae by,
I will come back and marry you
    And tak' ye to Strathspey."

" The Hielan' hills are very high,
    And, O, they're ill to clim',
And I fear if ance ye get owre them
    Ye'll no come back again.

" Besides, your father he will fret,
    Your mither she will frown,
Your sisters they will say to me,
    Gae hame, ye lowland dame."

" Ye dread sae muckle ill o' me,
    I fear ye'll smell the rue;
And if ye slight my parents dear,
    I will bid you adieu."

He's ta'en his pikestaff in his hand,
    His kilt abeen his knee;
Says, " Fare-ye-weel, my bonnie lass,
    For ye'll get nae mair o' me."

He's gane hame to his mither,
    But nae sleep could wink his e'e
For thinkin' o' the bonnie lass
    He left into Dundee.

" What aileth thee, my only son?
    Ye've lost your mirth and glee;
I fear your heart it is not here,
    Ye've left it in Dundee.

" Ye'll tak' your pikestaff in your hand,
    Wi' your kilt abeen your knee;
It's only like three score o' mile
    Until ye cross the Dee."

He's put on his Sunday coat,
    Wi' his kilt abeen his knee,
And he's ta'en the lassie by the hand
    That he left in Dundee.

Kissin's good in Februar',
  And clappin's good in May;
But I hae married my bonnie lass,
  And ta'en her to Strathspey.

WI' HIS APRON ON.

COME all ye young lovers, I pray give attention,
  And listen a wee, wee whilie to me;
I'll sing ye a sang concerning twa lovers—
  A bonnie mason laddie comin' frae Lochee.
    Singin', Fal the reedle airie, rodi, rodi,
    Singin', Fal de reedle airie, rodi, O.

Oh, lang has he courted the bloomin' young lassie.
  And oft to her father's dwellin' he cam';
She was not afraid to go out in the gloamin'
  And meet her mason lad wi' his apron on.
    Singin', Fal the reedle airie, etc.

One evening they walked out the road thegither,
  And wandered till daylight was almost gone;
They sat them down on a bank together,
  And he kissed his lass wi' his apron on.

Aye as he rolled her into his arms
  The charms of love began to flow;
He said, " Bonnie lass, will ye marry a mason?
  It's my intention this night to know."

" Indeed, bonnie laddie, I'll be plain and tell you,
  My heart and affections from others are gone,
You'll be welcome to wed me and then to bed me,.
  And kiss me aye wi' your apron on."

Now this couple they hae got married,
  And he has brought her safely home,
And now they sit at the fireside together,
  And he kisses her aye wi' her apron on.
    Singin', Fal the reedle airie, rodi, rodi,
    Fal al de eddle airie, rodi, O.

ERIN'S LOVELY HOME.

ALL ye that are at liberty,
  I pray ye will draw near;
A sad and dismal story
  I mean to let you hear.
Here in this foreign country
  I languish, sigh, and moan,
When I think on the days I spent
  In Erin's lovely home.

When I was young and in my prime
  My age was twenty-one;
Then I became a servant
  Unto a gentleman.
I served him right honestly,
  As to everyone is known,
Until cruelly he banished me
  From Erin's lovely home.

The reason of my banishment
  I mean to let you know;
It's true I loved his daughter,
  And she loved me also.
She had a handsome fortune,
  And riches I had none;
That's the reason why he banished me
  From Erin's lovely home.

It was in her father's garden,
  All in the month of June,
The flowers they were springing,
  And roses in full bloom;
She said, " My dearest Billy,
  If you with me will roam,
You'll never fret for those you left
  In Erin's lovely home.

That very night I gave consent,
  I mean to let you know;
And from her father's dwelling
  Along with her did go.
The night was bright with the moonlight,
  When we set off alone,
Still hoping to get safe away
  From Erin's lovely home.

When we arrived at Belfast town
  About the break of day,
She said, " Prepare, my jewel,
  Our passage for to pay."
Five hundred pounds she did lay down,
  Saying, " That is all your own;
So never fret for those you left
  In Erin's lovely home."

But to my sad misfortune,
  I mean to let you hear,
In two or three days after
  Her father did appear,
He marched me off to Omagh Jail,
  In the county of Tyrone;
And cruelly he banished me
  From Erin's lovely home.

When word came to the jail-gate,
  To take us all away,
My true love she came up to me,
  And thus to me did say—
" Cheer up your heart, dear Billy,
  I'll never you disown,
Until that you return again
  To Erin's lovely home."

There's seven links upon my chain,
  And every link a year,
Before I can return again
  To the arms of my dear.
So in this foreign country,
  I languish, sigh, and moan,
Far from my parents and my friends
  In Erin's lovely home.

THE BONNIE MASON LADDIE.

SIMMER's gaun awa',
   And the winter's comin' on,
And the bonnie mason laddies
   They'll be comin' home
Wi' their pockets fu' o' siller,
   And their lasses for to see;
And the bonnie mason laddie
   He will marry me.

I winna hae the sailor
   That sails on the sea;
Nor yet will I the ploughman
   That ploughs on the lea;
But I will hae the mason,
   For he's a bonnie lad,
And I'll wash the mason's apron,
   And think it nae degrade.

I winna hae the blacksmith
   That burns a' the airn;
Nor yet will I the weaver
   That works the creeshy yarn;
But I will hae the mason
   And the mason he'll hae me,
And the bonnie mason laddie
   I'll mount the scaffold wi'.

JAMIE AND JEANIE—A DUET.

Jeanie—

WHAT is the way ye're lookin' sae glum
   And why are ye turnin' awa?
I'm sure I've deen naething, at least that I ken,
   That's likely to grieve ye ava.

Jamie—

Yestreen at the ball, ye mind it fu' weel,
   Ye danced wi' nae less than ither three;
And if that's nae eneuch noo to grieve me fu' sair,
   For ye ken ye were promised to me.

Jeanie—

I danced at the ball as a lassie wad dee,
    I ken ye wad ta'en me and a';
But I'll dance wi' a chiel gin I like him fu' weel,
    Ay, and that tee when ye are awa'.

Jamie—

Oh, little dee ye ken o' the pain at my heart,
    Ye're sighin' again to be free;
Ye can gang if ye wish to anither man's airms,
    But ye ken ye were promised to me.

Jeanie—

Here is the ring ye gied me afore,
    I'll wear it nae langer ava;
I'll get a lad as guid that'll dae as he's bid,
    Ay, and that tee when ye are awa'.

Jamie—

Tak' back the ring, Jeanie, tak' it again,
    For, oh, it wad grieve me fu' sair;
Ye'll ne'er get a chiel that'll lo'e ye sae weel,
    For ye ken ye were promised to me.

Jeanie—

I'll tak' back the ring, Jamie, tak' it again,
    And together through life we will fare;
Until death does us pairt, ye will reign in my heart,
    And, Jamie, we'll quarrel nae mair.

Both.

Noo I am thine (Jamie),
(Jeanie), noo I am thine,
    And together through life we shall be;
Till death do us part ye shall reign in my heart,
    For (I) ken (I am) promised to (thee)
       (ye)   (ye are)   (me).

PEGGY IN THE MORNING.

Noo, mither, confess, a' the lasses ye saw
Yestreen at the wedding, sae trig and sae braw,
And wasna my Peggy the flooer o' them a',
   Like a new - blown rose in the mornin'?

My Peggy she's fair, and my Peggy she's fine,
Her cheeks are like lilies all dipped in wine,
Her eyes how they sparkle, how brightly they shine,
   Like the stars on a fine frosty mornin'.

" O Johnnie, O Johnnie, your prospects are sma',
Gin ye marry Peggy ye'll soon ruin's a';
She busks and she dresses and she gangs aye sae braw,
   But what time does she rise in the mornin'?

" She lies in her bed till eleven o' the day,
And then she prepares for her toast and her tea;
Your freens will be angry, and that widna dee,
   Sae, Johnnie, be wise and tak' warnin'.

" O Johnnie, O Johnnie, your prospects are fine,
Your meal-pocks and rag-bags sae finely they'll shine,
Brak' ye the vow and the faut shall be mine,
   For you'll ruin yersel' and your mither."

I saw Peggy's father just this very day,
And tauld him I was takin' his daughter away—
Widna that noo be perjury black as a slae
   To leave her and go to anither?

" O Johnnie, O Johnnie, and what did he say,
When ye said ye were takin' his Peggy away,
When ye said ye were takin' his Peggy away
   To mak' her your ain in the mornin'?"

He said he wad gie me twa horse and a coo,
A hun'er o' his sheep and three packs o' oo,
To plenish a place at the back o' the broo,
   To be wark to my Peggy in the mornin'.

" O Johnnie, O Johnnie, your Peggy's better noo,
When I think o' the danger o' brakin' your vow;
Your auld mither's blessin' gang wi' Peggy and you
   And be wi' ye baith evenin' and mornin'."

THE GREEN WOODS O' AIRLIE.

THE bonniest lass in a' the countryside
  Has fa'en in love wi' the ploughman laddie;
But little did she think that her heart was betrayed,
  At the fit o' the green woods o' Airlie.

Refrain.

  O, my lad, my bonnie ploughman lad,
    The lad I lo'e so dearly;
  Though I were to search the country all around,
    There's nane to me like my dearie.

Sweetly she sang till a' the woods rang,
  And, oh, she sang so cheerie,
For at every ither turn he made her heart to burn,
  Her heart it was wounded fairly.

    O, my bonnie lad, etc.

Sweet were the flowers and sweet was the dew
  On a bonnie simmer's mornin' early;
But sweeter is the bonnie lad that holds the painful plough,
  At the fit o' the green woods o' Airlie.

    O, my bonnie lad, etc.

Love's hottest glow is kindled in my breast,
  And, oh, but it beats so sairly;
There is none in this world can bring me comfort and rest
  But my handsome ploughman laddie.

    O, my bonnie lad, etc.

If I could indite I would soon a letter write,
  And send it on to my dearie,
To say that my heart it had been betrayed
  At the fit o' the green woods o' Airlie.

    O, my bonnie lad, etc.

Now the ploughman lad he has come owre the lea,
  And it was to the bower o' his dearie,
For the day was appointed that married they should be
  At the fit o' the green woods o' Airlie.

    O, my bonnie lad, etc.

Now they are married and in ae bed laid,
  And, O, but they sing cheerie;
And sae happy they will be, for in love they agree,
  At the fit o' the green woods o' Airlie.
    O, my lad, my bonnie ploughman lad,
      The lad I lo'e so dearly,
    Though I were to search the country all around,
      There's nane to me like my dearie.

MY BONNIE LADDIE'S LANG, LANG O' GROWING.

THE trees they are ivied, the leaves they are green,
The days are awa that I hae seen,
On the cauld winter nichts I hae to lie my lane,
  For my bonnie laddie's lang, lang o' growing.

O, father dear, ye have done me great wrong,
You have wedded me to a boy that's too young,
He's scarce twelve, and I'm but thirteen,
  And my bonnie laddie's lang, lang o' growing.

O, daughter dear, I have done you no wrong,
I have wedded you to a noble lord's son,
He'll be the lord, and ye'll wait on,
  And your bonnie laddie's daily growing.

O, father dear, if you think it fit,
We'll send him to the college a year or twa yet;
And we'll tie a green ribbon round about his hat,
  And that will be a token that he's married.

And, O, father dear, if this pleases you,
I will cut my hair aboon my brow;
Coat, vest, and breeches I will put on,
  And I to the college will go wi' him.

She's made him shirts o' the Holland sae fine,
And wi' her ain hands she sewed the same;
And aye the tears cam' trickling down,
  Saying, my bonnie laddie's lang, lang o' growing.

In his twelfth year he was a married man,
And in his thirteenth he had got a son,
And in his fourteenth his grave it grew green,
  Sae that put an end to his growing.

THE BONNIE PARKS O' KILTY.

On the south-east of Perth there lived a fair maid,
She wandered late and ear' and she never was afraid,
She walked both late and ear' and she never was afraid
   For meeting wi' the young laird o' Kilty, O.

It's out it spake her mother and she spoke wi' a smile,
Says, I wonder very much that you walk so late, my child,
You walk both late and ear' and you never are afraid
   For meeting wi' the young laird o' Kilty, O.

She has fastened up her yellow locks a little above her e'e,
And she's kilted up her petticoats a little below her knee,
And so neatly as she walked by the harrows and the ploughs,
   And she's down through the bonnie parks o' Kilty, O.

She had not left her father's house I think but scarce a mile,
When she heard a voice behind her say, stay, my pretty child,
She heard a voice behind her say, stay, my pretty child,
   Don't you know you're in the bonnie parks o' Kilty, O?

She turned her gently round about a sad tear blint her e'e,
Says, I will turn back again if I've offended thee,
Says, I will turn back again if I've offended thee,
   For I know I'm in the bonnie parks o' Kilty, O.

O, stay wi' me, my darling, just stop a little while,
When the harrows and the ploughs are loosed I'll go wi' you a
    mile,
When the harrows and the ploughs are loosed I'll go with you a
    mile,
   I'll convoy you from the bonnie parks o' Kilty, O.

He's ta'en her by the middle sma' and gently laid her down,
Where the apples and the cherries were a' hanging down,
The lilies and the green grass were growing all around
   Where they lay on the bonnie parks o' Kilty, O.

What will you tell your mother, my dear, when you go home?
Who will you say to your mother has done ye a' the wrong?
What will you say to your mother, my dear, when you go home?
   Will you say it was the young laird o' Kilty, O?

Just as she was going to make him some reply,
It's up it starts her father just from a bush nearby;
Says, You'll wed my daughter quickly or down her tocher pay,
  Or I'll forfeit your bonnie parks o' Kilty, O.

O, hold your tongue, old man, and do not angry be,
Although that your daughter is of a low degree,
I'll raise her to a higher, a lady for to be,
  Make her lady o' the bonnie parks o' Kilty, O.

Now, he loved this pretty girlie, as dearly as his life,
He loved this pretty girlie and made her his wedded wife,
And she sits in his house and is happy as a queen,
  For she's lady o' the bonnie parks o' Kilty, O.

BOGIE'S BRAES.

Air—" Logan Water."

By Bogie's streams that rin sae deep,
Fu' aft wi' glee I've herded sheep:
I've herded sheep, or gathered slaes
Wi' my dear lad on Bogie's Braes.
But waes my heart thae days are gane,
And fu' o' grief I herd my lane;
While my dear lad maun face his faes,
Far, far frae me and Bogie's Braes.

Nae mair at Huntly kirk will he
Atween the preachings meet wi' me—
Meet wi' me or when it's mirk
Convoy me hame frae Huntly kirk.
I weel may sing thae days are gane,
Frae kirk and fair I come my lane;
While my dear lad maun face his faes,
Far, far frae me and Bogie's Braes.

I picked up these lines from the singing of an old woman named
Mrs. Green who resided in Huntly. They are simply a parody on Logan
Braes and were sung to the air of Logan Water.

SALLY MUNRO.

COME all ye young females, I pray you attend
Unto these few verses that I have here penned,
I'll tell you the hardships I did undergo
With my bonnie young lassie called Sally Munro.

James Dickson's my name, I'm a blacksmith to trade,
In the town of Ayr I was born and bred,
And from that to Belfast I lately did go,
'Twas there I got acquainted with young Sally Munro.

I to this young lassie a letter did send,
It was by a comrade, I thought him a friend,
But instead of a friend to me he proved a foe,
He ne'er gave my letter to young Sally Munro.

He told her old mother to beware of me,
He said I'd a wife in my own countrie;
O, then said her mother, now since it is so,
He ne'er shall enjoy his young Sally Munro.

For two months and better I never could hear
A word from the maid that I once loved so dear,
Until that one evening, 'twas in Sandy Row,
It's who did I meet but young Sally Munro.

I told her if she'd come to Newry with me,
In spite of her parents there married we'd be;
She said no objections have I now to go
If ye will prove constant to Sally Munro.

Now, here is my love and here is my heart,
Till death separate us we never will part;
Next day in a coach we to Newry did go,
And there I got married to Sally Munro.

'Twas at Warren's point the ship Munro lay,
With four hundred passengers ready for sea,
Then we paid our passage for Quebec also,
And there I embarked with young Sally Munro.

On the fourteenth of April from the point we did sail,
And bore down the channel with a pleasant gale;
The parting of friends made some tears for to flow,
But I was quite happy with my Sally Munro.

On the second evening there came on a fog,
There on the Welsh coast our vessel did log,
In Carnarvon Bay when all merry below,
I never thought of parting with Sally Munro.

At nine o'clock that night near Bradsea we drew,
But the mist hid both light and land from our view,
The women and children were all down below,
And amongst the rest was my Sally Munro.

Here, dreading no danger, we met a great shock,
'Twas all of a sudden our ship struck a rock;
Three hundred and sixty who were down below
Were drowned—so I lost my young Sally Munro.

Many a man in this voyage lost his wife
And children he loved as dear as his life,
Though my life was preserved yet my tears down do flow,
And I sigh when I think of young Sally Munro.

It was from her parents I took her away,
Which will trouble my conscience till my dying day;
It was not to injure her that I did do so,
All my life I will mourn for my Sally Munro.

JEAN AND CALEDONIA.

Sair, sair was my heart, when I parted frae my Jean,
And sair, sair I sighed, while the tears stood in my e'en,
For my daddie is but poor and my fortune is but sma';
Which gars me leave my native Caledonia.

When I think on the days now gane, and how happy I hae been,
While wanderin' wi' my dearie where the primrose blaws unseen;
I'm wae to leave my lassie, and my daddie's simple ha',
Or the hills and healthfu' breeze o' Caledonia.

But wherever I wander, still happy be my Jean,
Nae care disturb her bosom where peace has ever been!
Then, though ills on ills befa' me, for her I'll bear them a',
Though I aft will heave a sigh for Caledonia.

But should riches e'er be mine, and my Jeanie still be true,
Then blaw ye favourin' breezes till my native land I view;
Then I'll kneel on Scotia's shore, while my heart-felt tear shall
    fa',
And I'll never leave my Jean and Caledonia.

CALEDONIA.

Twa Scottish lovers sat down to mak' their moan,
When by cam' ane o' their ain countrymen,
Says, " Rise ye up, my bonnie lass, mak' haste and come awa',
There's a vessel lying bound for Caledonia."

.   .   .   .

" Oh," says the sailor, " are ye willin' for to pay
Five hundred guineas before on board ye gae?
Ye must pay them plack and farthin' before on board ye go,
And we'll tak' ye to your bonnie Caledonia."

" Oh," says the lassie, " I'm willin' for to pay
Five hundred guineas before on board I go,
I'll pay them plack and farthin' before on board I go,
If ye'll tak' me to my pretty Caledonia."

" Oh," says the sailor, " her money we will tak',
And when she's on seas we'll throw her over deck,
Or we'll sell her for a slave lang or she win there ava,
And she'll never see her pretty Caledonia."

" Oh," says the captain, " that would never do,
There are no slaves sold intil oor country noo;
They would kill us every man, they would hang us ane and a',
If we offered a slave for sale in Caledonia."

They sailed east, and they sailed west,
They sailed past many a seaport bonnie;
The seas they did beat and the winds they did blaw,
And it caused them a' to weep for Caledonia.

One night as the captain was lying upon his bed
He dreamed a dream that something to him said—
" Tak' care o' yon bonnie lass that ye hae brocht awa,'
For she's caused ye a' to weep for Caledonia."

The captain away to the sailor has gone,
Says, " Where is yon bonnie lass that ye brocht from home?
Where is the bonnie lass that ye brocht far awa'?
For she's caused us a' to weep for Caledonia."

" Oh," says the sailor, " she's lying down below,
Bound hand and foot ready overboard to throw,
Bound hand and foot ready overboard to throw,
And she'll never see her sweet Caledonia."

The captain away to this fair maid has gone,
Says, " What is the reason that ye lie here so long?
What is the reason that ye lie here ava'?
For you've paid your passage dear for Caledonia."

" Oh," says the lassie, " oh, waes me,
That ever I was born sic hardships for to see,
But the sailor's got a sweetheart he likes better far than me,
And it causes me to weep for Caledonia."

" Oh," says the captain, " if a promise you will make,
That when we get to land then upon me you will wait,
If I would spare your life and let nobody know,
And we'll maybe see our pretty Caledonia."

" Oh," says the lassie, " a promise I will make,
That when we get to land then upon you I will wait,
If ye will spare my life and let nobody know,
And we'll maybe see our pretty Caledonia."

The captain away to the sailor he has gone,
He's taen him by the neck and him overboard has thrown;
" Tak' this cup o' water, though the liquor be but sma',
And drink your lassie's health to Caledonia."

They sailed east, and they sailed west,
And they've reached the land that they lo'ed best,
Tho' the seas they did beat, and the winds they did blaw,
And they've a' safe arrived at Caledonia.

They hadna been there but three-quarters o' a year,
When fine silks and satins he's made her for to wear,
When in fine silks and satins he's made her for to go,
And she lives the captain's wife in Caledonia.

SWEET TAYSIDE.

As I walked down by sweet Tayside
    One morning sweet and clear,
It was there I saw twa lovers meet
    As I was drawing near.

I leaned myself to the back o' a bush
  To hear what he would say;
I leaned myself to the back o' a bush
  To hear him her betray.

He kissed her, he clapped her,
  And that right willingly;
" Oh, what like a world would it be
  If I were to favour thee?"

" To favour me, young miss," he said,
  " It would be a great sin;
Besides there was no love-token
  Between us to begin."

" What want ye for a love-token?
  Dear love, what can I gie?
What want ye for a love-token?
  Oh, what can I gie thee?"

" Gie me the ring frae your finger sae bright,
  And the garter from off your knee;
Gie me the brooch from your bosom so white
  A love-token to be."

She's gi'en him the ring from her finger sae bright
  And the garter from aff her knee;
And she's gi'en him the brooch from her bosom so white,
  A love-token to be.

The girl turned right and round about,
  With the tear stains in her e'e—
" Is there any one in the high court above
  That will take care of me?"

" Hold well your sighs, hold well your cries,
  Hold well your modestie;
Hold well the flower of your fair bodie,
  It will never be ruined by me."

He's ta'en this fair maid by the hand,
  And that right willingly;
And he's ta'en her to St. Johnston's Tower,
  That wedded they might be.

DAVIE AND HIS KYE THEGITHER.

Davie and his kye thegither
  Cam' hame ae gloamin' frae the glen;
Davie ran to meet his mither,
  Some good news to lat her ken.

    Whirn a raw, a rue, a raw,
    Whirn a raw, a rue, a ree.

Davie, lad, ye're in a hurry,
  Fat mak's a' the spree the nicht?
Owre the hills I maun be trudgin',
  For to court a while, he said.

Dinna be like Geordie Morgan,
  Dinna court for sake o' brass;
Although he gets the name o' siller,
  He's just as puir's the auld kirk moose.

Yes, I ken ye are my mither,
  Yes, I ken ye wad be true,
For thirty years we've lived thegither,
  But a wife I maun hae noo.

He trippit owre the muir and heather,
  Until he cam' to his love's hoose,
And there they kissed and clapp'd thegither,
  And there they coorted unco croose.

Meg and Davie they've got mairret,
  They're as happy as could be;
But scarce they liv'd a month thegither
  When Meg kicked up an unco spree.

Meg ran but, and Meg ran ben,
  Meg ca'd Davie sulky loon;
She broke the porridge pot and pan,
  And crackit Davie on the croon.

Davie ran oot in a hurry
  When he found his heid was sore;
He met the parson come to visit,
  And nearly crushed him in the door.
Davie lad, ye're in a hurry,
  And your breeks I doot you've tore.

Then said Davie in a hurry,
　Ere he got time to dry his cheek,
This hoose o' mine will surely kill ye,
　I've got a most confounded reek.

The parson went into the cottage,
　Little kennin' o' the rig;
Maggie, thinkin' it was Davie,
　Knockit aff the parson's wig.

The parson turned in the passage,
　Ran to the door wi' angry speed,
Says, Davie lad, it's true ye've tell't me,
　Wae's me for your reek indeed.

People think that they are happy
　When I join them twa an' twa;
But if this be matrimony, Davie,
　I think nae mair o't we will hae.

　　　Whirn a raw, a rue, a raw,
　　　Whirn a raw, a rue, a ree.

BONNIE GLASGOW GREEN.

As I went out one morning fair,
On Glasgow Green to tak' the air,
I spied a lass wi' yellow hair
　And twa bewitchin' e'en, O.
And she spread her claes fu' early,
Fu' lovely and fu' cheerily,
She spread her claes fu' early
　On bonnie Glasgow Green, O.

Says I, My sweet and charming lass,
Ye're early on the dewy grass,
I think wi' me ye'll tak' a pass,
　And gang to Aberdeen, O.
For there's nane to match your beauty,
Your sweet and winsome beauty,
There's nane to match your beauty,
　Nor your claes on Glasgow Green, O.

O laddie, ye are surely mean,
I never lo'ed a lad but ane,
And he's my Jamie that hews the stane,
    To mak' our toon look braw, O.
Sae I canna leave my laddie,
My bonnie mason laddie,
I canna leave my laddie
    Nor my claes on Glasgow Green, O.

O lassie, can ye be so mad
As trust a rovin' mason lad?
For he may leave you wae and sad
    For a' that ye may ken, O.
Sae come wi' me, my lassie,
My blythe and charming lassie,
Sae come wi' me, my lassie,
    Leave your claes on Glasgow Green, O.

She ceased a while, then gave consent,
And doon Clyde's flowery banks we went;
But I think that day was gey weel spent
    Ere we wan to Aberdeen, O.
But she soon forgot her laddie,
Her bonnie mason laddie,
She soon forgot her laddie
    And her claes on Glasgow Green, O.

This couple they've got married noo,
And they've got bairnies one or two;
The lassie's got nae cause to rue
    The day she left her hame, O;
For she's aye since syne my dearie,
Sae lovely and sae cheery,
She's aye since syne my dearie
    On the flowery banks o' Don, O.

Come a' ye sporters, young and fair,
That gang to market, kirk, or fair,
Be sure and tak' the mornin' air,
    And gang to Glasgow Green, O;
For it's there ye'll find a lassie,
A bonnie winsome lassie,
It's there ye'll find a lassie,
    Like me on Glasgow Green, O.

NELLIE DOUGLAS.

It's, O and alas, and O wae's me,
  The term time is drawing so near me,
That I maun awa' for to leave you a',
  And the bonnie lad that I love so dearly.

It's no' for the leaving of this bonnie place,
  Nor my master nor mistress that grieves me;
But it's for the sake o' my kind comrades a'
  And the bonnie lad that I love so dearly.

Young Abram stands in his stable door
  Hearing young Nellie weeping;
"Oh, hold your tongue, Nellie Douglas," he cries,
  "You've got a' my keys in your keeping."

"Oh, hold your tongue, dear master," she says,
  And not hold me up in my folly;
For how could I think to be your wedded wife
  And me but your father's scogie[1]."

Silk and satin mak's mony a bonnie lass,
  Gowd and gear mak's a lady;
But it's better to marry a well-doing lass
  Than to marry a spending hizzie.

He has ta'en her upstairs, a poor servant maid,
  Brought her down an honoured lady;
And he ta'en her through amang his servants a',
  Saying, "Ca' her nae mair a scogie."

"Ye hae ca'd her Nellie Douglas," he says,
  "Baith but the house and ben, O;
But never let me hear a servant o' mine
  Ca' her Nellie Douglas again, O.

"Here you must stand wi' your hat in your hand,
  Ca' her young Abram's lady;
And pay her the honour that's due to her rank,
  For she's lady o' Balgay and Logie."

[1] Servant.

THE OLD RUSTIC BRIDGE BY THE MILL.

I'M thinking to-night of the old rustic bridge
    That bends o'er the murmuring stream,
'Twas there, Maggie dear, with our hearts full of cheer,
    We strayed 'neath the moon's gentle gleam.
'Twas there I first met you, the light of your eyes
    Awoke in my heart a sweet thrill;
Though now far away, still my thoughts fondly stray
    To the old rustic bridge by the mill.

        Beneath it the stream gently rippled,
          Around it the birds loved to trill;
        Tho' now far away, still my thoughts fondly stray
          To the old rustic bridge by the mill.

I think how I waited and watched there for you,
    And hoped you were coming to me;
While the whispering breeze mov'd the sad willow trees,
    And I wondered how long you would be.
When we met in the twilight, when no one was nigh,
    Our promises sweet to fulfil,
With our hearts full of love, 'neath the pale stars above,
    At the old rustic bridge by the mill.

How often, dear Maggie, when years passed away,
    And we plighted lovers became,
We rambled the path to the bridge day by day,
    The smiles of each other to claim.
But one day we parted in pain and regret,
    Our vows then we could not fulfil;
Oh, may we soon meet, and our fond love repeat,
    On the old rustic bridge by the mill.

I keep in my memory our love of the past,
    With me 'tis as bright as of old;
For deep in my heart it was planted to last,
    In absence it never grows cold.
I think of you, darling, when lonely at night,
    And when all is peaceful and still,
My heart wanders back in a dream of delight
    To the old rustic bridge by the mill.

This song has an English ring about it although it is well known all over
the North-east of Scotland.

THE BRAES O' STRATHBLANE.

As I was a-walking one morning in May
Down by yon green meadow I carelessly did stray,
I espied a fair maid, who was standing her lane,
While bleaching her claes on the braes o' Strathblane.

I stepped up towards her, as I seemed to pass.
" You are bleaching your claes here, my bonnie young lass;
It's twelve months and better since I had you in my min',
All for to get married if you would incline."

" To marry, to marry, lad, I am too young;
Besides, you young men have a flattering tongue.
My father and mother would both angry be
If I were to marry a rover, a rover like thee."

" Oh, haud your tongue, lassie, and do not say so,
You know not the pain that I do undergo.
Consent, my dear lassie, for to be my ain,
And we will live happy on the braes o' Strathblane."

" Oh, tempt me no longer," the fair maid did say,
" It's better for you to jog on your way.
It's better for me to bide here my lane
Than to pass my life with you on the braes o' Strathblane."

I turned about with a tear in my e'e,
Saying, " I wish you a good man whoe'er he may be.
I wish you a good one, as we are here alane,
And I'll court another on the braes o' Strathblane."

" Oh, stay a while, laddie, you have quite won my heart,
And here is my hand, love, we never shall part;
No, we never shall part till the day that we dee;
May all good attend us wherever we be."

" It's now you've consented, but quite out of time,
Since you spoke these few words I have changed my mind;
The clouds lower heavy, I'm afraid we'll have rain—"
So we shook hands and parted on the braes o' Strathblane.

Come all ye pretty, fair maids, where'er ye may be,
And ne'er slight a young man for his poverty;
For slighting of this young man I'm afraid I'll get nane,
But single I must wander on the braes o' Strathblane.

In some parts of Aberdeenshire " The Braes o' Strathdon " are substituted
for " The Braes o' Strathblane," but there seems to be little doubt but that
the song belongs to the Blane valley.

THE GAUGER.

THERE was a captain of the fleet,
A bonnie lassie he did entreat,
A bonnie lassie he did entreat
　　For to wed wi' him a sailor.

Oh, says the bonnie lassie, that winna dee,
For my minnie she wad angry be,
My minnie she wad angry be
　　If I wedded wi' you a sailor.

Then what contrivance can we make,
Or what contrivance can we take,
What contrivance can we make
　　For to beguile your mammy?

Oh, ye'll cast aff your trousers blue,
And ye'll on wi' the garb o' the gauger crew,
Ye'll on wi' the garb o' the gauger crew,
　　And ye'll come to oor toon a gauger.

And when ye come into oor toon,
Blythe and lauchin' ye'll come ben,
Sayin', Hae ye ony maut or gin?
　　For here am I the gauger.

He's casten aff his claes o' blue,
And he on wi' the garb o' the gauger crew,
He's on wi' the garb o' the gauger crew,
　　And he's gane to their toon a gauger.

And when he cam' into their toon,
Blythe and lauchin' he gaed ben,
Says, Hae ye ony maut or gin?
　　For here am I the gauger.

Oh, says the lassie, come awa',
Maybe we hae a cask or twa,
Maybe we hae a cask or twa,
　　Gin ye be the new-come gauger.

It's he ca'd but and he ca'd ben,
He's ca'd out and he's ca'd in;
But ne'er a drap o' gin could he fin',
　　For he hadna the wiles o' the gauger.

Come awa, lassie, and lat me see
Faur that caskie o' gin may be,
If I getna the gin, lassie, I'll tak' thee
    For beguilin' me the gauger.

Oh, says the auld wife, that's weel deen,
For she's aye ready wi' ilka ane,
She's aye ready wi' ilka ane
    And maist wi' the new-come gauger.

But lang or ever a month was gane,
The gauger and the lassie baith were ane,
He's married her and aff she's gane,
    She's awa wi' a rovin' sailor.

THE AMERICAN STRANGER.

I'M a stranger in this country,
    From America I came,
There is no one here knows me,
    Nor can tell my name;
I came over to this country
    For to wander for a while,
Far, far from my darling,
    For many a lang mile.

I have travelled this country
    Both early and late,
My hardships have been many,
    My trials have been great.
I courted a fair lassie,
    But she has me disowned,
Oft times she has denied me,
    But I'll try her again.

It is very well known
    That her parents were rich,
She was not my equal,
    Which grieved me very much;
But though father and mother
    And all should say so,
Yet through this wide world
    With my darling I'll go.

Some say I am rakish,
　　Some say that I am wild,
And some say I am guilty
　　Fair maids to beguile;
But I'll prove them all liars
　　If she'll go along with me
To the plains of America,
　　My darling to be.

The sun that's in the firmament
　　May give no more light,
And the stars in the elements
　　May fall in one night;
The rocks may rend asunder,
　　And the mountains may move,
Before that I prove false
　　To the girl that I love.

The ship that's on the salt sea
　　She may sail without sails,
And the smallest of fishes
　　Turn into big whales;
In the middle of the ocean
　　There may grow a myrtle tree,
Before that I prove false
　　To the girl that loves me.

Give my compliments to Nancy
　　Who lives on yon shore,
And likewise to Betsy,
　　She's the girl I adore;
Give my kind love to Susan,
　　She's my whole heart's delight,
I could roll her in my arms
　　In a cold winter's night.

Now this couple they've got married,
　　To America set sail,
May the Heavens go with them
　　And a brisk and pleasant gale!
And when they do get landed,
　　They may dance and they may sing,
On the plains of America
　　They're serving the King.

From the reading of the sixth verse one would infer that this song was written prior to the days of the steamship, and from the last verse it would appear that it was at least written before the American war of Independence.

AS I CAM' OWRE YON HIGH, HIGH HILL.

As I cam' owre yon high, high hill,
  I met a bonnie lassie;
She looked at me, and I at her,
  And, wow, but she looked saucy.
    But I love my love, and I love my love,
      And I love my love most dearly;
    My whole delight's in her bonnie face,
      And I long to have her near me.

The first thing that I asked of her,
  What was her father's name?
But the answer that she gave to me,
  " Ye're a curious man to ken."
    But I love my love, etc.

The next thing that I asked of her,
  Did he live here about?
And the answer that she gave to me,
  " His peatstack stands thereout."
    But I love my love, etc.

The next thing that I asked of her,
  Gin she wad tak' a man?
But the answer that she gave to me,
  " 'Tis nocht but what I can."
    But I love my love, etc.

The next thing that I asked of her,
  Gin she wad marry me?
And the answer that she gave to me,
  " If you and I agree."
    But I love my love, etc.

Then fare ye weel, my bonnie lass,
  May joy and peace be wi' ye;
And ye'll be on a better tune
  When I come back to see ye.
    But I love her yet, I love her yet,
      I love her yet most dearly;
    My whole delight's in her bonnie face,
      And I long to have her near me.

THE BANKS OF CLAUDY.

'Twas on a summer's evening, all in the month of May,
Down by a pleasant garden I carelessly did stray;
I overheard a fair maid, in sorrow to complain,
All for her absent lover, and Johnny was his name.

I stepped up unto her and put her in surprise,
I own she did not know me, I being in disguise;
I said, "My fairest creature, my joy, and heart's delight,
How far have you to wander this dark and stormy night?"

"It's to the banks of Claudy, if you the road will show,
And pity a poor stranger that knows not where to go;
I'm searching for a young man, and Johnny is his name.
And it's on the banks of Claudy I'm told he does remain."

"These are the banks of Claudy, fair maid, whereon you stan',
But do not trust young Johnny for he's a false young man,
Do not depend on Johnny, for he'll not meet you here;
But tarry with me in this green, green wood, no danger need
    you fear."

"If Johnny was here this night he would keep me from all
    harm,
For on the field of battle all in his uniform,
For on the field of battle his foes he does defy,
Like a Royal King of honour upon the walls of Troy."

"It's six long weeks and better since Johnny left this shore,
To cross the raging ocean where foaming billows roar,
To cross the rolling ocean for honour and for fame;
But his ship was wrecked and he was drowned upon the coast of
    Spain."

When she heard that dreadful news she fell into despair,
With the wringing of her hands and the tearing of her hair;
Says, "Since my Johnny is drowned, no man alive I'll take,
Through lonesome woods and valleys I'll wander for his sake."

When I saw her loyalty, no longer could I feign,
But clasped her in my arms and said, "Betsy, I'm the man,
My Betsy, I'm the young man that caused you a' the pain,
But since we've met on Claudy's banks we'll never part again."

IRISH MOLLY, O.

O, who is yon foreigner that's lately come to town?
And, like a ghost that cannot rest, he wanders up and down;
He's a poor unhappy Scottish youth, if more you want to know,
He's dying for the sake of his Irish Molly, O.

> She's young and she's beautiful, the fairest that I know,
> She's the primrose of Ireland, all for my guinea, O;
> She's the primrose of Ireland, all for my guinea, O,
> And the only one entices me is Irish Molly, O.

I said, " My pretty, fair maid, if you will go with me
I'll show you the straight road across the countie ";
" My parents would be angry if they should come to know,
And they would lay the blame upon my Scottish laddie, O."

> She's young and she's beautiful, etc.

When Molly's old father he came to know
That she was being courted by a Scotch laddie, O;
He sent for young M'Donald and unto him did say,
" If you court my daughter, Molly, I'll send you far away."

> She's young and she's beautiful, etc.

Since Molly has deceived me all by her father's ways,
In lonesome woods and valleys I mean to spend my days;
Like a poor forlorn pilgrim I'll wander to and fro,
And it's all for the sake of my Irish Molly, O.

> She's young and she's beautiful, etc.   *

When I am dead and buried, there's one thing I would crave,
To have a marble tombstone at the top of my grave,
And written on that stone an inscription should be laid,
" M'Donald lost his life for his pretty Irish maid."

> She's young and she's beautiful, etc.

So all ye pretty, fair maids, a warning tak' by me,
And never build your hopes at the top of any tree;
For the green leaves will wither and the root it will decay,
And the beauty of a fair maid will soon fade away.

> She's young and she's beautiful, etc.

THE UNCONSTANT LOVER.

Down in yon valley there was a fine wedding,
  And, oh! but the bride she had proved unkind,
When looking back on her bygone lover,
  This bygone lover came in at the time.

Supper being ended and all things over,
  It was proposed to sing the bride a song;
The song it was sung by her bygone lover,
  And unto the bride and the song it was sung.

" Many's the one has been seven years absent,
  Many's the one has returned again,
But I hae been but three years absent,
  An unconstant lover to me ye hae been.

" Oh, why can ye sit at another man's table?
  Oh, why can ye drink of another man's wine?
And how can ye lie in another man's arms?
  When oft times ye've said, love, that ye would be mine.

" It's the ripest apple that's aye the soonest rotten,
  It's aye the hottest love that is the soonest cauld,
Lang out of sight, love, aye soon forgotten,
  Oh, why were ye so ready for another man's call?

" Where's the piece of gold that we broke when we parted?
  Where's that piece of gold? Oh! return it again,
I ga'e it to you as a true lover's token,
  Return it to me as a false lover's one."

The bride being seated at the head of the table,
　　She heard every word and she acted so gay;
But to keep up the company no longer was she able,
　　And unto her bridegroom these words she did say—

" Bridegroom, oh bridegroom, I'm going to ask a favour,
　　And being the first one you'll grant it to me,
Only this ae nicht to lie wi' my mother,
　　Then aye, aye and after, love, I'll lie wi' thee."

In asking and pleading the favour was granted,
　　Sobbing and sighing she went to her bed;
And early, early the very next morning,
　　This beautiful damsel was found lying dead.

Surprising, surprising to all ye young women,
　　To see one so early cut off in her bloom;
To-night ye may be walking and wi' sweethearts talking,
　　And to-morrow ye may be cold in the tomb.

First I'll put on a coat o' green velvet,
　　And I will wear it for a week or two,
Then I'll put on a coat o' green and yellow,
　　And then aye and after that the orange and the blue.

If any one should ask me why I do wear it,
　　Or why I do wear such a costly array,
I will tell them just the very reason
　　Is that my true love lies cauld in the clay.

PITCAITHLY'S WELLS.

It fell about the Lammas time,
　　A fine time o' the year,
When youthful girlies a-sporting went
　　To drink the waters clear.

But there was ane amang the rest,
　　Her name I daurna' tell;
For as far as the sun an' moon extends
　　Her beauty does excel.

I've wandered east, I've wandered west,
    I've been by hill an' dell;
But the bonniest lass that e'er I saw
    Lives at Pitcaithly's well.

The first time that I saw my love,
    I think nae shame to say,
I asked if she wad be my bride,
    But she blushed and said me nay.

I asked if she wad take a walk;
    She said we wad be seen;
But at length we went and took a walk
    Down by Pitcaithly's green.

We walkèd up, sae did we doon,
    To breathe the cauler air,
And ilka laddie had his lass,
    And I my Jeanie fair.

We wandered east, sae did we west,
    Kind nature took my part;
We wandered by Belvandon's bank,
    Till I gained my Jeanie's heart.

I wish I were a shepherd's son,
    To skip the heather bell,
I wad dawt yon girlie in my arms
    That lives at Pitcaithly's well.

Oh, happy, happy wad I be,
    If I could call her mine;
I wad treat her in my father's house
    With the country cheer sae fine.

There is a legend in the North-east of Scotland that this song was written upwards of 200 years ago by the Earl of Kinnoul in honour of Jeanie Oliphant, daughter of the Laird of Pitcaithly.

I have seen a version of the song which had the following verse at the end:—

    Lang may Pitcaithly's wells run fine,
        And lang may they run there,
    And mony a ane frequent the place
        Where I gained Jeanie fair.

THE MAID OF DON.

As I rode ower the haughs o' Newe,
   And doon Strathdon upon my pownie,
I met a may baith brisk and gay,
   I asked her name; she said, " It's Downie."

She'd cherry cheeks and coal-black hair,
   Her eyes appeared to me like lamer[1];
I viewed this fair maid up and down
   Till my head grew light and my feet did stammer.

" Young man," she said, " you're surely drunk,
   Or in your mind there is some frolic;
For in courtin' me you've little share,
   You can neither dance nor speak the Gaelic."

" I canna speak your Highland tongue,
   Because my mother never had it;
But for to dance I'll do my best,
   Since my profession does not forbid it."

All that night we sat and drank,
   And after that we rose and danced;
But as for me I had little share,
   For on my love's toes I always tramped.

But if I could dance as weel's M'Lean,
   Then would my heart be light and cheery;
And if I could speak the " Phairson " tongue,
   Then I would go and woo my dearie.

For the like of her's not on Ericht banks,
   On Ericht banks nor in a' Glen Gairn;
And far she excels yon Kitty Kate
   That lives as you cross ower the Cairn.

The like of her's not on Ericht banks,
   On Ericht banks nor Girnock water;
And I carena what wad me betide
   If I only had the luck to get her.

[1] Amber.

F

OH! NO, NO.

COME here, dearest Peggy, you're my whole heart's delight,
But the fairest of days, love, brings on the dark night;
So fain I wad bide, love, but away I must go,
And ye canna win wi' me, love, oh! no, no.

You see yonder mountains so gloomy and high?
They have parted mony a lover, and they'll part you and I;
So fain I wad bide, love, but away I must go,
And ye canna win wi' me, love, oh! no, no.

You see yonder seas, love, how they do arise?
They've caused mony's the lover to give heavy sighs;
They've sinnert mony sweethearts and they'll sinner us also,
And ye canna come wi' me, lovie, oh! no, no.

You see yonder soldiers how they march along,
With their guns in good order and their swords are all drawn?
So fain I wad bide, love, but away I must go,
And ye canna come wi' me, love, oh! no, no.

If ye were in India, love, 'neath the sun and the rain,
Your colour would fade and your beauty would stain:
And I would be sorry to see my love so,
So ye canna come wi' me, love, oh! no, no.

If I were in Canada, love, 'mong the frost and the snow,
I wad stand at your back, love, and keep off the foe;
I wad stand at your back, love, and fight every foe,
But I canna win wi' ye, love, oh! no, no.

I'll go to some nunnery and there spend my life,
I never will marry nor be called a man's wife;
I'll never be married, to a nunnery I'll go,
Since I canna win wi' ye, love, oh! no, no.

Hold down your hands, Peggy, why tear your hair so?
I never intended away for to go;
I never intended away for to go,
And ye'll aye win wi' me, love, where'er I go.

THE WEE TOTUM.

Some say to live single it is the best plan,
But I was ne'er happy till I got a man,
When I got a man I soon got a wean,
A wee little totum to toddle its lane.

Chorus.
It gangs toddlin' but, and gangs toddlin' ben,
The wee little totum gangs toddlin' its lane.

When my guidman comes hame as tired as can be,
He nae sooner sits doon than it's up on his knee,
And he'll kiss it and clap it and ca' it his ain,
The wee little totum that toddles its lane.

When supper is over we then go to bed,
And on my love's bosom I then lay my head;
Oh! what a great pleasure to sleep wi' ane's ain,
And hae a wee totum to toddle its lane.

When mornin' comes in we rise wi' the lark,
John goes to his labour and I the hoose wark;
What pleasure and comfort to toil for ane's ain,
And hae a wee totum to toddle its lane.

It gangs toddlin' but, and gangs toddlin' ben,
My wee little totum gangs toddlin' its lane.

BUNDLE AND GO.

Frae Clyde's bonnie hills where the heather was blooming.
And lassies and lads sang o' love a' the day,
I have come, my dear lassie, to mak' the last offer,
Sae mak' up your mind now, and dinna delay.
My mithers she's gane, and the house it is eerie,
This night you may rue if you answer me no,
'Tis now in your power for to aye be my dearie,
Rise up, bonnie lassie, and bundle and go.

Bundle and go, bundle and go,
Rise up, bonnie lassie, and bundle and go.

My daddie is dead, but he left me some siller,
And bade me ne'er marry anither but you,
I'll tak' this advice, for lang, lang I hae courted,
And ye canna say but I'm constant and true.
Although we be poor, yet our minds shall be cheerie,
Our hearts shall ne'er sink tho' our purse it be low,
I'll count myself happy wi' lugging my dearie,
Rise up, bonnie Annie, and bundle and go, etc.

We'll marry for love, and we'll then work for siller,
Industry frae poortith will soon set us free;
And snugly we'll live on yon hillside together,
And virtue and peace our companions shall be.
Contentment's my tocher, good health a' my riches,
A heart leal and kindly, come weal or come woe;
We'll be happier far than the laird wi' his hundreds,
Make haste—are ye willing to bundle and go? etc.

'Tis true I hae courted wi' Matty and Tibby,
And other daft gaukies at kirk and at fair,
But nane o' them a' set my bosom a-dunting,
Or gart my heart dirl 'tween hope and despair.
When out o' their sicht I care naething mair for them,
The caper once o'er they get leave for to go,
But you, my sweet lass, I hae lo'ed lang so dearly—
Now, give your consent, rise, and bundle and go, etc.

Her young tender mind it began for to swither,
And said, while the tears in abundance did flow,
"'Tis hard to be press'd thus between love and duty,
And yet I would wish for, to bundle and go.

But if I should gang without telling my father,
  My tocher he'll keep, sheets and blankets also,
My mither will rage and forever disown me,
  Yet fain, very fain would I bundle and go, etc.

A fig for excuses, come kilt up your coaties,
  O'er moor and thro' mosses ye ken we've to gang.
There is danger to linger wi' sitting and thinking,
  The day will be breaking before it be lang;
Your father and mother nae doubt will be angry,
  But affection soon in its old channel will flow,
When they see our wee totums around the fire dancing,
  Are you willing and ready to bundle and go? etc.

Love lent wings to both, in a blink they were kippled,
  In peace and in pleasure their years flow along;
Their young sprouts are innocent, noisy, and healthy,
  And Tam, to please Annie, lilts o'er a sweet song.
His Annie is a' his delight and his treasure,
  Their bosoms wi' love to each other do glow;
She blesses the day she left father and mother,
  And took his advice and did bundle and go, etc.

BUNDLE AND GO.
(ANOTHER VERSION)

THE winter is gane, love, the sweet spring again, love,
  Bedecks the blue mountain and gilds the dark sea;
Giein' birth to the blossom, and bliss to the bosom,
  And hope for the future to you, love, an' me.
For far to the West, to the land of bright freedom,
  The land where the vine and the orange-trees grow,
I fain would conduct thee, my ain winsome dearie—
  They, hey, bonnie lassie, will ye bundle and go?

The vales and the wild wood, the scene of our childhood,
  Will ever be dear to your memory an' mine,
But cauld blasts o' poortith that sweeps Scotland's mountains
  Gars mony a fond heart in sorrow repine,
Mak's aft the leal laddie to lose his dear lassie,
  Or opens the fount for her saut tears to flow;
But the land o' fair promise invites us, my Mary,
  Then, hey, bonnie lassie, will ye bundle and go?

Weel, weel hae I lo'ed thee, an' lang hae I wooed thee,
  An' faes to our sweet future hopes there are nane;
Then why should we tarry, my ain bonnie Mary,
  Or sever twa hearts that will aye beat as ane?
Frae poortith to shield thee, in bliss to upbuild thee,
  Will aye be the first dearest wish I can know;
To mak' thy hame cheery, and tend thee, my dearie,
  Then, hey, bonnie lass, will you bundle and go?

To the deep verdant valleys and braid hills sae fertile,
  Where wealth's for the winning, if will guides the hand;
Where flowers bloom fairer, and landscapes are rarer,
  And the skies are more bright than in our fatherland;
Where great rolling rivers are laden wi' treasures,
  Upon the inhabitants wealth to bestow;
To the West, to the land o' bright freedom and plenty,
  Rise up, bonnie lass, an' we'll bundle and go.

I ken, my dear laddie, it's true a' you've tauld me,
  An' I'll say nae langer that I winna gang,
Though I'm wae to leave my sweet hame in the Hielands,
  An' a' the dear friends wha hae lo'ed me sae lang.
But my father and mither are happy thegither,
  I ken noo, my laddie, they winna say no,
For baith hae consented that I should gae wi' you,
  Then up, my dear laddie, we'll bundle and go.

THE PEDLAR.

Air—" Come Under My Plaidie."

THE pedlar cam' in by the House o' Glenneuk,
When the family were thro' wi' the breakfast and beuk,
The ladies were kaimin' and curlin' their hair,
For to gang to the weddin' o' Maggie M'Nair.
" Guid morn," quo' the pedlar fu' frank and fu' free,
" We'll see wha this day will be handsel to me;
And gin an ill bargain ye chance for to mak',
Losh! ye'll get mysel' and the hale o' my pack."

Chorus.

Wi' my fal dreedle aldreedle, aldreedle al,
Fal aldreedle, aldreedle, aldreedle al.

"Na," quo' the guid-wife, " gin I hae ony skill,
But that wad be makin' a waur oot o' ill;
Troth, dochters, I think that the work wad be slack,
Ere thro' the hale country ye trudged wi' a pack."
" Oh, na! " said the pedlar, " it was but a joke,"
As he threw down his wallet and showed them his stock;
When she viewed his rich cargo she rued she'd e'er spak'
Sae lichtly o' either the pedlar or pack.
    Chorus.

The lasses drew roon wi' their gleg, glancin' e'en,
And viewed his rich pearls micht hae deen wi' a queen;
They bocht aff his trockies, silk ribbons and lace,
Till they raised many a thraw in the laird's auld niggard face.
At brooches and bracelets wi' diamonds enriched
They glowered till their hearts and their e'en were bewitched,
But yon bonnie, blithe Nellie stood aye a wee back
Stealin' looks at the pedlar, ne'er mindin' the pack.
    Chorus.

The looks o' that lassie his heart it did move,
For he saw that her looks were the glances o' love;
He gae her a bracelet wi' pearls beset,
Sayin', " Wha wad ken but we may be mairriet yet ";
The blush flushed her cheek, and the tear filled her e'e,
She gaed oot to the yaird and sat doon 'neath a tree;
And something within her aye silently spak',
" I cou'd gang wi' yon pedlar and carry his pack."
    Chorus.

Her heart it lap licht ilka time he cam' roon,
Till he telt her he'd taen a braw shop in the toon;
The rose left her cheek and her head licht did reel,
For she thocht it would be his hinmost fareweel.
" Cheer up your heart, lassie, and don't let it fa',
Tho' your father may fret and your minnie may jaw,
They'll a' rue the day yet that they their jokes cracked.
When a' thro' the country I trudged wi' a pack.
    Chorus.

The auld wife kent nocht o' the secret ava'
Till ae day to the kirk she gaed vogie and braw;
Her heart till her mou' lap, and the sweat on her brak ,
When she heard Nell cried out to the chiel wi' the pack.

She sat up wi' a face nearly roasted wi' shame,
Syne awa at twal hours she gaed scouring straucht hame,
She min't nae the text nor a word the priest spak',
A' her thochts were taen up wi' the chiel an' the pack.
    Chorus.

" Od," quo' the auld laird, " ye are hame unco sune,
The kail's but new on: is the day's service dune?"
" Na," quo' the auld wife, " but I've gotten an affront
That for months yet to come will my bosom gar dunt.
Yon glaikit slut Nell that we've reared up sae weel,
She's woun' us a pirn that will sair us to reel,
And tho' she has cost us baith pounds and a plack,
Faith, she's cried thrice to-day to the chiel wi' the pack.
    Chorus.

" Oh," says the auld laird, " gin she's been sic a fule,
He'll get her as bare as the birk tree at Yule;
Whaur is she, the jaud? gin I could but her fin',
The deil haud my hands but I'd reestle her skin!"
But Nellie weel kent what the upshot wad be,
Sae she gaed owre the hill to a freen's hoose a wee,
And lang in the mornin', ere daylight did brack,
She's awa wi' the pedlar, unfashed wi' the pack.
    Chorus.

They were lawfully spliced by the Reverend J. P.,
Which the hale country roon in the *Herald* may see;
They were weel stockit for bed and for back,
That was started wi' ballads and trumps in a pack.
He raise up to riches, he raise up to fame,
Noo the title o' Bailie's attached to his name;
And the laird o' Glenneuk about naething will crack
But aye o' the Bailie—ne'er hintin' the pack.

      Wi' my fal dreedle, aldreedle, aldreedle al,
      Fal aldreedle, aldreedle, aldreedle al.

This is the bothy version of " The Pedlar " as sung by an old man named Robert Mellis, Westfolds, Huntly, at the beginning of the present century.
The book version was by William Watt (1792-1859), one of our best minor poets. Watt, who was also the author of " The Tinkers' Wedding " and " Kate Dalrymple," was for a long time precentor in the Parish Church of East Kilbride near Glasgow.

PEGGY O' GREENLAW.

I AM a bold, undaunted youth,
　　George Hewitt is my name,
And Threipland is my dwelling-place,
　　On Deveron's banks my hame;
And there I had a sweetheart,
　　Her like ye never saw,
She's the bonniest lass in a' the place,
　　My Peggy o' Greenlaw.

But woe to yon worthless man!
　　His name it was M'Call,
He took me to the town o' Banff,
　　Unto a ploughman's ball.
'Twas there I met a fair maid,
　　Before I never saw,
She made me to forget my love,
　　My lassie o' Greenlaw.

In six weeks we were married,
　　And that's but four and twa;
The seventh I was lamenting
　　My lassie o' Greenlaw.
My married life soon wearied me,
　　Frae her I've run awa',
And I'll evermore lament for
　　My Peggy o' Greenlaw.

Come, all ye roving young men,
　　A warning tak' by me,
And leave off your late walking,
　　And shun bad company;
Bad company enticed me,
　　And led me first awa',
And it's parted me for ever
　　Frae my lassie o' Greenlaw.

This is a song with a moral. It was written by Alexander Shaw, for some time beadle at the Parish Church of Alvah, in Banffshire.

THE FOUNDLING BABY.

Two sailors walking, together talking,
    Two sailors walking, I've heard them say;
And as they walked, together talked,
    They met a fair maid by the way.

She had a baby rolled in a basket,
    And for to give the damsel ease,
One of them asked for to carry her basket;
    She lightly answered, " If you please.

" But it is eggs that is in my basket,
    And of them you must take great care,
And if you chance to outgo me,
    The half-way house you'll leave them there."

The sailors they being brisk with liquor,
    They nimbly tripped out-o'er the lea;
But Nancy slowly followed after,
    And on the sailors she kept an e'e.

When they came to the inn for breakfast,
    They called the cook to divide the spoil;
But instead of feasting they got nursing,
    And instead of eggs a lovely child.

One of the sailors flew in a passion,
    The landlord laughed most heartily—
" The babies they are growing so plenty,
    Some wily girl has beguiled thee."

Out it spake then one of the sailors,
    " To frown it is not worth the while,
We'll call a nurse for our foundling baby,
    One hundred pounds shall go with the child."

Out it spake then the babe's own mother,
    And none did know that she was there,
Says, " Give me the baby before another,
    And of it I will take great care."

They both kissed it, and they both blessed it,
  The money it was then paid down;
They both kissed it, and they both blessed it,
  And then they sailed from the town.

The sailors had a prosperous voyage,
  And they returned safe back again;
The sailors having a prosperous voyage,
  They had some money for to spend.

Then out it spake one of the sailors,
  "Brother seaman, since we are here,
We'll go and see the foundling baby
  That we left here the other year."

When they came to the nurse's gates,
  They knocked high, and they knocked low:
"Are ye the nurse of our foundling baby
  That we left here a year ago?"

"I am the nurse of your foundling baby
  That was left here the other year;
And now your child is both well and healthy,
  The very same as you left it here."

They took the child into their arms,
  They kissed it first, and they blessed it syne;
"Since you've been so kind to our foundling baby,
  You shall have money to your mind."

"Don't you mind on Nancy whom you did fancy,
  When you roved on yon pleasant plain?
You are the father, and I'm the mother,
  And here's your Nancy to you again."

"If ye're the Nancy that I did fancy
  When I roved on yon pleasant plain,
I am the father and ye're the mother,
  And we shall never part again."

The baby it was then baptised,
  The wedding day was set also;
And our sailors all to it were invited,
  And many more that I do not know.

THIS IS THE NICHT MY JOHNNIE SET.

Air.—" Low Down He's in the Broom."

THIS is the nicht my Johnnie set,
　　And promised to be here,
Oh, what can stay his longing step?
　　He's fickle grown, I fear.
Wae worth this wheel, 'twill no rin roun',
　　I hae nae heart to spin;
But count each minute wi' a sigh
　　Till Johnnie he steal in.

How snug that canty fire it burns
　　For twa to sit beside;
And there fu' aft my Johnnie sat,
　　And I my blushes hid.
My father now he snugly snores,
　　My mother's fast asleep;
He promised aft, but, oh! I fear,
　　His word he winna keep.

What can it be keeps him frae me?
　　The road it's no so lang;
And frost and snaw are nought ava,
　　If folks are fain to gang.
Some ither lass wi' bonnier face
　　Has caught his wanderin' e'e:
Than thole their jeers at kirk and fair,
　　Oh! sooner let me dee.

Oh! if we lasses could but gang
　　And woo the lads we like,
I'd run to thee, my Johnnie dear,
　　Nor stop at bog or dyke.
But custom's such a powerfu' thing,
　　Men aye their will maun hae,
While mony a bonnie lassie sits
　　And mourns from day to day.

But wheest! I hear my Johnnie's fit,
　　It's just his very jog,
He snecks the fa'-yett saftly too—
　　Oh, hang that collie dog!

And now for mony sugar'd words,
    And kisses no a few;
Oh, but this world's a paradise.
    When lovers they prove true.

GREEN BUSHES.

WHEN I was a-walking, one morning in May,
To hear the birds whistle and the nightingales play,
I heard a young damsel, so sweetly sung she,
Down by the green bushes, there he thinks he'll meet me.

" I'll buy you fine beavers and a fine silken gown,
I'll buy you fine petticoats flounc'd to the groun',
If you will prove loyal and constant to me,
Forsake your true love and marry wi' me."

" I want none of your beavers and fine silken hose,
For I ne'er was so poor as to marry for clothes;
But I will prove loyal and constant to thee,
I'll forsake my own lover and married we'll be."

" Come, let us be going, kind sir, if you please,
Come, let us be going from under these trees,
For yonder a-coming my true love I see,
Down by the green bushes where he thinks to meet me."

But when he got there and found she was gone,
He stood like some lambkin when left all alone;
" She's gone with some other and forsaken me,
So adieu to green bushes, forever adieu.

" I'll be like some schoolboy, spend my time in play,
For I never was so foolishly deluded away,
There's no falsehearted woman shall serve me so more,
So adieu, ye green bushes, it's time to give o'er."

Reprinted from an old chapbook similar to those sold at **Feeing Markets**
half-a-century ago. It is an Irish Folk-song and is printed in **Petrie's**
collection.

MITHER, I MAUN HAE A MAN.

" Noo, mither, I maun tell ye,
 I'm gaun to be a wife;
For I'm sure it's nae pleasure
 To live a single life;
For be I weel, or be I ill,
 Of this I'm very sure,
That there's naething can be harder
 Than what I now endure.

" You raise me every mornin'
 Lang ere it be licht,
And keep me hard at labour
 Till it be late at nicht;
And syne when I gae to my bed,
 In it I find no rest,
For thinking on the labours
 With which I am opprest.

" Noo isna it a pity
 That such a one as I
Should be a drudge to anyone
 As you require of me?
For I am fit companion
 For any brisk young man,
So I wish that I was joined
 Into some marriage band."

" I think he'd be in want o' a wife
 That wad hae ane like you;
Ye hiv mair need to bide at hame
 Some household work to do.
Or else gae to the schule awhile,
 And that I dare to say,
For the maist pairt o' the lear ye got
 It's a' been thrown away."

" Noo, mither, ye maun hold now,
 I think it is full time,
Your speech has no foundation,
 It's like unto a rhyme;
You talk about it like a child,
 Suppose that you be old;
But may your speech bewray you,
 And to your shame be told.

" For man could never happy be
  While he was yet alone,
For Eve was sent just for his help,
  Because that he had none;
And he among the righteous,
  All creatures that were made,
But there was none among them
  That he could love indeed."

" Oh, if I had but profit,
  Though my pleasures were but sma';
For Eve has been the ruin
  Of us baith ane and a';
He trusted too much to her,
  I'm sure he was nae wise,
For she soon turned out his ruin
  In the loss o' Paradise."

" I know the Scriptures bind me
  Obedient to be;
But not in things unlawful,
  As you require of me;
Forbidding me to tak' a man
  When time and chance do come;
But it's that I'll do in spite o' you,
  So you needna' fash your thoom.

" For I hae read the Testaments,
  Baith aul' and new indeed,
And several other histories
  Which I have also had;
And marriage is nae forbidden,
  Nor yet is it a sin,
But to increase and multiply,
  And that is the comman'.

" And that comman' I mean to keep,
  As weel as a' the rest;
And for to use the means o' that,
  I wyte I'll dae my best.
An' syne there'll be nae mair required,
  If I dae all I can;
So I'll conclude as I begood—
  I mean to tak' a man."

OH, BUT I'M WEARY.

" OH, but I'm weary, weary waitin',
  Oh, but I'm weary nicht and day;
Oh, mither, gie me the man
  Will tak' this weariness away."

" O, daughter dear, wad ye marry a man
  Wha mak's his livin' by the ploo?"
" Oh, no, mother," she says,
  " The ploughman's wife has much to do."
    Oh, but I'm weary, etc.

" O, daughter, dear, wad ye marry a man
  That mak's his livin' building stanes?"
" Oh, no, mither," she says,
  " He might fall to the earth and brak' his banes."
    Oh, but I'm weary, etc.

" O, daughter, dear, wad ye marry a man
  That mak's his livin' by the mill?"
" Oh, no, mither," she says,
  " The smell o' the dust wad mak' me ill."
    Oh, but I'm weary, etc.

" O, daughter, dear, wad ye marry a man
  That mak's his livin' by the gun?"
" Oh, no, mither," she says,
  " He mith go out and never come in."
    Oh, but I'm weary, etc.

" O, daughter, dear, wad ye marry a man
  That mak's his livin' by the sea?"
" Oh, no, mither," she says,
  " The ship might wreck and ruin me."
    Oh, but I'm weary, etc.

" O, daughter, dear, wad ye marry a man
  That mak's his livin' by the pen?"
" Oh, yes, mither," she says,
  " My heart delights in gentlemen."
    Oh, but I'm weary, etc.

THE BAD WIFE.

As soon as I got married, a happy man to be,
My wife turned out a sorry jade, we never could agree;
For what I thought my greatest bliss was grief without compare,
And a' the cause o' my complaint's she's mine forever mair.

For she's aye plague, plaguing, and she's aye plaguing me;
She's aye plague, plaguing, and never lets me be.

About a week or something less, a bonnie thing she was,
But e'er the second Sunday cam' she made me cry, alas!
Oh! aftentimes I cry, alas! 'tis needless here to tell,
For a' the cause o' my complaint, the jade she kens hersel'.

And she's aye plague, plaguing, etc.

And if I choose to speak a word she flies like fire frae flint;
I daurna ca' my house my ain, nor anything that's in't,
My very hair I daurna' cut, my claes I daurna wear,
An' o' baith claes and siller, too, she keeps me naked, bare.

For she's aye strip, stripping, etc.

Richt weel she kens I dearly lo'e a dainty dish o' meat,
But she cooks it sae dirtily a bit I canna eat,
And if I turn my mouth awry, or chance to shake my head,
She ca's me filthy loun, and says, I'm very ill to feed.

And she's aye starve, starving, etc.

When I am for soberness she gangs distracted mad,
And when I am for merriment, oh, then she's always sad;
And when I wish to hear her speak she silent sits and dumb,
And when I ask for quietness she rattles like a drum.

For she's aye drum, drumming, etc.

Last nicht my neighbour Tam an' I went out our throats to wet,
She thunder'd in my lugs sae loud I think I hear her yet;
And when her warlike moods are on, which aften is the case,
The first thing that comes to her hand she dashes't in my face.

For she's aye dash, dashing, etc.

That marriage is a Paradise I've aften heard folk tell,
But for my ain part, first and last, I think it worse than hell;
An' yet there is a comfort left, ae comfort and nae mair,
The pangs o' death will break the bonds and bury a' my care.

For she'll soon, soon bury, an' she'll soon bury me,
She'll soon, soon bury, an' then she'll let me be.

THE ROAD TO DUNDEE.

Cauld winter was howling o'er muir and o'er mountains,
    And wild was the surge on the dark-rolling sea,
When I met, about daybreak, a bonnie young lassie,
    Wha asked me the road and the miles to Dundee.

Said I, " My young lassie, I canna weel tell ye,
    The road and the distance I canna weel gie;
But if ye'll permit me to gang a wee bittie,
    I'll show you the road and the miles to Dundee."

At once she consented, and gave me her arm;
    Ne'er a word did I speir wha the lassie might be,
She appeared like an angel in feature and form,
    As she walked by my side on the road to Dundee.

At length, wi' the Howe o' Strathmartine behind us,
    And the spires o' the toon in full view we could see;
She said, " Gentle sir, I can never forget ye
    For showing me so far on the road to Dundee.

" This ring and this purse take to prove I am grateful,
    And some simple token I trust ye'll gie me,
And in times to come I'll the laddie remember
    That showed me the road and the miles to Dundee."

I took the gowd pin from the scarf on my bosom,
    And said, " Keep ye this in remembrance o' me."
Then bravely I kissed the sweet lips o' the lassie
    Ere I parted wi' her on the road to Dundee.

So here's to the lassie—I ne'er can forget her—
    And ilka young laddie that's listening to me;
And never be sweer to convoy a young lassie,
    Though it's only to show her the road to Dundee.

THE WASHING-DAY.

THE sky with clouds was overcast, the rain began to fall,
My wife she beat the children and raised a pretty squall;
She bade me with a frowning look to get out of the way,
The deil a bit of comfort's there upon the washing-day.

    For it's thump, thump, scold, scold, thump, thump, away,
    The deil a bit of comfort's there upon the washing-day.

My Kate she is a bonnie wife, there's none more free from evil,
Except upon the washing-day and then she is the deevil!
The very kittlins on the hearth they dare not even play,
Away they jump wi' many a thump upon the washing-day.

    For it's thump, etc.

On that fatal morning when I rise I make a fervent prayer
Unto the gods that it may be throughout the day quite fair,
That not a gown or handkerchief may in the ditch be laid,
For should it happen so, egad, I'd catch a broken head.

    For it's thump, thump, scold, scold, thump, thump, away,
    The deil a bit o' comfort's there upon the washing-day.

A GUID, GUID WIFE.

Air.—"Highland Laddie."

To hae a wife, and rule a wife,
    Tak's a wise, wise man, tak's a wise, wise man;
But to get a wife to rule a man,
    O, that ye can, o' that ye can.

So the wife that's wise we aye maun prize,
    For they're few, ye ken, they're scarce, ye ken;
O, Solomon says ye'll no fin ane
    In hundreds ten, in hundreds ten.

When a man's wed, it's often said,
    He's aye owre blate, he's aye owre blate;
He strives to improve his first calf luve
    When it's owre late, when it's owre late.

Ye maun daut o' them, and mak' o' them,
    Else they'll tak' the barley hood, the barley hood;
Gin the honey-moon wad ne'er gang dune,
    They wad aye be guid, they wad aye be guid.

Gin ye marry when ye're auld,
    Ye will get jeers, ye will get jeers;
And if she be a bonnie lass
    Ye may get fears, ye may get fears.

For gin she's tall, when she grows baul,
    She'll crack your crown, she'll crack your crown;
An' if ye plea wi' ane that's wee,
    She'll pou ye doun, she'll pou ye doun.

Sae he that gets a guid, guid wife,
    Gets gear eneuch, gets gear eneuch;
An' he that gets an ill, ill wife,
    Gets care eneuch, gets care eneuch.

A man may spend and hae money to lend,
    If his wife be ocht, if his wife be ocht;
But a man may spare and aye be bare
    If his wife be nocht, if his wife be nocht.

THE MANTLE SO GREEN.

As I was a-walking one evening in June,
To view the green fields and the meadows in bloom,
I spied a fair female, she appeared like a queen,
In her costly fine robes and her mantle so green.

I stood in amazement, and gazed with surprise,
I thought it was an angel had dropped from the skies;
Her eyes shone like diamonds, and her cheek like the rose,
She was one of the finest that Nature did compose.

Says I, " My lovely fair one, now if thou wilt agree,
It's joined in wedlock and married we shall be;
I'll dress you in rich attire, you'll appear like a queen,
In your costly fine robes and your mantle so green."

Says she, " Oh! my young man, I must be excused,
For I will wed no man, so you must be refused,
To the green woods I'll wander, to shun all men's view,
Since the lad that I loved lies in famed Waterloo."

Says I, " My pretty fair one, pray tell me your lad's name,
For I have been in battle and might have known the same."
" Draw near into my mantle, and there can be seen
His name is embroidered in my mantle so green."

In the raising of the mantle it's there he did behold
His name and his surname in letters of gold,
" Young William O'Riely it appeared to my view,
He was my chief commander in famed Waterloo.

" We fought for three days, and the bullets thick did fly,
I was on the field of battle your own true love did lie;
We fought for three days until the fourth after noon,
He received his death summons on the 18th of June.

" As he lay a-dying I heard his last sigh,
' If you were here, my lovely Nancy, contented I'd die ';
But peace is now proclaimed and the truth I must declare,
This is your true love's token—the gold ring that I wear."

The longer she viewed it, the paler she grew,
She flew into my arms with a heart full of woe,
Crying, "To the green fields I'll wander to shun all men's view,
Since the lad that I love lies in famed Waterloo."

"Oh! Nancy, lovely Nancy, it's thou hast won my heart,
It was in your father's garden that day that we did part,
It was in your father's garden, where no one had us seen,
I rolled you in my arms in your mantle so green."

The couple soon got married, and I heard people say
They had nobles to attend them upon their wedding day;
"For peace is proclaimed and the wars are all o'er,
So you're welcome to my heart, lovely Nancy, evermore."

Many songs and ballads have been written about the battles of Waterloo
and Alma. John Buchan entitled one of his books *The Green Mantle*.
Green was never a favourite colour, and, indeed, has invariably been
considered unlucky. The 300 Caithnessmen who marched over the Ord to
Flodden, and only one of whom returned, wore green tunics.

THE BACK O' RAREY'S HILL.

It was on a Saturday's evening,
    As I went to Dundee,
I met in wi' an old sweetheart,
    And he being on the spree,
His company I did incline,
    So with him I did go;
But to my sad misfortune
    He's proved my overthrow.

I travelled east, I travelled west,
    His company to shun,
Until the train, it was away,
    Nae mair for to return;
My love he followed after me
    Wi' heart and hand guidwill,
That very nicht, and I lost my way
    At the back o' Rarey's hill.

When we awoke in the morning
    We were lying in each other's arms,
When we awoke in the morning
    From enjoying each other's charms;

My love brought forth a bottle,
  Likewise a glass to fill,
And we drank, shook hands, and parted
  At the back o' Rarey's hill.

My love wrote me a letter
  Which made me weep and mourn;
My love wrote me another
  That he would never return;
But if I'd come to sweet Dundee
  His wedded wife to be,
Wi' heart and hand in wedlock band,
  So happy we would be.

Oft in my lover's arms
  My love to him I've told,
And in my lover's arms
  He oft did me enfold;
But, girls, keep your secrets,
  Let no one know your mind
That talks of love and marrying you
  When it's far from his design.

Oh, may you never prosper,
  And may you never thrive,
Nor anything you take in hand
  As long as you're alive;
And the very grass you travel on,
  May it refuse to grow,
If ever I loved anyone
  So dear as I love you.

So all ye Aberdeen lassies,
  A warning tak' by me,
And be sure and choose your company
  When ye gang to Dundee;
And beware o' young bachelor laddies
  Down by yon Baxter's Mill,
For they're sure to gar ye lose your way
  At the back o' Rarey's hill.

Rarey's or Rarie's hill, the locus of the incidents in this song, is situated
near to Broughty Ferry.

THE BUTCHER AND CHAMBER MAID.

It's of a brisk young butcher, as I have heard them say,
He started for Newcastle town upon a certain day;
He says, a frolic I will have, my fortune for to try,
And I'll set off to Morpeth some cattle for to buy.

When he arrived at Morpeth town he alighted at an inn,
He called for an hostler and boldly stepped in;
He called for liquor of the best, being a roving blade,
And presently he fixed his eyes upon the chamber maid.

He called for a candle to light him up to bed,
And when she came into the room, these words to her he said—
One sovereign I will give for to enjoy your charms;
So all that night this maid she lay within the butcher's arms.

'Twas early the next morning he rose to go away—
The landlord says your reckoning you have forgot to pay;
No, then, says the butcher, so do not think it strange,
One sovereign I have given your maid and have not got the
    change.

The chamber maid was called forth and charged with the same,
One sovereign she did lay down for fear of getting blame.
The butcher than returned home well pleased at what had passed;
But soon this lovely chamber maid grew thick about the waist.

'Twas in a twelvemonth after, he came to town again,
And there as he had done before he stopped at the inn,
'Twas then the lovely chamber maid happened him to see—
She brought a child just three months old and placed it on his
    knee.

The butcher then did wonder much and at the child did stare—
But when the joke he did find out, how he did stamp and swear.
She says, kind sir, it is your own, so do not think it strange—
One sovereign you gave to me and I have brought your change.

The company did loudly laugh, the joke went freely round,
And soon the tidings of the same was spread through Morpeth
    town;
Unto the justice they did go, who happened to live near,
One hundred pounds he did pay down before he could get clear.

Come all you brisk and lively lads, a warning take by me,
And look well to your bargain before you money pay,
For fear your fortune you might rue, and cause you for to range,
For if you sport with chamber maids you are sure to get your
     change.

WHEN YOU AND I WERE YOUNG.

I WANDERED to-day by the mill, Maggie,
   To watch the scene below;
The creek and the creeking old mill, Maggie,
   As we used to do long ago.
The green grove is gone from the hill, Maggie,
   Where first the daisies sprung;
The creeking old mill is still, Maggie,
   Since you and I were young.

Chorus.

But now we are agèd and gray, Maggie,
   And the trials of life nearly done;
Let us sing of the days that are gone, Maggie,
   When you and I were young.

A city so silent and lone, Maggie,
   Where the young, the gay, and the best,
In polished white masions of stone, Maggie,
   Have each found a place of rest.
It is there that the birds used to sing, Maggie,
   And we joined in the songs that were sung,
For we sang as well as they, Maggie,
   When you and I were young.

     But now we are agèd, etc.

They say I am feeble with age, Maggie,
   My steps are less sprightly than then;
My face is a well-written page, Maggie,
   But time alone was the pen.
They say you are aged and gray, Maggie,
   As sprays from the white breakers flung,
But, to me, you're as fair as you were, Maggie,
   When you and I were young.

     But now we are agèd, etc.

THE HANDSOME CABIN BOY.

It's of a pretty female, as you shall understand,
She had a mind for roving unto a foreign land;
Attired in sailor's clothing she boldly did appear,
And engaged with the captain to serve him for a year.

She engaged with the captain a cabin-boy to be,
The wind it being in favour so they put off to sea;
The captain's lady being on board she seemed in great joy,
So glad the captain had engaged the handsome cabin boy.

So nimble was the pretty maid to do her duty well,
But mark which followed after, the time itself will tell;
The captain and the pretty maid did often kiss and toy,
For he soon found out the secret of the handsome cabin boy.

Her cheeks appeared as roses, with her locks all in curl,
The sailors ofttimes smiled and said, he looks like a girl;
By eating captain's biscuits she her colour did destroy,
And the waist did swell of pretty Nell, the handsome cabin
    boy.

As through the Bay of Biscay their gallant ship did plough,
One night among the sailors there was a pretty row;
They bundled from their hammocks, it did their rest destroy,
And laughed about the growing of the handsome cabin boy.

Oh doctor! oh doctor! the cabin boy did cry,
The sailors swore by all that's good the cabin boy should die.
The doctor ran with all his might, and smiling at the fun,
For to think a sailor lad should have a daughter or a son.

The sailors when they heard the joke they all began to stare,
The child belonged to none of them they solemnly did swear;
The lady to the captain said, my dear, I wish you joy,
For it's either you or I betrayed the handsome cabin boy.

So they all took up a bumper and drank success to trade,
And likewise to the cabin boy though neither man nor maid;
And if the wars should rise again the sailors to destroy,
We will ship some other sailors like the handsome cabin boy.

LOW DOWN IN THE BROOM.

My daddie is a canker'd carle,
   He'll no twin wi' his gear;
My minnie she's a scaulding wife,
   Hauds a' the house a-steer.

     But let them say, or let them do,
       It's a' ane to me;
     For he's low down, he's in the broom,
       That's waiting on me;
     Waiting on me, my love,
       He's waiting on me;
     For he's low down, he's in the broom,
       That's waiting on me.

My auntie Kate sits at her wheel,
   And sair she lightlies me;
But weel ken I, it's a' envy,
   For ne'er a jo has she.

     But let them say, etc.

My cousin Kate was sair beguil'd
   Wi' Johnnie in the glen,
And ay sin' syne, she cries, Beware
   O' false, deluding men.

     But let them say, etc.

Gleed Sandy he cam wast ae night,
   And speer'd when I saw Pate?
And ay sin' syne the neighbours round
   They jeer me air and late.

     But let them say, or let them do,
       It's a' ane to me;
     For I'll gae to the bonnie lad
       That's waiting on me;
     Waiting on me, my love.
       He's waiting on me;
     For he's low down, he's in the broom,
       That's waiting on me.

MY BONNIE IRISH BOY.

WHEN first that I was courted
  By a bonnie Irish boy,
He called me his darling,
  His heart's delight and joy.

It was in Dublin city,
  That place of note and fame,
Where first my bonnie Irish boy
  A-courting to me came.

His cheeks they were like roses,
  His eyes as black as sloes;
He breaks the hearts of all the girls
  Wherever that he goes.

When fields they were green,
  And meadows they were gay,
Me and my bonnie Irish boy
  Did often sport and play.

The lambkins they are sporting,
  The birds did sweetly sing,
And to my bonnie Irish boy
  Sweet kisses I did bring.

A long time I kept his company,
  In hopes to be his bride,
Now he has gone and left me
  To cross the seas so wide.

I'm afraid some other fair maid
  She does my love enjoy,
And I am left lamenting
  For my bonnie Irish boy.

So I'll pack up my clothing
  And in search of him I'll go,
And travel through this country,
  Through hail, wind, and snow.

When I'm footsore and tired,
  I'll set me down and cry,
And think upon the joys I had
  With my bonnie Irish boy.

Oh! when that I am dead and gone,
    There's one request I crave,
To take my bones to Ireland
    And lay them in the grave,

And write upon the tombstone,
    To tell the passers by,
That I died quite broken-hearted
    For my bonnie Irish boy.

THE DAWNING OF THE DAY.

ONE morning early I walked forth
    By the margin of Loch Lene,
The sunshine dressed the trees in green,
    And summer bloomed again;
I left the town and wandered on
    Through fields all green and gay;
And whom should I meet but Coolen-dhas
    By the dawning of the day.

No cap or cloak the maiden wore,
    Her neck and feet were bare;
Down to the grass her ringlets fell
    Her glossy golden hair;
A milking pail was in her hand,
    She was lovely, young, and gay;
She bore the palm from Venus bright,
    By the dawning of the day.

On a mossy bank I sat me down,
    With the maiden by my side;
With gentle words I courted her
    And asked her for my bride;
She said, "Young man, don't bring me blame,
    But let me go away,
For morning light is shining bright
    By the dawning of the day."

This is another Irish Folk-song. A copy of it, set to music, appears
in Joyce's *Ancient Irish Music*, published by M. H. Gill & Son, Limited,
Dublin, 1912.

I'M TO BE MARRIT IN MAY.

THE win' at the window is rattlin',
  The sheep huddle close on the brae,
The birdies are caldrif an' chirpin',
  And the clouds are frownin' an' grey.
But what care I for the weather?
  I'm happy's a queen a' the day;
I've got the consent o' my mither,
  And I'm to be marrit in May.

Chorus.

  For I'm to be marrit in May,
  Oh! I'm to be marrit in May!
  I've got the consent o' my mither
  And I'm to be marrit in May.

My Johnny's the pride o' Portlethen,
  Sae strappin', sae blythe, and sae trig,
He's naething, they say, in his muggin,
  But for riches I carena a fig.
There's nane o' them a' like my Johnny
  Can handle a pair on the lea,
His rig is the strachtest o' ony,
  An' his heart aye beats faithfu' to me.

  Chorus.

Sma' won'er it is then I'm cheerfu',
  An' sing like a queen a' the day,
While ithers, I hear, are gey tearfu',
  'Cause Johnny's to tak' me away.
Blaw, blaw ye win's wi' your sleetin',
  For the caul' blast I carena a strae,
The sun in the Heavens will be shinin'
  The day I get marrit in May.

  Chorus.

This song was sent to me by James M. Taylor, 13 Fraser Street,
Aberdeen, when I was collecting Folk-songs through the columns of a
weekly magazine. Mr. Taylor informed me that he was the author of the
song himself. It has the true bothy ring about it.
  Half-a-century ago the farm servants of the north-eastern counties of
Scotland did not trouble themselves about the May marriage superstition.
The May term was their favourite time for getting married.

THE MILL, MILL, O.

BENEATH a green shade I found a fair maid,
  Was sleeping sound and still, O;
A' lowan wi' love my fancy did rove
  Around her wi' good will, O.
Her bosom I prest, but sunk in her rest
  She stir'dna my joy to spill, O,
While kindly she slept, close to her I crept,
  And kiss'd and kiss'd her my fill, O.

Oblig'd by command in Flanders to land,
  To employ my courage and skill, O,
Frae her quietly I flaw, hoist sails and awa,
  For the wind blew fair on the hill, O.
Twa years brought me hame where loud-fraising fame
  Tauld me with a voice richt shrill, O,
My lass, like a fool, had mounted the stool,
  Nor kend wha had done her the ill, O.

Mair fond of her charms, with my son in her arms,
  I ferlying speir'd how she fell, O;
Wi' the tear in her eye, quoth she, " Let me die,
  Sweet sir, gin I can tell, O."
Love gave the command, I took her by the·hand,
  And bade her a' fears expel, O,
And nae mair look wan, for I was the man
  Wha had done her the deed mysel', O.

My bonnie sweet lass, on the gowany grass
  Beneath the Shillinghill, O,
If I did offence, I'll mak' ye amends
  Before I leave Peggie's Mill, O.
O the mill, mill, O, and the kill, kill, O,
  And the coggin' of the wheel, O;
The sack and the sieve, and a' ye maun leave,
  And round wi' a sodger reel, O.

THE KING OF THE FAIRIES.
(NURSERY SONG.)

A WEE, wee man came to our toon en',
    Fiddledum, faddledum, fee, fee, fee;
An' he sang sae sweet that the hale o' our men
    Lap aff their looms the carle to see.

His cap was red and his breeks were green,
    Fiddledum, faddledum, fee, fee, fee;
An' his jacket the shortest that ever was seen,
    An' the queerest colour you ever did see.

His nose was as flat as the back o' my han',
    Fiddledum, faddledum, fee, fee, fee;
An' his feet wad hae covered an acre o' lan',
    Yet his boots came up o'er the lid o' his knee.

His e'en were grey without any white,
    Fiddledum, faddledum, fee, fee, fee;
An' his teeth were as black as the middle o' the night
    When the moon has forsaken this countrie.

His legs were as bow'd as the half o' a hoop,
    Fiddledum, faddledum, fee, fee, fee;
An' his arms were sae lang he ne'er needed to stoop,
    For he picked up preens without bending his knee.

He laughed, and the hale o' the men o' our toun,
    Fiddledum, faddledum, fee, fee, fee,
Lap out o' their wits and fell doun in a swoon,
    The fent ane o' them had the power to flee.

He sang, and they sprang to their feet in a crack,
    Fiddledum, faddledum, fee, fee, fee;
Now what I relate is a notable fact,
    For I was sleeping when I did it see.

He play'd them a jig and the dancing began,
    Fiddledum, faddledum, fee, fee, fee;
And he led them to where a big water down ran,
    Where he douked them till they were like to dee.

This queer wee man lap up on a hill,
  Fiddledum, faddledum, fee, fee, fee;
And he opened his mouth like the door o' a mill,
  I hope sic a mouth I will never again see.

But thunder ne'er gied sic a terrible roar,
  Fiddledum, faddledum, fee, fee, fee,
As when he announced that the dancing was o'er,
  And bade them fareweel and awa did flee.

Weary and wet our men came hame,
  Fiddledum, faddledum, fee, fee, fee;
An' swore the wee man was surely to blame
  For using sic freedom in ony countrie.

Ye'll wonder what came o' this wee, wee man,
  Fiddledum, faddledum, fee, fee, fee;
He bought a green coat—an' to fairy lan' ran,
  An' now he is king o' that countrie.

CRADLE LULLABY.

BALOO, loo baby, now baloo, my dear,
Now baloo, loo lammie, your mammie is here:
What ails my wee lammie? what ails it the nicht?
What ails my wee lammie? is bairnie no richt?

Baloo, loo lammie, now baloo, my dear,
Does wee lammie ken that its daddy's no here?
You're rockin' fu' sweetly on mammie's warm knee,
But daddy's a-rockin' upon the saut sea.

Now hush-a-ba, baby; now hush-a, my dear,
Now hush-a-ba, lammie, your minnie is here,
The wild wind is ravin' an' mammie's he'rt's sair,
The wild wind is ravin' an' ye dinna care.

Sing baloo, loo lammie, sing baloo, my dear,
Sing baloo, loo lammie, your mammie is near,
My wee bairnie's noo dozin', it's dozin' noo fine,
And, oh! may its wauk'nin' be blyther than mine.

JOHNNIE LAD.

(NURSERY SONG.)

I BOUGHT a wife in Edinburgh
  For ae bawbee,
I got a farthing back again
  To buy tobacco wi';
We'll bore a hole in Aaron's nose,
  And put therein a ring,
And straight we'll lead him to and fro,
  Yea! lead him on a string.

Chorus.

And wi' you, and wi' you,
  And wi' you, Johnnie lad,
I'll drink the buckles o' my sheen
Wi' you, my Johnnie lad.

When auld King Arthur ruled this land
  He was a thievish king,
He stole three bows o' barley meal
  To mak' a white pudding.
    And wi' you, etc.

The pudding it was sweet and good,
  And weel mixed up wi' plumes,
The lumps o' suet into it
  Were big as baith my thooms.
    And wi' you, etc.

There was a man in Nineveh,
  And he was wondrous wise,
He jumped into a hawthorn hedge
  And scratched out baith his eyes.
    And wi' you, etc.

And when he saw his eyes were out
  He was sair vexed then,
He jumped into anither hedge
  And scratched them in again.
    And wi' you, etc.

O, Johnnie's nae a gentleman,
  Nor yet is he a laird,
But I wad follow Johnnie lad,
  Although he was a caird.

    And wi' you, etc.

O, Johnnie is a bonnie lad,
  He was ance a lad o' mine,
I never had a better lad,
  And I've had twenty-nine.

    And wi' you, and wi' you,
      And wi' you, Johnnie lad,
    I'll drink the buckles o' my sheen
      Wi' you, my Johnnie lad.

PART I.

(b) Songs of the Forsaken and Jilted.

———

SEVEN YEARS O'ER YOUNG.

KEY A. { .s₁ | s₁ :s .l₁ | d :- .m | r .,m :r .d |d,l₁.- :s₁ .l₁ }

{| f .m :r .d | d :d .m | f :f .l | s :- .m | f :f .l | s :- .m,m}

{| f .m :r .d | l₁ :d .l₁ | s₁.,l₁ :d .d |d,s.- :- .m | r :- .,d | d :-.||

'Twas in between twa bonnie woods and valleys
  Where I and my love aye met so rare,
And all the world it will never know it
  What my laddie said to me there.

And aye so kindly he smiled upon me,
  And aye, he said, " Love, will ye wed?"
And aye the answer that I gave to him
  Was—" I'm seven years o'er young to wed."

If that ye be seven years o'er young, love,
  Your love and my love can ne'er agree;
But aye so kindly I said unto him—
  " When will ye come to my bower and see?"

One night as we sat in my chamber
  Talking o'er some frivolous thing,
I smiled and said unto my lover,
  "When will ye wed me wi' a ring?"

If I should wed you wi' a ring, love,
  Some other fair maid might on me frown;
But sing me the song that ye sang afore, love,
  That ye are seven years o'er young.

I winna sing the song that I sang afore, love,
  For daily and hourly that I would rue;
But I'll sing a song that I ne'er sung afore, love,
  I will sing that I am years enow.

Then touch not the nettle while it is hot, love,
  Down in yon valley so green it grows,
And love not the lad ye will never get,
  For the bands o' love they are ill to loose.

For I love the lass wi' the gowen hair, love,
  And the lass wi' the gowen hair loves me;
I love the lass wi' the amber locks, love,
  And that makes me care the less for thee.

Then I love the lad wi' the dark brown hair, O,
  And the lad wi' the dark brown hair loves me,
I love the lad wi' the dark brown hair, O,
  And that makes me care the less for thee.

Of all the flowers in yonder garden
  Be sure that ye pu' the rue and the thyme,
Since all other flowers are quite out of fashion,
  Wi' a false-hearted laddie aye on my mind.

In 1816 James Hogg, the Ettrick shepherd, sent to *Albyn's Anthology* a ballad entitled "A Year O'er Young." In a letter to the editor which accompanied the ballad, Hogg wrote as follows:—"The first half of this song only is mine—the latter, very old. As I have often told you I got the verses and tune from a maniac, and I never heard anyone else sing them." When in Huntly, Strathbogie, in August, 1907, I heard an old gentleman Mr. Robert Mellis, singing the above song, and I subsequently received a copy of it from him. There seems to be little doubt but it is the original of Hogg's ballad, and it is of great interest to the student of Folk-song to find in Aberdeenshire a complete version of a ballad nearly a hundred years after Hogg picked up in some place near the Borders three verses of it from the singing of an insane person.

ON LONGSIDE ROAD; or THE FALSE LOVER.

On Longside Road I've often trod
  When the moon was shining clear,
'Twas there I spied another maid
  In the arms of my dear.

Another maid now fill your arms
  Where I've been many a time,
And she enjoys the favours now
  Which I did once langsyne.

Oh, may she flourish in your arms,
  And happy may she be;
For she's innocent and ignorant
  Of what you've done to me.

You think that I could love you still?
  But, oh, how can this be?
For I am quite resolved now
  To shun your company.

I'm every bit as good as you,
  And of as good a kin;
So you're as welcome to go by
  As you were to come in.

Though you were fair as Absalom,
  Or Alexander brave,
If you canna gie love for love again,
  I can never be your slave.

But ye hae ta'en your ain road,
  The thing you'll maybe rue;
But mine's a heart that will not break
  For such a one as you.

But if I chance to hae a house,
  A house I can ca' mine,
I'll welcome in my auld sweethearts
  For the days o' auld lang syne.

OH, YE'VE BEEN FALSE; or THE CURSE.

As I cam' in by yon bonnie waterside,
  And down by yon bonnie bush o' broom,
There I spied my ain dear love,
  And I left my heart wi' him.

> Oh, ye've been false, and very, very false,
>   And your words hae been far frae true;
> The woman never shall follow at your back
>   That will love you so well as I do.

The church you're mairriet in, young man,
  Oh, may she sink in sand;
And the minister that marries you, young man,
  To the hills mad may he gang.

> Oh, ye've been false, etc.

Muckle, muckle sorrow to your new mairriet wife,
  And ill, ill may she thrive;
And every year a burial,
  Till she bury to you sons five.

> Oh, ye've been false, etc.

A curse rest on your corn, young man,
  A curse rest on your hay;
And muckle, muckle sorrow to your new mairriet wife,
  And a dwinin' baith nicht and day.

> Oh, ye've been false, etc.

The meadows ye ride through, young man,
  Oh, sharp pins may they grow,
And the wee horn cows that in them feed
  Haud up their heads and low.'

> Oh, ye've been false, etc.

The waters ye ride through, young man,
  Oh, red blood may they rin;
And the little fishes that in them swim,
  May they sink and lose their fin.

> Oh, ye've been false, etc.

For the sinnerin' o' me and my bonnie love,
　For the sinnerin' o' him and me;
I wish their heads may ne'er be whole
　That sinnert him and me.
　　Oh, ye've been false, etc.

THE FAUSE YOUNG MAN.

'Twas in the gay, merry month of May,
　When birds sing always so sweet,
I did me to my own chamber door,
　And saw two lovers meet.
I saw two lovers meet all alone,
　And heard what they did say;
But I wished to know some more of their mind
　Before that they gaed away.

" You're welcome to me, young man," she said,
　" But I hear that you've changed your mind,
I hear that your after another pretty maid,
　And your heart is no longer mine;
But when your heart was mine, young man,
　And your hand upon your left breast,
You'd have made me believe by the fause oaths you swore
　That the sun aye rose in the west.

" Oh, fause ha'e you been to me, young man,
　And sair ha'e you changed your min';
You are a deceiver of our ain female sex,
　A deluder of young women.
But I'll never believe an old man," she said,
　" For it's high time that he was gone;
Nor will I believe a young man's faith and troth,
　For he swears to many a one.

" He swears to many a one," she said,
　" And many fause tale does he tell;
He delights to be in young maids' company,
　Till he knows their minds full well.
I will never believe a man any more,
　Let his hair be white, black, or brown,
Save he were on the top of a high gallows tree,
　And swearing he wished to come down."

IT WASNA MY FORTUNE TO GET HER.

I COURTED a lassie for mony a lang day,
And aye conter'd them that against her did say,
And noo she rewards me by saying me nay,
   And she's to be wed to another.
When I saw the bonnie lass a' drest in white,
Wi' tears in my e'en she dazzl'd my sight,
I thought wi' mysel' I could never be right,
   Since it was not my fortune to get her.

When I saw the bonnie lass to the church go,
Wi' her young men and maidens who made a fine show,
I followed after wi' heart full of woe,
   Since it wasna my fortune to get her.
When I passed the bonnie lass in the church style,
I tramp'd on her gown though I didna it fyle;
She turned to me and said wi' a smile,
   "Young man ye are troubl'd about nothing."

Mess John of the parish he gave a loud cry—
"If any object now, I pray they'll draw nigh";
I thought to mysel' good occasion hae I
   For it hasna been my lot to get her.
When I saw the bonnie lass in the church stand,
Wi' the ring on her finger and glove in her hand,
I wish'd him that got her both houses and land,
   Though it wasna my fortune to get her.

Now after the wedding we sat down to dine,
I took up the bottle and served out the wine,
And drank to the bride that should ha'e been mine,
   Though it wasna my fortune to get her.
They a' got sae merry that I couldna byde,
I leant o'er the table, shook hands wi' the bride,
I bade her farewell that should been by my side,
   But oh! I was wae then to leave her.

Now ye'll dig my grave baith lang, wide, and deep,
Put a stone at my head, a green turf at my feet,
And there I'll lie down and tak' a long sleep,
   And when I awake I'll think on her.
So they dug his grave, made it lang, wide, and deep,
Put a stone at his head, a green turf at his feet,
And there he was laid down to tak' a lang sleep;
   But he will tak' lang to think on her.

THE RAMBLING BEAUTY.

ALL ye that follow the rambling beauty,
　I warn ye a' tak' special care,
And not depend on false young women,
　They'll be sure to draw ye into a snare.

A merchant's daughter callèd Nancy,
　Dressed in silks and satins fine,
For her I had the greatest fancy
　I ever had for womankind.

One day I went to pay her a visit,
　And offered her the wedding ring;
How scornfully she did refuse it,
　And said she would have no such thing.

She then went straight unto her father
　To let him this awful story know;
His cruelty was worse than his daughter's,
　He bade me from his presence go.

He swore that I had his daughter ruined,
　And into prison he did me throw;
And there I lived upon bread and water
　Till my condition was very low.

And now she's married to Prince Orai,
　A reckless youth in yonder town,
Who neither loves nor yet regards her,
　But tries to trample her courage down.

One day as I was out a-walking,
　My false lover I chanced to meet,
She being in a poor condition
　And I myself in a thriving state.

I put my hand into my pocket
　And took out guineas one, two, three,
Says, " Take ye this, ye poor heartless woman,
　D'ye mind how false ye were to me?"

She wrung her hands and she fell a-weeping,
   Alas, her sorrows were fresh and green;
Says, "Once I thought I had a heart a-keeping,
   But how unfortunate I hae been."

Now all ye young women frae me take warning,
   And never throw your first love away;
For. oft a dark and a misty morning
   Turns out a bright and a bonnie day.

I'LL CHEER UP MY HEART.

As I was a-walking ae May morning,
   The fiddlers and youngsters were making their game;
And there I saw my faithless lover,
   And a' my sorrows returned again.

Well, since he's gane, joy gang wi' him,
   It's never be he shall gar me complain:
I'll cheer up my heart, and I'll get another,
   I'll never lay a' my love upon ane.

I couldna get sleeping yestreen for weeping,
   The tears ran down like showers o' rain;
An' hadna I got greetin' my heart wad a-broken,
   And O! but love's a tormenting pain.

But since he is gane, may joy gae wi' him,
   It's never be he shall gar me complain:
I'll cheer up my heart, and I'll get another,
   I'll never lay a' my love upon ane.

When I gaed into my mither's new house,
   I took my wheel and sat down to spin;
'Twas there I first began my thrist;
   And a' the wooers came linking in.

It was gear he was seeking, but gear he'll nae get,
   And it's never be he that shall gar me complain,
For I'll cheer up my heart, and I'll soon get another;
   I'll never lay a' my love upon ane.

THE BREWER LAD.

THERE lived a lad in the town o' Perth,
   A brewer to his trade, O;
He courted Peggy Royal,
   A very handsome maid, O.

He's courted her for seven lang years,
   Thinkin' to gain her favour;
But there cam' a lad frae the south-sea banks,
   And he swore that he would have her.

It's will ye go along wi' me,
   And will ye go, my honey;
And will ye go along wi' me
   And leave your ain dear Johnny?

Yes, I will go along with you,
   And along with you I'll ride, O;
Yes, I will go along with you,
   Though I'm the brewer's bride, O.

The brewer he cam' home at e'en,
   Enquiring for his honey;
Her father he made this reply—
   I've ne'er seen her since Monday.

Wasna that a nasty trick,
   Wadna anyone been offended,
To court wi' a lad for seven years
   And leave him at the end o't?

But since she's gone, pray let her go,
   No more shall she thus grieve me;
For I'm a brisk and a bonnie lad,
   And little will relieve me.

There's as good fish into the sea
   As ever yet was taken;
And I'll cast out my net again
   Although I am forsaken.

She's rambled up, she's rambled down,
   She's rambled through Kirkcaldy;
And mony's the time she rues the day
   She jilted her brewer laddie.

He's ta'en his course, where'er he's gane,
　The country he has fled, O;
And he's left nae sark upon her back,
　Nor blanket on her bed, O.

The brewer he set up in Perth,
　And there he brews guid ale, O;
And he has courted anither lass
　And ta'en her to himsel', O.

Ye lovers all, where'er ye be,
　By this now take a warnin',
And never slight your ain true love
　For fear ye get a waur ane.

THE DAYS ARE AWA THAT I HAE SEEN.

THE flowers are bonnie and the trees are green,
But the days are awa that I hae seen,
Another is chosen where I hae been,
　And my lad will never mair come near me.
But to try him again I'll deck my hair,
And tie it up wi' a green ribbon fair,
And tie it up wi' mickle care,
　Though he says he will never mair come near me.

Then I'll gae to him and stand by his side,
And I'll wait on him and I'll be his guide;
For he may yet mak' me his bride,
　And I'll go to him though a' should see me.
But he said, " I've chosen another maid ";
I answered, " What have I done or said
To make you choose another maid?
　And me loving you so dearly."

" Nothing you've done and nothing you've said,
To make me choose another maid,
To vex me; another I've chosen," he said,
　" Sò go now I'll never more love thee."
I left him there and said, " Do not rise,
For I have played a foolish guise,
In time to come I shall be more wise,
　I'll go and never more will love thee."

WHEN FORTUNE TURNS HER WHEEL.

Come, fill a glass, let's drink about,
　　This night we'll merry be,
For harmony and friendship free,
　　Likewise my comrades free,
To meet ye a' ance mair, my friens,
　　A sacred joy I feel,
Though far awa I noo maun stray
　　Till Fortune turns her wheel.

The changes of a comrade's state
　　Ne'er make true friendship less;
For a true Caledonian's heart
　　Feels warmer for distress;
For I hae met some trusty friens,
　　And to me they've aye been leal;
Though far awa I noo maun stray
　　Till Fortune turns her wheel.

'Tis not vain clothes nor gold, he says,
　　That's the estimate of man;
For when we meet a frien in straits,
　　We shake a frienly hand;
With them we sit, with them we drink,
　　And to them our minds reveal,
And friens we'll be whatever way
　　Blind Fortune turns her wheel.

But, oh, I loved a bonnie lass,
　　And her I'll justly blame;
For when hard Fortune frowned on me
　　She denied she knew my name;
But falsehood by remorse is paid,
　　And to her I'll never kneel,
I'll sweethearts find baith fair and kind
　　When Fortune turns her wheel.

It's mony the time my heart's been sair
　　And like to brak in twa;
Mony's the time my feet's been cauld,
　　Comin' in frae the frost and snaw;

Wi' nae ane to pity me,
　Nor yet to wish me weel,
But maybe I'll repay them back
　When Fortune turns her wheel.

Some of my once pretending friens,
　If friens I may them ca',
Proved false and turned their backs on me
　When mine was at the wa';
But in this glass I'll let it pass,
　I'm sure I wish them weel;
If my hard fate on them await
　May Fortune turn her wheel.

Adieu, ye hills of Caledon,
　Likewise sweet Avondale,
For friendship binds the strongest ties,
　Love tells the softest tale.
Adieu, my friens and comrades here,
　I ken ye wish me weel;
And I maybe yet can pay my debt
　When Fortune turns her wheel.

GO AND LEAVE ME IF YOU WISH IT.

One I loved with fond affection,
　All his thoughts they were for me;
Until a dark girl did persuade him,
　And then he thought no more of me.
But now he's happy with another,
　One who has bright gold in store;
It's he that caused my heart to ponder,
　I'm left alone because I'm poor.
Chorus.
　Go and leave me if you wish it,
　　Never let me cross your mind;
　If you think me so unworthy,
　　Go and leave me, never mind.

Many days with you I've wandered,
　Many hours with you I've spent;
I thought your heart was mine forever,
　But now I find 'twas only lent.

My heart has failed me, and you know it,
　The heart that fondly beats for thee,
However could I tell another
　The tales of love I told to thee?
　　Chorus.

Many a night when you are sleeping,
　Partaking of your sweet repose,
I, poor girl, lie broken-hearted,
　Listening to the wind that blows.
Farewell, friends and kind relations,
　Farewell to you, my false young man,
It's you that caused my pain and sorrow,
　I never can return again.
　　Chorus.

GREEN GROWS THE LAUREL.

I ANCE had a sweetheart, but now I've got nane,
She's gane and she's left me to weep and to moan,
She's gane and she's left me, but contented I'll be,
For I'll get another far better than she.
　Green grows the laurel, and sweet falls the dew,
　Sorry was I, love, when parting with you;
　But by our next meeting I hope you'll prove true
　And change the green laurel to the violet so blue.

She wrote me a letter, four sweet rosy lines,
She wrote me another all twisted and twined;
Keep your love letter and I will keep mine,
And write to your sweetheart and I'll write to mine.
　Green grows the laurel, etc.

She passes my window both early and late,
And the looks that she gives me they make my heart break,
And the looks that she gives me a thousand times o'er—
" You are the sweetheart I once did adore."
　Green grows the laurel, etc.

I ofttimes do wonder why young maids love men,
I ofttimes do wonder why young men love them;
But by my experience I now ought to know
Young maids are deceivers wherever they go.
　Green grows the laurel, etc.

FALSE MALLIE.

Oh, did ye hear how Mall was courted?
  Oh, did ye hear how Mall was woo'd?
Or did ye hear how Mall was courted
  By a young sailor brisk and bold?

Now Jamie swore that he loved Mallie,
  And Mallie swore that she loved him;
But still he cried, " How can we be parted,
  Perhaps never for to meet again?"

I must go face a bloody battle,
  Perhaps receive the fatal stroke;
But when the wars they all are over,
  If life remains, lovie, I'll come back.

Jamie swore that he loved Mallie,
  And Mallie swore that she loved him,
A piece of gold was broke between them
  For a love-token to remain.

Now Mall's convoyed her bonnie laddie
  Now Mall's convoyed him to the shore;
And she's parted wi' her brisk young sailor,
  And hopes never for to see him more.

He hadna sailed frae bonnie Dundee,
  Oh, nae a mile by far awa',
When Mall has married a ploughman laddie,
  Her vows to Jamie were but sma'.

Oh, mony a letter he sent to Mallie,
  Oh, mony a letter frae far awa',
Oh, mony a letter he sent to Mallie,
  But he never received ane at a'.

Oh, mony a pledge he sent to Mallie,
  And among the rest he sent his glove;
Seven guineas in a letter lockèd,
  Which was a token of his love.

Oh, mony a letter he sent to Mallie
  Frae Portugal to the British shore;
But he never did receive an answer
  Till old England he did come o'er.

Oh, when he heard his Mall was married,
  He wished that he had died in Spain;
But before that he had gone any further,
  In strong Bedlam he was lain.

Oh, mony a lady went to see him,
  In strong Bedlam where he lay bound;
But he roared so loud in his own shackles,
  He was like to pull strong Bedlam down.

Oh, hold your tongue, ye bonnie Jamie,
  Oh, hold your tongue and take your ease;
It's for your sake we will transport her,
  And send her far owre the raging seas.

Oh, hold your tongue, ye bonnie lady,
  And do not talk of Mallie more,
For when I hear her name but mentioned
  It rends my flesh to the very core.

Ye'll go down to my ship's cabin,
  And there you'll find a looking-glass;
Oh, it's so false and it's so deceiving,
  It's like unto false Mallie's face.

And ye'll go down to yonder cottage,
  And maybe ye'll be lookin' in;
When ye'll see Mall rockin' a ploughman's baby
  When she should hae been rockin' mine.

I ploughed the ground and I sowed the seed,
  I thought the increase would be my own;
But there came a blackbird frae the north,
  And he's reaped all that I hae sown.

Oh, that I was ever born,
  Or yet into a cradle laid,
To love a fair maid, and love her dearly,
  And after all to be denied.

And still he cried out to the porter
  To go and bring false Mallie in,
That he could grind her into a mortar,
  And make her powder for his gun.

And aye he cried out unto the porter,
  " Oh, can't you bring false Mallie in,
For I could grind her into mouldings,
  And I could blow her owre to Spain."

Time will make an end of all things,
  And love will make an end of me;
But surely there's some place of torment
  To punish Mallie for slighting me!

THE BONNIE WOODS O' HATTON.

YE comrades and companions, and all ye females dear,
To my sad lamentations I pray ye give an ear;
Once I lo'ed a bonnie lass, I lo'ed her as my life,
It was my whole intentions to make her my wedded wife.

I courted wi' this bonnie lass a twelve months and a day,
Sometimes amang the green grass, sometimes amang the hay;
I courted her a lea-lang nicht and part o' the next day
Till she said, " My dearest Sandy, it's time you were away."

Says I, " My pretty Betsy, when will you set a time
When you and I'll get married, love, and hands together join;
You'll sit in our wee cottage and you'll neither spin nor sew,
While your ain kind-hearted hireman lad gangs whistling at
  the plough."

There's Castem and there's Cadem Mills and Leather Mills
  likewise,
There are woods and waters mony more that's present to my
  eyes;
But the bonnie woods o' Hatton, they a' grow green in May,
'Twas there the bonnie lassie lived that stole my heart away.

I'll speak about yon bonnie lass though I be far awa,
I'll speak about yon bonnie lass to those she never saw,
I'll tell them that I lo'ed her weel although she proved untrue,
And left me doon by Hatton's woods my follies for to rue.

But blessings on yon bonnie lass, wherever she may be,
I wish no evil unto her although she slighted me;
I only hope she'll say some day, before that she does dee,
" I wish I'd wed yon hireman lad that sang sae sweet to me."

BLOOMING CAROLINE O' EDINBURGH TOWN.

COME all ye men and maidens, and listen to my rhyme,
It's of a lovely damsel that was scarcely in her prime;
Her cheeks were like the roses red, and her hair was deep dark
      brown,
She was called the blooming Caroline of Edinburgh town.

Young Henry being a Highland lad, a-courting her he came,
And when her parents came to know they were angry at the
      same;
Young Henry, being offended, these words to her did say,
" Arise, my dearest Caroline, and we will run away.

" We will go to London, love, and there we'll wed with speed,
And then, my lovely Caroline, is happiness indeed."
She came tripping down the stair, with her hair all hanging
      down,
Away went blooming Caroline from Edinburgh town.

O'er hills and lofty mountains together they did roam,
Till they arrived in London, far from her happy home.
She said, " My dearest Henry, pray never on me frown,
Or you'll break the heart of Caroline of Edinburgh town."

They had not been in London not passing half-a-year,
When cruel, hard-hearted Henry proved to her severe;
Says he, " My dear, I'll go to sea, since your friends will on me
      frown,
So beg your way, without delay, to Edinburgh town.

" The ships are fitting out, and to Spithead dropping down,
And I will join the gallant fleet to fight for King and Crown,
The gallant tars may feel the scars, or in the water drown,
But I will never return again to Edinburgh town."

Then many a day she passed away in sorrow and despair,
Her cheeks, that once like roses were, grew like the lilies fair.
She cried, " Where is my Henry?" and oft-times she did swoon,
Crying, " Sad's the day I ran away from Edinburgh town."

Oppress'd with grief, without relief, this damsel she did go
Into the wood to eat such food as on the bushes grow;
Some strangers they did pity her, and some did on her frown,
And some did say, " What made you stray from Edinburgh
      town?"

Beaneath a lofty spreading oak this maid sat down to cry,
To see the gallant ships of war as they were sailing by;
She gave three shrieks for Henry, and plunged her body down—
She was once the blooming Caroline of Edinburgh town.

A note, likewise her bonnet, she left upon the shore,
And in the note a lock of hair, with words, " I am no more,
For in the deep I'm fast asleep, the fishes watch all round;
I was once the blooming Caroline of Edinburgh town."

Now, all ye tender parents, ne'er try to part true love,
Or you're sure to see in some degree the ruin it will prove.
Likewise, young men and maidens, ne'er on your lovers frown;
Think of the fate of Caroline of Edinburgh town.

THE ROSE AND THE THYME.

I'M sorry, I'm sorry that my fortune's been so bad,
Since I've fa'en in love wi' a young sailor lad;
He courted me by night and he courted me by day,
And now he has left me and went far away.

My love sent me a letter that he was lying bad,
I sent him another I did not him regard;
He sent me another wi' the red rose so fine,
But I sent him another wi' the rue and the thyme.

Keep ye the red rose, love, and I'll keep my thyme,
Drink ye to your true love, and I'll drink to mine;
I'll eat when I'm hungry, and drink when I'm dry,
And rest when I am wearied, contented am I.

Oh! are ye waiting your fortune to advance?
Or are ye awaiting a far better chance?
Or are ye keeping me laid up for you in store?
Or do ye mean to tell me that ye love me no more?

I am not waiting my fortune to advance,
Nor am I awaiting a far better chance;
Nor am I keeping you laid up for me in store,
Nor do I intend for to mind you any more.

Once I did love you but now I you disdain,
And it's not for all the world I would e'er love you again;
The more that I loved you the prouder still you grew,
So ye may keep the thyme, love, and I will keep the rue.

THE FLOWER OF FRANCE AND ENGLAND, O.

As I was on my rambles,
I came from Dover to Carlisle;
The town was full of rebels,
You might have heard them for a mile;
I called at " The Grapes " to see
What entertainment I could find;
Not being brisk, I ran the risk,
And called for a pint o' wine,
And saw a smiling bonnie lass,
The flower o' France and England, O.

As I was in a hurry,
I for a private room did call;
They sent me to the cadie,
The boy that rings the morning bell.
But in there came this brisk young dame
And said, " Kind sir, come follow me,
It is not fit for you to sit
Among such roving company:
You hearty smiling bonnie lad,
The flower o' France and England, O.

She led me to a private room,
Where everything was neat and clean,
And said, " Young man, it is not fit,
You should have somewhat on to dine."
The table soon she covered,
And dinner soon she did bring in,
She looked not like an idle slut,
Nor one that was not taught to spin:
The hearty smiling bonnie lass,
The flower o' France and England, O.

But I could take no dinner
For thinking on the pretty maid,
And, if I could but win her,
I would not care how long I stayed;

I rang the bell, she heard the knell,
And soon to me she did repair,
I said, " My dear, the table's drawn,
Sit down by me upon this chair:
My hearty smiling bonnie lass,
The flower of France and England, O.

She said, " Young man, you are as bad
As any in this house this night,
For they are drunk, and you are mad,
Or else you would not speak the like.
Take up the cup and drink it up,
And drive such fancies out by sleep,
For if you dream you had me wed,
I'm sure you would rise up and weep:
You hearty smiling bonnie lad,
The flower of France and England, O."

I could not fall a-sleeping,
For thinking on the bonnie lass,
That spent some time a-scouring
Among the pewter and the brass.
I rang the bell, she heard the knell,
And soon to me she did repair;
Said I, " We'll to St. Mary's Church
And there we will undo the care:
My hearty smiling bonnie lass,
The flower of France and England, O."

We went unto St. Mary's,
And there the priest the knot did tie;
I hied home my bonnie bride
As fast as ever I could hie;
Through Scotland broad we took the road,
Until we came to Balquidder braes;
The servants all did skip and dance
To see their Lord and Lady's face:
The hearty smiling bonnie lass,
The flower of France and England, O.

We spent some days a-feasting
Among our friends and neighbours all,
The bride did think't no jesting,
When they did on the lady call;

Now she's a lady frank and free,
And needs no more to toil or spin;
And all her friends may bless the day
That e'er I came " The Grapes " within,
To get a hearty smiling lass,
The flower of France and England, O.

This song from the reference in the third verse to Carlisle being " full of
rebels " evidently dates back to the Rebellion of 1745. I never heard the
song sung but once, and that was about forty-five years ago at a farm-house
in Aberdeenshire.

THE BLAEBERRY COURTSHIP.

" WILL ye gang to the Hielands, my jewel, wi' me ?
Will ye gae wi' your true love the mountains to see;
It is healthy, dear lassie, to breathe the sweet air,
And to pu' the blaeberries in the forest sae fair."
" Wi' thee to the Hielands, love, I daurna gang,
The mountains are dreary, the journey is lang;
I love this fair valley and sweet cornfield
Mair than all the blaeberries your wild forests yield."

Then out spake her father, a haughty auld man,
" Gae seek ye a mistress amang your ain clan;
We lo'e nae the proffer, 'mang wild Hieland fells,
O' your wealth o' blaeberries and blue heather bells."
Awa' she's gane wi' him in spite o' them a',
Awa to a country her e'en never saw;
Ower broad moss and mountain on foot she did gang:
And aye he said, " Lassie, think nae the road lang."

" I'm foot sair and weary, my shoes are all rent,
Sae far hae we travelled, I'm ready to faint;
And were it not, dearest, for your company,
Amang the lang heather I'd lie down and dee."
As onward they wandered they came to a grove,
Where sheep out o' number a-feeding did rove;
And Allan stood musing, his hirsels to see,
But to her, his dear lassie, nae joy could they gie.

A sprightly young laddie, wi' green tartan trews,
And twa bonnie lassies were buchting his ewes;
He said, "Honoured master, fu' blessed may ye be!
Baith you and your lady we lang look'd to see."
'Midst warmest o' welcome she entered the ha',
And sic a fine mansion she scarce ever saw;
Wi' ale and gude whisky they drank her health roun',
And they made her braw bed o' heather and down.

He led her neist morn to the hayfield near by,
And bade her look roun' her as far's she could spy:
"These lands and possessions are yours, love, for aye,
And ye winna gang roun' them in a lang summer's day."
"O Allan, O Allan, why came ye to me?
Sure I am unworthy your mistress to be!"
"Look up, winsome lassie, ye needna think shame,
And call me not Allan, for Sandy's my name."

"Are you, then, the Sandy whom I loved so dear?
Why heard I not from you for many a year?
O, oft, faithful Sandy, wi' thinking on thee,
When others were sleepin', I ne'er closed an e'e."
"Alas! both my parents I lost when a child,
And far from these valleys was I then exiled;
But years came and plenty was shower'd upon me,
So I wish, dearest jewel, to share it with thee.

"We loved other dearly, with love let us end,
While in innocent pleasure our days we will spend;
And again to your father together we will go,
It will ease the old farmer of trouble and woe."
With men and maid servants to wait them upon,
Away to the Lowlands again they have gone;
They drove to the window before they would stand,
While down came the father with bonnet in hand.

"Come, keep on your bonnet, and don't let it fa',
It sets not the peacock to bow to the craw!"
"Forbear, gentle Sandy, and dinna taunt me,
My Jean's undeserving your leddy to be."
There's mirth in the kitchen, delight on the green,
Sae pleased was the mother tears blinded her e'en;
To make ilka ane happy nae siller was spared,
And now the auld farmer's a douce-looking laird.

THE FLOWER O' NORTHUMBERLAND.

A MAID passed by the prison door
  (Maids' love whiles is easy won)
She saw a prisoner standing there,
  And wishing to be in fair Scotland.
" O, fair maid, will ye pity me?
  (Maids' love whiles is easy won)
Ye'll steal the keys, let me gang free,
  And I'll make ye my lady in fair Scotland."

" I'm sure ye hae nae need o' me
  (Maids' love whiles is easy won)
For ye hae a wife and bairns three
  That live at hame in fair Scotland."
Then by a sacred oath he has sworn
  (Maids' love whiles is easy won)
He ne'er had a wife since he was born,
  But lived a free lord in fair Scotland

She went into her father's room
  (Maids' love whiles is easy won)
And mony a key from it she's stown,
  And let him out o' prison strong.
She went into her father's stable
  (Maids' love whiles is easy won)
And stown a steed baith wight and able
  To carry them on to fair Scotland.

They raid till they came to a moss
  (Maids' love whiles is easy won)
He bade her light aff her father's best horse,
  And return again to Northumberland.
When she gaed back to her father's ha'
  (Maids' love whiles is easy won):
She looted her low amongst them a',
  Though she was the flower o' Northumberland.

Out spoke her father, he spoke bold
  (Maids' love whiles is easy won)
" How could ye do so at fifteen years' old,
  And you the flower o' Northumberland?"
Out spoke her mother, she spoke with a smile
  (Maids' love whiles is easy won):
" She's nae the first he tried to beguile,
  Ye're welcome back to Northumberland."

THE HAUGHS O' NEWE.

As I gaed up the Haughs o' Newe,
　And through Strath Don upon my pony,
I met a may baith young and gay,
　Wha said to me her name was Downie.
Wi' cherry cheeks and coal black e'en—
　Her e'en appeared to me like lammer—
I view'd her ower frae tap to tae,
　Till my head grew licht, and my tongue did stammer.

There's nae her like on Tweed or Tay,
　Nor in Strath Don, nor yet Lochearn;
She far excels yon cutty quean
　That stays where ye gang through the Cairn.[1]
The lads and lasses a' convened,
　And ate and drank, and syne they dancèd:
But 'mang them a' I shared but sma',
　Though aft in that may's face I glancèd.

She said, " Young man, you are not wise,
　Or in your head there is some frolic;
For ye can neither sing nor dance
　Nor can ye speak our Hielan' Gaelic."
" The Gaelic tongue I dinna hae,
　Because my mither never had it;
But for to dance I weel may try,
　As my profession does not forbid it.

" But could I dance like young MacLean,
　To him I would gie my grey meirie;
And could I speak Macpherson's tongue
　I would gae on and court you, dearie.
And could I get your own consent,
　And syne had you upon my pony,
I would nae mair range through a fair,
　But stay at hame wi' my love Downie."

[1] Cairn o' Mount.

I picked this song up from the singing of an old man namèd Robert
Mellis, Westfolds, Huntly, Aberdeenshire, in the harvest of 1909.

THE BELT WI' COLOURS THREE.

THE moon shone bright upon my pillow
    Into the chamber where I lay;
I could not sleep that cauld winter's nicht,
    But up I rose at the break of day.
And though the nicht was cauld and frosty,
    My mantle green held me in heat;
I did me down into the garden,
    And gaed in at the garden yett.

And there I heard a fair maid sighing
    And tearing at her yellow hair:
She was tearing at her dark green claithing,
    And fyling a' her face so fair.
She cried, " For me there is no comfort,
    And for me now there's no supplie;
Lat ne'er a lass love any young man
    Until she know that she loved be.

" The firsten thing my lad gae to me,
    It was a cap well lined wi' lead;
And aye the langer that I wore it
    It grew the heavier on my head.
Oh, for me now there is no comfort,
    And for me now there is no supplie;
Lat ne'er a lass love any young man
    Until she know that she loved be.

" The nexten thing my lad gae to me,
    It was a mantle wi' sorrow lined;
And lang will I wear that black mantle
    Till one to borrow it I can find.
Oh, for me now there is no comfort,
    And for me now there's no supplie;
Lat ne'er a lass love any young man
    Until she know that she loved be.

" The thirden thing my lad gae to me,
    It was a belt wi' colours three;
The first was shame, the next was sorrow,
    And the last of all sad miserie.

Oh, for me now there is no comfort,
  And for me now there's no supplie;
Lat ne'er a lass love any young man
  Until she know that she loved be.

" But I may climb as high a tree yet,
  And there find out as rich a nest;
And come down from it without e'er falling,
  And marry a lad I may loe the best.
Yet, for me now there is no comfort,
  And for me now there's no supplie;
Lat ne'er a lass love any young man
  Until she know that she loved be."

" Oh, why should ye now climb a tree, may.
  Or pull the cherries ere they be ripe?
For if the gardener do ance you see, may,
  He'll throw ye o'er the garden dyke."
Then up she rose, and gaed on slowly,
  And stately steppèd o'er the lea;
And by this samin it is weel kennin',
  That mourners crave nae company.

THE BEAUTY OF GARMOUTH.

NEAR the foot of the Backhill there lives a fair dame,
And fain would I court her, fair Annie by name;
Her eyes are like bright stars, and have wounded me,
She's the beauty of Garmouth, my bonnie Annie.
Her voice is like an instrument new set in tune,
Her cheeks are like roses that blossom in June,
Her teeth are like ivory, so bonnie to see—
She's the beauty of Garmouth, my bonnie Annie.

If my hand, with my mind, could my pen rightly hold,
I would set forth her praises in letters of gold;
Ye high powers above us, take pity on me!
And soften the heart of my bonnie Annie!
Oh, mony a day ha'e I courted this maid,
And mony a sweet hour wi' her I ha'e stayed;
On my first voyage to Garmouth my love I did see,
And I hope we'll be joined yet in sweet unity.

FOR A' THAT AND A' THAT.

Be gude to me as lang's I'm here,
　I'll maybe win awa' yet;
He's bonnie coming o'er the hills,
　That will tak' me frae ye a' yet.
For a' that and a' that,
　And thrice as muckle's a' that;
He's bonnie coming o'er the hills,
　That will tak' me frae ye a' yet.

He wears a bonnet for a hat,
　A napkin for a gravat,
He wears a jacket for a coat,
　But he'll be mine for a' that.
For a' that and a' that,
　And twice as muckle's a' that,
He's coming here and will be here,
　To tak' me frae ye a' yet.

And maybe I'll hae hose and sheen,
　When ye maun a' gang barefit;
And maybe I'll gang neat and clean,
　When ye gang wet and drablit;
For a' that and a' that,
　And thrice as muckle's a' that;
Ye'll maybe sit in my cot-town,
　When I sit in my ha' yet.

There's nane o' you been gude to me,
　But I'll reward ye a' yet,
You'll maybe need a peck o' meal
　When I can gie ye twa yet;
For a' that and a' that,
　And thrice as muckle's a' that,
I'll hae fine kilns, and fine meal mills,
　And muckle mair than a' that.

Our national poet—Burns—appears to have used this old bothy song as a
model for his "A Man's a Man for a' That."

THE DUKE OF ARGYLE'S COURTSHIP.

DID ever ye hear of a loyal Scot
Who was never concerned in any plot?
" I wish it could fa' to be my lot
    To marry you, my dearie."

" I'd clout your hose, I'd mend your shoon,
And gin ye should chance to have a son,
I'll mak' him a laird when a' is done,
    If ye will be my dearie."

" Your clouted hose I couldna wear,
Your mended shoon I couldna endure,
And o' your lairdship I'm nae sure,
    So I'll never be your dearie."

" O, if I had you in Cantire,
To follow me through dub and mire;
Then I would have my heart's desire,
    And marry you, my dearie."

" Altho' you had me in Cantire,
To follow you through dub and mire,
I would hae naething I could desire,
    And I'll never be your dearie."

" Did you but see my bonnet blue,
Which is right comely for to view,
It's walted roun' wi' ribbons new,
    You'd marry me, my dearie."

" Wi' your bonnet blue ye think ye're braw,
But I ken nae use for it at a'
But be a nest for our jackdaw,
    And I'll never be your dearie."

" I am a lord o' high renoun,
My name's Argyle when I'm in town,
The cannon balls fly up and down,
    And ye'll never be my dearie."

" Oh, great Argyle, now pardon me,
For the offence I've done to thee;
O'er Hie'lan' hills I'll go wi' thee,
     And I long to be your dearie."

" There ne'er was a jilt in London town
Will e'er set foot on Campbell's groun';
I'm near related to the Crown,
     And ye'll never be my dearie."

" O, great Argyle, I'm sick in love,
There's nane but you can it remove,
If I getna' you I'll die for love,
     For I long to be your dearie."

" You mean to flatter, as I suppose,
Wi' your pauky face and Roman nose;
Go, get you down among my foes,
     For you'll never be my dearie."

The hero of this ballad was probably John, Duke of Argyle and Greenwich,
who commanded the Royal army at the battle of Sheriffmuir.

MY MITHER SHE FEED ME:

OR THE CRUEL MISTRESS.

My mither she feed me when I was o'er young,
'Twas to a kind master that had a cruel dame;
My mistress and me could never agree,
And a' frae the kindness my master shew'd me.
She thocht frae his kindness he was fain o' me,
And, oh, meikle sorrow she made me to dree;
Gin it werna for thinking on the lad I lo'e best,
I am sure, in my mind, I could never ha'e a rest.

Oh! wae is my heart, for my lad didna ken,
How dearly I lo'ed him, when she did me blame,
But I'll live in hope thinkin' time will shew me true,
And expect aye to get him wha dearly I lo'e.
But sair it is to byde for a young honest heart
To be suspected fause, though the thocht mak's it smart;
I'll lippen aye to Providence to clear up it a'.
And maybe I'll get him that's now far awa.

THE BANKS OF INVERURIE.

ONE day as I was walking,
  And down as I did pass
On the banks of Inverurie
  I met a bonnie lass;
Her hair hung o'er her shoulders broad,
  And her eyes like stars did shine;
On the banks of Inverurie,
  And, oh, gin she were mine.

I did embrace this fair maid
  With all the haste I could,
Her hair hung o'er her shoulders broad
  All in its threads of gowd,
Her hair hung o'er her shoulders broad,
  And her eyes like drops of dew;
" On the banks of Inverurie
  I long to walk with you."

She says, " Young man, give over,
  And not delude me so;
For after kissing wooing comes,
  And after wooing woe;
My tender heart ye will ensnare,
  And I'll beguiled be;
On the banks of Inverurie
  I'll walk alone," said she.

She said, " Young man, give over,
  My company refrain;
I know you are of gentle blood,
  But of a graceless clan;
I know your occupation, lad,
  And good you cannot be;
On the banks of Inverurie
  I'll walk alone," said she

He said, " My pretty, fair maid,
  The truth I'll ne'er deny,
On the banks of Inverurie
  Twelve maids beguiled have I.

I used to flatter fair maids,
But now I'll faithful be,
On the banks of Inverurie,
　If you will walk with me."

He put a horn to his lips,
　And he blew both loud and shrill,
Till six-and-thirty armèd men
　Came to their master's call;
He said, " I used to flatter maids,
　But now it shall not be,
On the banks of Inverurie
　My wedded wife you'll be.

" Come then my pretty, fair maid,
　And mount on horse-back high,
And to a parson we will go,
　And that immediately;
And I will sing these lines with joy
　Until the day I dee,
To the praise of Inverurie's banks
　Where first I met with thee."

THE SHANNON SIDE.

'TWAS in the month of April,
　One morning by the dawn,
When cowslips and violets
　Were strewn upon the lawn;
When flowers, like to a mantle,
　Bedecked the fields with pride,
I met a comely damsel
　Upon the Shannon side.

I said, " My pretty, fair maid,
　Why walk ye here so soon,
How far then do you go this way,
　And why are you alone?"
With cheeks like blooming roses,
　This damsel then replied:
" I go to seek my father's sheep
　Upon the Shannon side."

I said, "My pretty, fair maid,
  I'll bear you company,
If you have no objections
  That I should go with thee."
"Oh no, kind sir, excuse me,
  But my parents would me chide,
If I were seen with any man
  Upon the Shannon side."

I threw my arms around her,
  And gave to her a kiss;
She said, "Young man, be civil,
  What do you mean by this?"
The ground being wet on which we stood,
  Her feet from her did slide,
And we both fell down together
  Upon the Shannon side.

Three times I kissed her ruby lips
  As she lay on the grass;
On coming to herself again
  'Twas then she cried: "Alas!
Now since you've ta'en your will o' me
  Make me your lawful bride,
And do not leave me here to mourn
  Upon the Shannon side."

I said, "My pretty, fair maid,
  From mourning aye refrain,
And we will talk of marriage
  When I return again;
But do not let your courage fail,
  Whate'er may you betide,
And I'll come back and see you
  Upon the Shannon side."

So we kissed, shook hands, and parted,
  And from her I did steer;
I did not pass that way again
  For more than half a year;
But while I was passing
  Along yon flowery walk,
Whom did I meet but my true love,
  And she could scarcely walk.

I seemed to take no notice,
  But walked on my way,
When my true love she shook her head,
  Desiring me to stay.
The tears like crystal fountains
  Down from her eyes did glide,
" Don't you mind the fall you gave to me
  Upon the Shannon side.

" Oh, but it was an awful fall,
  For I'm with child to thee,
And surely you'll consent, kind sir,
  Now for to marry me;
There's fifty guineas in bright gold
  My parents will provide,
And sixty acres of good land
  Upon the Shannon side."

I said, " My pretty, fair maid,
  I like your offer well,
But I've already chosen,
  The truth to you I'll tell;
A tall and handsome maiden,
  Who is to be my bride,
A wealthy gauger's daughter,
  Upon the Shannon side."

" Now, since you will not marry me,
  Pray, tell to me your name,
And when my child is baptized
  I may call it the same."
" My name is Captain Thunderbolt,
  And it I'll ne'er deny,
And I've got soldiers guarding me
  Upon yon mountain high."

So we kissed, shook hands, and parted,
  And from her I did steer,
But as I turned myself away
  These words I chanced to hear:
" I hope 'twill be a warning,
  So all fair maids betide,
And never trust a young man
  Upon the Shannon side."

An Irish Folk-song common all over the North-east of Scotland.

IT'S BRAW SAILIN' ON THE SEA.

THERE cam' a letter late yestreen,
  Our ship maun sail the morn;
Alas, says the bonnie lass,
  That ever I was born,
To sit so late wi' my true love,
  And part wi' him the morn.

When he cam' to her father's gate,
  At twelve o'clock at noon,
This girlie, being proud-hearted,
  She widna lat him in;
This girlie, being proud-hearted,
  She wadna lat him in.

It's braw sailin' on the sea,
  When wind and weather's fair;
It's better being in my love's arms,
  And O gin I were there;
It's better being in my love's arms,
  And O gin I were there.

It's braw drinkin' Glasgow beer,
  It's better drinkin' wine;
But it's better being in my love's arms,
  Where I've been mony's the time;
But it's better being in my love's arms,
  Where I've been mony's the time.

He's taen the ring from his pocket,
  Which cost him guineas three;
Says, " Tak' ye that, ye weel-faur'd maid,
  And aye think weel o' me ";
Says, " Tak' ye that, ye weel-faur'd maid,
  And aye think weel o' me."

She's taen the ring frae her pocket,
  Which cost him shillin's nine;
Says, " Tak' ye that, my bonnie lad,
  For I hae changed my min' ";
Says, " Tak' ye that, my bonnie lad,
  For I hae changed my min'."

THE FLOWER OF FOCHABERS.

IT was on the bonnie banks o' Spey
  To muse I sat me down;
The small fish were a-sporting,
  The birds sang sweet aroun';
I spied a pretty, fair maid,
  In modesty and youth,
She was the flower o' Fochabers
  And the beauty of the North.

I gently steppèd up to her,
  And thus to her did say—
" Ye fairest of all womankind,
  Ye've stolen my heart away;
Pray, don't despise my humbleness,
  Tak' pity on my youth,
For ye are the flower o' Fochabers
  And the beauty of the North."

My tale of love did not her please,
  As you shall quickly hear,
For unto it she gave no heed,
  To it she gave no care.
Could I but make this girl to love,
  I would give all I'm worth,
For she is the flower of Fochabers
  And the beauty of the North.

Ye powers above, who first caused love,
  Pray ease my troubled mind,
And take me from this world below,
  No comfort here I find;
But at my death, with my last breath,
  I'll seal it with an oath,
That I died for Peggy Clapperton,
  The beauty of the North.

GEORDIE ASKING MISS TIPTOE IN MARRIAGE.

A MAID of vain glory, with grandeur and pride,
Was asked by a ploughman for to be his bride;
But she turned up her head and the white o' her e'e,
" I'd rather the garret than a ploughman," quo' she.

Says Geordie, " I'll get a bit house and a cow,
While ye could sit couthie, and little to do
But wash my bit rags and darn my hose,
And get plenty to sup o' good pottage and brose."

Out she spoke like a fury, like a drunkard in drink,
" Could I sup your pottage or brose, d'ye think?
A sight o' them's plenty, in pot or in plate,
And your oatmeal cakes I do mortally hate."

" Oh, then," says Geordie, " but it would be something strange,
Gif we getna whiles taties and kail for a change,
And maybe on Sunday we would get a drap tea;
Though I could not promise ilka day this to gie."

" Your kail and potatoes, they never will do,
Your pottage nor brose, your house, nor your cow;
I must have what I choose each day that I dine,
With .a servant to do whate'er I incline.

" It may do with poor servants that's still at the frame,
Who work like yoursel', and eat of the same,
But it never will do with a lady like me;
So I'd rather the garret than a ploughman," quo' she.

" And you know, every morning I rise out of bed
The servant must have my breakfast well made;
With beef steaks and biscuits, buns, sugar, and tea,
As something like treatment for ladies like me."

" Since I know now," says Geordie, " that this is your plan,
I'll swear you shall never get me for a man;
You may gang to the garret, or gang to the deil,
It's a' ane to Geordie; guid nicht, and fareweel!"

In the counties of Aberdeen, Banff, and Elgin " porridge" is pronounced
" pottage."

This old bothy favourite was written some sixty or seventy years ago
by Mr. John Milne, of Demick, Glenlivat, better known by the country
folks as " John Milne o' Livat's Glen," and was published in 1871 at
Aberdeen, in a small booklet entitled, *Selections of Songs and Poems* by
John Milne of Glenlivat.

Milne was born in the parish of Dunnottar, Kincardineshire, in 1792.

PART II.

Songs relating to Farm Life and Work

PART II.

Songs Relating to Farm Life and Work.

DRUMDELGIE.

THERE's a fairmer up in Cairnie,
  Wha's kent baith far and wide
To be the great Drumdelgie,
  Upon sweet Deveronside.

The fairmer o' yon muckle toon
  He is baith hard and sair,
And the cauldest day that ever blaws
  His servants get their share.

At five o'clock we quickly rise
  And hurry doon the stair;
It's there to corn our horses,
  Likewise to straik their hair.

Syne, after working half-an-hour
  Each to the kitchen goes,
It's there to get our breakfast,
  Which generally is brose.

We've scarcely got our brose weel supt,
  And gi'en our pints a tie,
When the foreman cries, " Hallo, my lads!
  The hour is drawing nigh."

At sax o'clock the mull's put on,
  To gie us a strait wark;
It tak's four o' us to mak' to her,
  Till ye could wring our sark.

And when the water is put aff,
  We hurry doon the stair,
To get some quarters through the fan
  Till daylicht does appear.

When daylicht does begin to peep,
  And the sky begins to clear,
The foreman he cries out, " My lads,
  Ye'll stay nae langer here!

" There's sax o' you'll gae to the ploo,
  And twa will drive the neeps,
And the owson they'll be after you
  Wi' strae raips roun' their queets."

But when that we were gyaun furth,
  And turnin' out to yoke,
The snaw dank on sae thick and fast
  That we were like to choke.

The frost had been sae very hard,
  The ploo she wadna go;
And sae our cairting days commenced
  Amang the frost and snow.

Our horses being but young and sma'
  The shafts they didna fill,
And they aft required the saiddler[1]
  To pull them up the hill:

But we will sing our horses' praise,
  Though they be young and sma',
They far outshine the Broadland's anes
  That gang sae full and braw.

Sae fare ye weel, Drumdelgie,
  For I maun gang awa;
Sae fare ye weel, Drumdelgie,
  Your weety weather and a'.

Sae fareweel, Drumdelgie,
  I bid ye a' adieu;
I leave ye as I got ye—
  A maist unceevil crew.

¹ The whip.

There are many versions of " Drumdelgie " differing in the number of
verses and in the description of the events referred to by the author. One
well-known version cemmences:—
  " Oh ken ye o' Drumdelgie toon
    Where a' the crack lads go?
  Stra'bogie braw in a' her boun's
    A better canna show."

THE WEARY FARMERS.

THERE's some that sing o' Cromar Fair,
  An' sound out an alarm,
But the best sang that e'er was sung
  It was about the term;
The term-time is drawing near
  When we will a' win free,
An' wi' the weary farmers
  Again we'll never fee.
      Singing, fal al al the derry,
        Fal al the dee;
      Fal al the diddle al the derry,
        Fal al the dee.

Wi' broad-tail'd coats and quaker hats,
  And whips below their arms,
They'll hawk and ca' the country roun'
  Until they a' get farms.
Their boots a' glawr an' glitterin',
  Wi' spurs upon their heels;
An' though ye ca' the country roun'
  Ye winna find such deils.

They'll tip you on the shoulder
  And speir gin ye're to fee;
They'll tell ye a fine story,
  That's every word a lee;
They'll tell ye a fine story,
  An' get ye to perform;
But, lads, when ye are under them
  Ye'll stand the raging storm.

They'll tak' ye to an alehouse
  And gie ye some sma' beer;
They'll tak' a drap unto themsel's
  Till they get better cheer;
And when the bargain's ended
  They'll toll ye out twa shillin's,
An' grunt and say that siller's scarce—
  The set o' leein' villains!

On cauld kail and tawties
  They'll feed ye up like pigs,
While they sit at their tea and toast,
  Or ride into their gigs.
The mistress must get "Mem"—and ye
  Maun lift yer cap to her;
And ere ye find an entrance
  The master must get "Sir."

The harvest time when it comes roun'
  They'll grudge ye Sabbath rest;
They'll let ye to the worship,
  But they like the workin' best.
The diet hour it vexes them,
  And then to us they'll say—
"Come on, my lads, ye'll get your rest
  When lyin' in the clay."

They'll say unto the foreman chiel,
  "Keep aye the steady grind,
And dinna let the orra lads
  Stand idle at the end;
For I pay them a' good wages,
  And I wish them to get on;
And when they are not able
  There's mair when they are done.

THE SCRANKY BLACK FARMER.

At the tap o' the Garioch, in the lands o' Leith-hall,
A scranky black farmer in Earlsfield did dwall;
Wi' him I engaged a servant to be,
Which makes me lament I went far frae the sea.

I engaged wi' this farmer to drive cart and plough;
Hard fortune convenit an ill-fated crew,
I ane o' the number, which causes me to rue
That e'er I attempted the country to view.

Up from the low country my course I did steer,
To the parish o' Kinnethmont you shortly shall hear;
Their customs and fashions to me a' seemed new,
My rapid proceedings full sore did I rue.

In the head o' the Garioch we all did appear,
From various counties some far and some near,
From the parish of Kinnethmont, Kilmarnock, and Keith,
From Aberlour, Rothiemay, and Fordyce.

The harvest in our country is both early and late,
And all kinds of drudgery of course we do get;
Our usage is rough and our ale is but pale,
It's the brown bree o' molasses that we get for ale.

It's early in the mornin' we rise to the yoke,
The storm and the tempest can ne'er make us stop;
While the wind it does beat and the rain it does pour,
And aye yon black farmer he on us does glower.

But the time is expiring and the day it will come,
To various counties we all must go home;
Bonnie Jeanie must travel, bonnie Bawbie also,
To the back o' beyont Montgomery must go.

So farewell, Rhynie, and adieu to you, Clatt,
For I hae been wi' ye baith early and late,
Baith early and late, baith empty and fu',
So farewell, Rhynie, I'll bid you adieu.

So farewell, Bawbie, and adieu to you all,
Likewise to the farmer that lives at Leith-hall,
For to serve this black farmer I'm sure is nae sport,
So I will be going to my bonnie seaport.

THE BARNYARDS O' DELGATY.

IN New Deer parish I was born,
    A child of youth to Methlick came;
And gin ye'll no believe my word
    The session-clerk will tell the same.

Linten adie toorin adie,
　　Linten adie toorin ae,
　　Linten, lourin, lourin, lourin,
　　　Linten lourin lourin lee.

Good education I did get,
　　And I did learn to read and write;
My parents they were proud o' me,
　　My mother in me took delight.

To bide upon my father's farm,
　　That was never my intent;
I lo'ed the lasses double weel,
　　And aye the weary drap o' drink.

As I cam' in by Netherdale,
　　At Turra market for to fee,
I fell in wi' a farmer chiel
　　Frae the Barnyards o' Delgaty.

He promised me the ae best pair
　　I ever set my e'en upon;
When I gaed hame to Barnyards
　　There was naething there but skin and bone.

The auld black horse sat on his rump,
　　The auld white meer lay on her wime,
And a' that I could hup and crack,
　　They wouldna rise at yokin' time.

Meg Macpherson mak's my brose,
　　An' her and me we canna gree;
First a mote and then a knot,
　　And aye the ither jilp o' bree.

When I gae to the kirk on Sunday,
　　Mony's the bonnie lass I see
Prim, sittin' by her daddy's side,
　　And winkin' owre the pews at me.

I can drink and nae be drunk,
　　I can fight and nae be slain,
I can court anither's lass,
　　And aye be welcome to my ain.

My can'le noo it is brunt oot,
　　The snotter's fairly on the wane;
Sae fare ye weel, ye Barnyards,
　　Ye'll never catch me here again.

OH CHARLIE, O CHARLIE.

Oh Charlie, O Charlie, come owre frae Pitgair,
    And I'll gie ye out all your orders,
For I maun awa to yon high Hielan' hills,
    For a while to leave the bonnie Buchan borders.

Oh Charlie, O Charlie, tak' notice what I say,
    And put every man to his station,
For I'm gaun awa to yon high Hielan' hills,
    For to view a' the pairts o' the nation.

To the loosin' ye'll put Shaw, ye'll put Sandison to ca',
    To the colin ye'll put auld Andrew Kindness,
Ye'll gar auld Colliehill aye feed the thrashin' mill,
    An' see that he dee't wi' great fineness.

To the gatherin' o' the hay ye'll put little Isa Gray,
    And wi' her ye'll put her cousin Peggy;
And in aneath the bands, it's there ye'll put your hands,
    And ye'll see that they dee't richt tidy.

As for you, Willie Burr, ye'll carry on the stir,
    And ye'll keep a' the lasses a-hyowin',
And beware o' Shaw and Jeck, or they'll play you a trick,
    And set a' your merry maids a-mowin'.

And for you, Annie Scott, ye'll put on the muckle pot
    And ye'll mak' milk pottage a-plenty,
For yon hungry brosers that's comin' frae Pitgair,
    They're keepit aye sae bare and scanty.

Oh Charlie, O Charlie, sae early's you'll rise,
  And see a' my merry men yokin';
And you, Missy Pope, ye'll sit in the parlour neuk
  And keep a' my merry men frae smokin'.

THE PLOUGHMAN.

THE ploughman he's a bonnie lad,
  And does his wark at leisure,
And when that he comes hame at e'en
  He kisses me wi' pleasure.
      Then up wi't noo, my ploughman lad,
        And hey, my merry ploughman;
      Of a' the lads that I do ken,
        Commen' me to the ploughman.

Now that the blooming Spring comes on,
  He tak's his yokin' early,
And whistling owre the furrowed field,
  He goes to fallow fairly.
      Then up wi't noo, etc.

When my ploughman lad comes hame at e'en,
  He's aften wat and weary;
Cast aff the wet, put on the dry,
  Come to your bed, my dearie.
      Then up wi't noo, etc.

I will wash my ploughman's hose,
  And I will brush his o'erlay;
I will mak' my ploughman's bed,
  And cheer him late and early.
      Merry but, an' merry ben,
        Merry is my ploughman,
      Of a' the trades that I do ken,
        Commen' me to the ploughman.

Plough yon hill, and plough yon dale,
  And plough yon faugh an' fallow;
Wha winna drink the ploughman's health
  Is but a dirty fellow.
      Merry but, and merry ben, etc.

Burns and Lady Nairne both wrote revised versions of this song, but the
old version (printed above) is still the favourite not only in the North-
eastern counties but throughout the whole of rural Scotland.

BARLEY RIGS A-RAKING.

It fell about a Lammas time,
When hay it was a-making;
A loving couple I did spy
  Some barley rigs a-raking.

    Sing, right fal al riddle, right fal aye,
    Right fal al riddle I do.

This smart young couple they did meet
For to have a jolly treat,
For to have a jovial treat
  Among the barley raking.

    Sing, right fal, etc.

This loving couple sat on the ground,
They thought the world was going round,
They thought the world was going round,
  Among the barley raking.

    Sing, right fal, etc.

When twenty weeks were past and gone
This fair maid fell a-sighing,
When forty weeks were past and gone,
  This fair maid fell a-crying.

    Sing, right fal, etc.

She wrote a letter to her love,
She says, " My joy and turtle dove,
If you'll return to your sweet love
 You'll ease her of her sighing."
  Sing, right fal, etc.

He took the pen and wrote again,
To think of me is all in vain,
For married life I do disdain,
 I dearly like my freedom.
  Sing, right fal, etc.

I have got as good a pair of shoes
As ever was made of leather;
I cock my beaver up in front
 And face both wind and weather.
  Sing, right fal, etc.

Oh! I've been east, and I've been west,
And I can find no place of rest ;
I'll turn again to yon sweet face
 Among the barley raking.
  Sing, right fal al riddle, right fal aye,
  Right fal al riddle I do.

SWAGGERS.

Come, all ye jolly ploughman lads,
 I pray you, have a care,
Beware o' going to Swaggers,
 For he'll be in Porter Fair.

He'll be aye lauch-lauchin',
 He'll aye be lauchin' there;
And he'll hae on the blithest face
 In a' Porter Fair.

Wi' his fine horse and harness,
 Sae well he'll gar ye true,
But when ye come to Auchterless,
 Sae sair's he'll gar ye rue.

He'll tell ye o' some plooin' match
   That isna far awa;
And gin ye clean your harness richt,
   Ye're sure to beat them a'.

For the tackle's gained the prize afore
   At every country show;
And gin that ye lat it fa' back,
   Ye'll be thocht little o'.

A pair o' blues that lead the van,
   Sae nimbly as they go;
A pair o' broons that follow them,
   That never yet said no.

A wee bit shaltie ca's the neeps,
   And, oh, but it is sma';
But Swaggers he'll declare to you
   It's stronger than them a'.

But he'll aye be fret-frettin',
   He'll aye be frettin' there;
And he'll gie ye regulations
   That are worn a' threadbare.

And Swaggers in the harvest time,
   He's got too much to do
For the twa-three jovial laddies
   That ca's his cairt and ploo.

Sae he'll gang on some twenty miles,
   Faur people disna him ken,
And he'll engage some harvest hands
   And bring them far frae hame.

He'll say unto the foreman chiel,
   " Keep aye the steady grind,
And dinna lat the orra lads
   Fa' idle back behind.

" For I pay ye a' guid wages,
   And sae ye maun get on,
And gin ye are not able,
   There's anither when ye're done."

He'll say unto the girlies,
   As they are comin' back,
"Come on, my girls, and hurry up,
   Gie them nae time to sharp."

But noo the cuttin's ended,
   And we've begun to lead,
And mony's the curious plan he tries
   For to come muckle speed.

And noo the sheaves they are all in,
   And formèd in the stack;
And noo the windy days are come
   When we maun hunt the brock.

When we maun hunt the brock, my boys,
   Wi' mony a fret and frown;
And Swaggers cries, "Come on, my boys,
   It's like for to ding on."

And when that we gang to the raips,
   He gets up wi' a bawl,
Says, "Come on, my girls, ply in the twine,
   Ye're sure to beat them all."

Now the harvest's ended,
   And a' thing is made snod;
The harvest hands wi' bundles big
   They now must pad the road.

They now must pad the road, my boys,
   Amang the frost and snaw;
And they hae sworn a solemn oath,
   They'll ne'er come back ava.

But Martinmas it has worn on,
   My fee's into my pouch;
And sae merrily, merrily, I will sing,
   "I'm oot o' the tyrant's clutch."

For he is the worst master
   That ever I did serve;
An' gin ye dinna me believe,
   Never mind ye this observe.

Porter Fair is a feeing market held twice a year at Turriff, Aberdeenshire, and Auchterless is the neighbouring parish to Turriff.

THE PAINFUL PLOUGH.

COME all the jolly ploughmen, of courage stout and bold,
That labour all the winter in stormy winds and cold,
To clothe the fields with plenty, your farmyards to renew,
To crown them with contentment, behold the painful plough.

" Hold, ploughman," said the gardener, " don't count your trade
        with ours,
Walk through the garden and view the early flowers,
Also the curious border and pleasant walks go view,
There's none such peace and plenty performed by the plough."

" Hold, gardener," said the ploughman, "my calling don't
        despise,
Each man for his living upon his trade relies;
Were it not for the ploughman, both rich and poor would rue,
For we are all dependent upon the painful plough.

" Adam in the garden was sent to keep it right,
But the length of time he stayed there, I believe it was one
        night,
Yet of his own labour, I call it not his due,
Soon he lost his garden and went to hold the plough.

" For Adam was a ploughman when ploughing first began,
The next that did succeed him was Cain, the eldest son;
Some of this generation this calling now pursue,
That bread may not be wanting remains the painful plough.

" Samson was the strongest man, and Solomon was wise,
Alexander for to conquer, 'twas all his daily prize;
King David was a valiant man, and many thousands slew,
Yet none of these brave heroes could live without the plough.

" Behold the wealthy merchant that trades in foreign seas,
And brings home gold and treasure for those who live at ease,
With fine silks and spices, and delicious fruits also,
They all are brought from India by virtue of the plough.

" For they must have bread and biscuits, rice pudding, flour, and
        peas,
To feed the jolly sailors as they sail o'er the seas;
And the man that brings them will own to what is true,
He cannot sail the ocean without the painful plough.

"I hope there's none offended at me for singing this,
For it is not intended for anything amiss;
If you consider rightly, you'll find that it is true,
That all that you can mention depends upon the plough."

Note.—In this song "painful" means laborious.

THE PLOOMAN LADDIE.

Air.—" The Rigs o Rye."   (See page 31.)

My love's a plooman and follows the ploo,
I promised to him, and I'll keep it true,
I promised to him, and I'll never rue
  The lovin' o' the plooman laddie.

    Then it's oh, oh, oh, it's bonnie oh,
    To hear him cry hup, hi, and wo,
    And mak' his horses straight to go;
      What's better than a plooman?

As my plooman lad gangs roon the toon
Wi' a' his irons ringin' roon,
And oh, he is a bonnie loon,
  And he whistles when he sees me.
    It's oh, oh, oh, it's bonnie oh, etc.

I micht hae got the miller in yonder mill,
But the smell o' the dust wad hae dune me ill;
I love my plooman, I love him still,
  I'm for a plooman laddie.
    It's oh, oh, oh, it's bonnie oh, etc.

I micht hae got the gairdner o' yonder tree,
But the smell o' thyme wad hae sickened me,
I'll love my plooman until I dee,
  He's my bonnie plooman laddie.
    It's oh, oh, oh, it's bonnie oh, etc.

I micht hae got the merchant in yonder shop,
But a' his goods they're nae worth a grot,
And for himsel' he's a drunken sot,
  He's nae like my plooman laddie.
    It's oh, oh, oh, it's bonnie oh, etc.

When I gang oot and gang to the stack,
I hear his whip gie the ither crack,
My very hert is like to brack
 For the love o' my plooman laddie.

  It's oh, oh, oh, it's bonnie oh, etc.

When I gang oot and look owre the burn
And see the ploo gie the ither turn;
My very heart is like to burn
 For my bonnie plooman laddie.

  It's oh, oh, oh, it's bonnie oh, etc.

I hae a father and mither good,
And o' my beauty they are prood,
But unto me they are very rude
 'Cause I love my plooman laddie.

  It's oh, oh, oh, it's bonnie oh, etc.

The plooman lad, being nae far away,
Heard a' his bonnie lass did say;
Cheer up your hert, love, and come away
 And be the plooman's dearie.

  It's oh, oh, oh, it's bonnie oh, etc.

It's I'll tak' aff my goon o' green,
And I'll put on my goon o' broon,
On a bed o' strae we'll baith lie doon,
 And I'll clap my plooman laddie.

  It's oh, oh, oh, it's bonnie oh, etc.

Gin that day week she was a bride,
And gin that day fortnicht she was wed,
And happy were they when in ae bed laid,
 And she got her plooman laddie.

  Then it's oh, oh, oh, it's bonnie oh,
  To hear him cry hup, hi, and wo,
  And mak' his horses straight to go;
   He's a bonnie plooman laddie.

SLEEPYTOWN.

It happened at last Whitsunday,
  I tirèd o' my place,
And I gaed up to Insch to fee,
  My fortune for to chase.

    And sing airrie erritie adie,
    And sing airrie erritie an.

I met in wi' Adam Mitchell,
  To fee we did presume,
He's a fairmer in Kinnethmont,
  And he lives at Sleepytown.

If you and I agree, he says,
  You'll have the fairest play,
For I never bid my servants work
  Above ten hours a day.

If a' be true ye tell to me,
  I think the place will suit;
Guid-faith, I think I'll gang wi' you,
  But ye're an ugly brute.

'Twas on a Monday mornin'
  I gaed hame to Sleepytown,
And he ranked us in guid order
  To lay his turnips down.

I was sent to drive the dung,
  Likewise my neighbour Knowles;
But soon the rain it did come on,
  And the order cam' to lowse.

The rain it still increasèd;
  The son was at the mill
For meal, old Adam Mitchell said,
  Our bellies for to fill.

The rain it soon went over,
  And the day began to break;
And our next orders were to scrape
  Our dinners frae the secks.

We'll ne'er refuse your orders,
  Whate'er ye bid us do;
But to eat the scrapin's o' your secks
  Is a thing we'll never do.

Do ye refuse what I command,
  Ye scoundrels that ye are?
Ye bargained for ten hours a day,
  Refuse then if ye daur.

But if the one thing winna dee,
  The ither I can try;
I go and get the kitchen-maid
  To mix it through the dry.

The order was to bed at nine,
  And never leave the town,
And for every time we left it
  We'd be fined half-a-crown.

Knowles he was fined mony's a time,
  But never lost the heart;
And I mysel' was fined a pound
  For turnin' up a cart.

We never heeded Adam,
  But aye we took the pass,
Sometimes to buy tobacco,
  Sometimes to see the lass.

But now the term's come at last,
  The trifle's safely won,
And we'll awa to Rhynie Muir,
  And there we'll hae some fun.

When we are owre in Alford,
  We'll gar the glass gae roun',
And we'll tell them o' the usage
  That we got at Sleepytown.

We'll maybe see old Adam yet
  Jist at his dish o' brose;
And we'll gie him oor pocket-napkin
  To dicht his snuffy nose.

    And sing airrie erritie adie,
    And sing airrie erritie an.

COURTIN' IN THE STABLE.

THE nicht was fine, 'twas after nine,
  The frost was biting keenly, O,
The rising moon owre Mormond's croon
  Was shinin' on serenely, O.

On sic a nicht the plooman wicht,
  Wi' whisky fine and cheery, O,
Has taen the gait we here relate,
  To visit Kate, his dearie, O.

The road was lang, but Jock aye sang,
  Oh Kate, ye are my charmer, O,
At Whitsuntide ye'll be my bride,
  And le'e the weary fairmer, O.

He reachèd to the trystin' gate,
  And in the stable enters, O,
To wait until his darling Kate
  Wad guide him to the kitchen, O.

He sat and thought, the whisky wrought,
  The whisky fine and cheery, O;
A workin' steer was standin' near,
  Jock thocht he was his dearie, O.

Come gie's a kiss to croon our bliss,
  And then we'll fix the waddin', O,
I'm noo full grown, I've twenty pound,
  And that will buy the beddin', O.

Turn roun' your face, ye're naething less
  Than jist a temptin' hizzie, O,
As sure as fate I'll leave ye, Kate,
  And tak' yer sister Lizzie, O.

Come gie's a kiss, ye saucy jaud,
  Altho' I'm fu' I'm cheery, O,
There's nane can gie sic joys to me
  As cuddlin' you, my dearie, O.

Turn roon your face and gie's a kiss,
  And nae be half sae saucy, O,
As sure's a doo, you've turned a coo,
  Ye're unco caul' and hairy, O.

But soon the sport was broken short
　　By Jockie's kind companion, O,
A woman ne'er beheld a steer
　　Embraced in sic a fashion, O.

This couple they've got married noo,
　　And lang may they be able, O,
To lauch at fate, and no forget
　　The courtin' in the stable, O.

GIEN THE NOWTE THEIR FODDER.

As I rode in by yon bonnie waterside,
　　It was in the wintry weather,
And there I spied a weel-faur'd maid,
　　She was gien the nowte their fodder.

Oh, will ye fancy me, fair maid,
　　And never mind another?
Ye winna hae to gang to yon barn or byre,
　　Nor gie the nowte their fodder.

I will not fancy you, kind sir,
　　Nor yet will I some other,
A ploughman laddie I maun hae,
　　Because I hae nae tocher.

He rode away, bade her good-day,
　　Begone, false man, forever;
But aye he min't on the weel-faur'd maid
　　Who was gien the nowte their fodder.

He rode home to his ain countrie,
　　In hopes to find some other;
But aye he min't on the very pretty maid
　　Who was gien the nowte their fodder.

As he rode in by yon bonnie waterside,
　　It was all in the pleasant weather,
And there he spied the same fair maid
　　That was gien the nowte their fodder.

Oh, will ye fancy me, fair maid,
And never fancy another?
Ye winna hae to gang to yon barn or byre,
Nor gie the nowte their fodder.

They set them down by yon bonnie waterside
Till the darksome night was over,
And now she rides in her gilded coach,
With servants to attend her.

Noo, all ye young men and maidens fair,
Think it nae degrade on another,
For I mysel' was a maiden fair,
And was gien the nowte their fodder.

But if I had gotten my heart's delight,
As I'm sure I wished nae other,
I wad hae casten aff the royal robes
And hae gien the nowte their fodder.

JOHN BRUCE O' THE CORNER.

At Martinmas term I gaed to the fair
To see the braw lasses and snuff the fresh air,
I feed wi' a mannie to ca' his third pair,
They ca' him John Bruce o' the Corner.

When I gaed hame to this man John Bruce,
He lives owre at Skene in a blue-sclated house,
Sae keen in the fair, but he lookit sae douce,
When I gaed hame to the Corner.

The first Sunday mornin', oor temper to tease,
Oot cam' aul' Johnny wi' a flagon o' grease
To rub oor horse legs frae the queets to the knees,
For they're a' cripple nags at the Corner.

The heat o' the horses sune melted the grease,
And oot there cam' a swarm o' flees;
Says we to oorsels, it's the plague o' flees
Sent doon on the lads o' the Corner.

Here's to oor gaffer, a cannie aul' man,
He'll neither swear at ye, curse, nor ban,
There's nae eneuch o' the deevil in him
For aul' John Bruce o' the Corner.

Here's to oor foreman, he comes frae Balquhine,
His name is M'Gilvray, he wrocht on the line,
He meats his horse weel, but he hauds on the twine,
   For the wark's aye ahin at the Corner.

Here's to oor second lad, a sturdy young chiel,
He sticks to his wark and it sets him richt weel,
But he wasna lang hame when he thocht he wad heel
   Frae aul' Johnny Bruce o' the Corner.

Here's to oor third ane—a rant and a reel,
A bit o' a poet, some half o' a feel;
But the lasses a' roon him they like him sae weel,
   He will sune win awa frae the Corner.

Here's to oor bailie, he comes frae Kinnaird,
A little wee mannie, some scant o' a beard,
At coortin' the lasses he aye would prefer't
   Till sortin' his stots at the Corner.

The loon he was feed to advance and retire
Atween the neep park and the aul' coo byre,
But he wasna lang hame or he seem'd for to tire
   O' aul' Johnny Bruce o' the Corner.

Here's to the dochter, the floo'er o' the glen,
She plays the piano, an' rants wi' the men,
She rins through the close to be keppit again
   By the rovin' young lads o' the Corner.

On Sunday to the kirk she wears a white veil,
And a yard o' her goon ahin her does trail,
And her hair is tied up like my aul' horse's tail
   To charm the lads o' the Corner.

The hairst it wis back, and the weather was bad,
And ae Sunday mornin' a ruckie we led,
And the rest o' the day we lay in oor bed
   And prayed for oor sins at the Corner.

The hairst bein' dune, and the weather bein' bad,
We were a' turned oot wi' a pick and a spad,
He tore aff his jacket, the aul'. nickum gaed mad—
   Hurrah for John Bruce o' the Corner.

THE BARNS O' BENEUCHIES.

Air.—" Hey! Johnny Cope."

My freens, ane and a', I'll sing ye a sang,
If ye a' haud your weeshts, it winna tak' me lang;
It's about a mannie Kempie, he's a cyaurd-tongued fang,
　　For he rages like the deevil in the mornin'.

He's a wee little mannie, wi' a fern-tickled face,
A' the days o' your life ye ne'er saw sic a mess;
Ye wad sweer he had deserted frae some tinkler race
　　Afore they had got a' wakened in the mornin'.

At the Barnyards o' Beneuchies he has lang been a grieve,
But come May the twenty-saxt he has to pad, I believe;
For he's seiged at his men till his maister's gien him's leave,
　　For he canna get them up in the mornin'.

But when he gets ye up, ye ne'er heard sic a soun',
For he'll curse ye and ban ye like ony dragoon,
He's a lang cyaurd-tongue, you'd hear't roun' the toon,
　　Afore he gets his breakfast in the mornin'.

Dinna gang to the Barns if ye wish to be weel,
A' the days o' your life ye ne'er saw sic a chiel,
He'll treat ye to a breakfast o' buttermilk and meal,
　　Wi' a drink o' sour ale in the mornin'.

We get beef-bree whiles weel seasoned wi' reek,
Wi' three seeds o' barley and the smell o' a leek,
If your nae pleased wi' that, he'll tak' nane o' your cheek,
　　But he'll pit ye frae his toon in the mornin'.

But if e'er sic a thing as a row should arise,
My freens, ane and a', tak' tent and be wise;
Keep quietness, ane and a', or his wife will rise
　　Dancin' mad in her stockin's in the mornin'.

'Twas ae mornin' in March, just as near as I can,
She cam' sweerin' frae the blankets we'd ill-used her man;
Wi' her sark-tail wiggle-waggle into the close she ran
　　Dancin' mad in her stockin's in the mornin'.

For an ill-tongued jaud she's the warst that I ken;
Lord bless me! sic a mornin' may I never see again!
Five or six naked bairnies a' rinnin' but and ben,
  Cryin', Od, mammie's mad in the mornin'!

Says she to the shepherd, Ye're nae freen o' mine,
For a'body kens ye're a cyaurd Hielan' thing,
Ye tauld them doon at Brunan I gied milk to the swine,
  And you sour ale to your porridge in the mornin'.

But it's May the twenty-saxt will be here in a crack,
And we'll a' leave the Barns never mair to gang back,
We'll gang blithely doon the road like an ill-tongued pack,
  Singin', Kempie he can follow in the mornin'.

Now, my name I will reveal, if sic a thing I ever hid,
It's but the country clype, I'll ne'er deny, Guid forbid,
My neebours a' that ken me weel they ca' me daft Jock Wid,
  Sae we'll up and leave the Barns in the mornin'.

BROOMHILL'S BONNIE DOCHTER.

'Twas at a summer feeing time,
  When ploughmen lads they fee,
That I engaged with Broomhill,
  His foremost lad to be.

    Broomhill's bonnie dochter,
      By all I ever saw,
    Geordie Wilson's bonnie Margaret,
      She's stown my heart awa.

When I went hame to Broomhill's toon,
  It fairly pleasèd me,
For ilka thing about the place
  Was trig as trig could be.

But oh, the maiden o' the place,
  Nae pen could her portray;
The first glint o' her winsome face
  It stole my heart away.

I usèd every lover's wile
  Her favour for to gain,
Likewise to please her kind father
  Myself I didna hain.

It was on a summer's evening,
  As I walked round the toon,
I met sweet Margaret on a bank,
  And there we baith sat doun.

I whispered, O, my dearest dear,
  My heart's gane out to thee,
If ye would give me love for love,
  Enraptured I would be.

Let's join ourselves in wedlock's bands,
  And live sae happilie;
There's nocht but what I'd dare to do
  If 'twere to pleasure thee.

With her head press'd to my bosom,
  She whispered lovinglie:
I felt that ye would be my mate
  First time I did you see.

    Broomhill's bonnie dochter,
      By all I ever saw,
    Geordie Wilson's bonnie Margaret,
      She's stown my heart awa.

THE JOLLY PLOUGHBOY.

THERE was a jolly ploughboy was ploughing at his land,
  With his horses all under the shade,
He whistled and he sang as the plough she went alang,
  His intention was to court a pretty maid, pretty maid,
  His intention was to court a pretty maid.

He whistled and he sang as his plough she went alang,
　　Says, this fair maid's above my degree;
And when that her parents they come for to know,
　　The place where they'll send me is to the sea, to the sea,
　　The place they'll send me to is the sea.

And when that her parents they came for to know
　　This young man was a-courting in the plain,
The press-gang was raised, and they hoisted him on board,
　　And they sent him to the wars to be slain, to be slain,
　　And they sent him to the wars to be slain.

A suit of men's clothing she then did put on,
　　With her pockets well lined with gold,
And she marched up the street, with the tear on her cheek,
　　And she's marchèd up like any soldier bold, soldier bold,
　　And she's marchèd up like any soldier bold.

The first that she met was a bold dragoon,
　　Oh, where have you sent my ploughboy?
We've sent him to the fleet, for to plough upon the deep,
　　But he says, my pretty girl, march along, march along,
　　But he says, my pretty girl, march along.

But she went to the ship that her true love was in,
　　To the captain she made a low moan,
Says, You've ta'en frae me my joy, my charming ploughboy,
　　And you've sent him to the wars to be slain, to be slain,
　　And you've sent him to the wars to be slain.

She's pulled out a purse of the purest of gold,
　　Five hundred guineas, ay, and more;
And she's paid it freely down for her charming ploughboy,
　　And she's rolled him in her arms to the shore, to the shore,
　　And she's rolled him in her arms to the shore.

Oh, happy is the day when true lovers they do meet,
　　When their troubles and their sorrows all are o'er;
She made the hills to ring as her sweet voice did sing,
　　When she's gotten the young man she adored, she adored.
　　When she's gotten the young man she adored.

THE DYING PLOUGHBOY.

THE gloamin' winds are blawin' saft
Aroun' my lonely stable laft;
Amid the skylight's dusky red,
The sunbeams wander roun' my bed.

The doctor left me in good cheer,
But something tells me death is near;
My time on earth has nae been lang,
My time has come and I must gang.

Ah, me! 'tis but a week the morn
Since I was weel and hairstin' corn,
As fu' o' health and strength and fun
As ony man amang the throng.

But something in my briest gaed wrang,
A vessel burst and blood it sprang;
And, as the sun sets in the skies,
They'll lay me down nae mair to rise.

Fareweel my horse, my bonnie pair,
I'll yoke and loose wi' you nae mair;
Fareweel my plough, wi' you this han'
Will turn ower nae mair fresh lan'.

Fareweel, my friends, my comrades dear,
My voice ye shall nae langer hear;
Fareweel to yonder setting sun,
My time has come and I must gang.

I've served my master weel and true,
My weel done wark he'll never rue;
And yet, forbye, I micht hae striven
To reach the pearly gates o' heaven.

'Tis weel my Maker knows my name,
Will he gae me a welcome hame?
As I should help in need afford,
Receive me in thy mercy, Lord.

Printed by permission of the author, the Rev. R. H. Calder, Parish Church Minister, Glenlivet.
This is one of the most popular Bothy Songs of the present day.

THE GUISE O' TOUGH.

I GAED up to Alford
　For to get a fee,
I fell in wi' Jamie Broon,
　And wi' him I did agree.

　　Tum a hum a-do,
　　Tum a hi dum day.

I engaged wi' Jamie Broon
　In the year o' ninety-one,
To gang hame and ca' his second pair
　And be his orra man.

When I gaed hame to Guise o' Tough
　'Twas in the evening clear,
And from about some orra house
　The gaffer did appear.

I'm the maister o' the place,
　And that's the mistress there;
And ye'll get plenty o' cheese and breid,
　And plenty mair to spare.

I sat and ate at cheese and breid
　Till they did at me stare,
And, fegs, I thocht that it was time
　To gang doon and see my pair.

I gaed to the stable
　My pairie for to view,
And, fegs, they were a dandy pair,
　A chestnut and a blue.

On the followin' mornin'
　I gaed to the ploo,
But lang, lang or lowsin' time
　My pairie gart me rue.

My ploo she wasna workin' weel,
　She wadna throw the fur,
The gaffer says, "There's a better ane
　At the smiddy to gang for."

When I got home the new ploo
　She pleased me unco weel,
But I thocht she would be better
　Gin she hid a cuttin' wheel.

I wrocht awa' a month or twa
　Wi' unco little clatter,
Till I played up some nasty tricks
　And broke the tattie chapper.

The gaffer he got word o' this,
　And orders did lay doon
That if I did the like again
　He wad pit me frae the toon.

We hae a gallant bailie,
　And Wallace is his name;
And he can fair redd up the kye
　When he tak's doon the kaim.

We hae a little bailie,
　And Jamieson's his name,
And he's gane doon to Alford
　And raised an awfu' fame.

He's gane doon to Charlie Watt's
　For to get a dram;
But lang, lang or I got doon
　The laddie couldna stan'.

We hae a gallant kitchie lass,
　And Simpson is her name,
And for to tell her pedigree
　I really wad think shame.

She dresses up on Sunday
　Wi' her head above the level,
Wi' twa raw o' ivory
　Wad scare the very devil.

Noo, my sang is ended
　And I wont sing any more,
And if ony o' ye be offended,
　Ye can walk outside the door.
　　Tum a dum a-do,
　　Tum a hi dum day.

LITTLE BENTON.

To Little Benton I did fee,
  In Rhynie feein' fair;
It was to be the foremost man
  And work the foremost pair.

I scarcely was a week gane hame
  When I did plainly see
The little mannie Benton
  And I could not agree.

Like mony o' my calling,
  I soon began to find
That Benton's study ever was
  His servants for to grind.

Oftentimes he laid a snare
  To catch me in a flaw;
The Banton thocht I was a hen
  To cooer when he did craw.

The craw jist o' the Banton cock
  It might surprise some men;
But weel could I withstand the shock,
  And loot the Banton ken.

From time to time the simmer past,
  Wi' strife, and scoff, and jeer,
The days to me like months did seem
  Beneath the Banton sneer.

But harvest it did now come on,
  To cut we did repair;
I from the Banton socht a scythe
  To cut his corn there.

A pair o' scythes in time was brought,
  And I did grip to mine;
The Banton he did quickly say
  " Ye are before your time."

Benton in a passion flew,
  Says, I will mak' ye blythe
To cut jist all the corn through
  Wi' an auld roosty scythe.

Tak' hame the new scythe, he did say,
  And bring your auld scythe here;
His orders I did soon abey,
  And home for it did steer.

I soon did bring the roosty scythe,
  And doon to him I threw;
The Banton he did not look blythe,
  It made him thraw his mou'.

For twa-three days I idle went,
  I wadna work a jot;
Benton quickly did repent,
  Back my new scythe I got.

Cuttin' being over,
  And leading weel begun,
The Banton thocht he wad get me
  Awa frae him to run.

It's to the Banton I stuck fast,
  As fast as ony brier;
I made him pay me every plack
  Or he o' me got clear.

Come, listen, all ye plooman lads,
  That do intend to fee,
If ye go to serve the Banton cock
  Ye'll rue as weel as me.

The Banton cock will crousely craw,
  When the servants gangs new hame;
But wi' the cock there's nane can live,
  Unless a cock that's game.

In Aberdeenshire Bantam becomes "Banton" hence Banton and Banton-cock—a spirited barnyard fowl of small size, much given to fighting.

THE PLOUGHING MATCH.

THE plooman lads at Hilton met,
Some looked bold and some looked blate,
That day there was mony a drap o' sweat
  Lost among the ploomen.

When they got their tickets oot,
For their rigs they looked about,
The Clerk to them he gaed a shout,
  And aff gaed a' the ploomen.

Alick Black got number one,
And wi' it he tried mony a plan,
Whiles his horse at the en' did stan',
    And thither drew the plooman.

Robbie Clark got number twa,
Sae cannily he slipt awa',
His horse and harness looked sae braw
    That day among the ploomen.

Charlie Duff got number three,
Though a haflin loon was he,
A pattern he did fairly gie
    When he put up his feerin'.

Davie Fife got number four,
Sae neatly as he turned it ower,
Spectators they at him did glower,
    Says, " Ye'll beat a' the ploomen."

Willie Park got number five,
He for the first prize sair did strive;
But in the well he took a dive
    That day among the ploomen.

Francie Grant got number six,
They thocht they had him in a fix,
But he stuck up like lime to bricks
    That day among the ploomen.

'Twas seven that Geordie Hill did get,
Altho' he didna ploo first-rate,
Gie him a scythe he'll no be beat
    By ony ither plooman.

Henry Isles got number eight,
He did his best to mak' it right;
He got it up as square and straight
    As ony o' the ploomen.

Lewie Jack got number nine,
Guid preserve us sic a shine!
He forgot to haud the line
    That day among the ploomen.

'Twas ten that Jamie Kirk got,
He up the rig jist at the trot;
But Willie Sim was on the spot,
    Cries, "Hie, it winna dee, man."

Eleven that Laurie Murdo drew,
His horse weel drest they ruggit too,
But he was awfu' like to spue
    That day among the ploomen.

The loons they a' ploo'd by themsel's,
Pleasure this and that to tell;
They held, they tramped, and jumped as well
    As ony o' the ploomen.

Jamie Broon he ploo'd fu' weel,
Tae tak' a prize he didna feel,
Ye ken he's nae a selfish chiel,
    Altho' he is a plooman.

Willie Petrie he cam' frae New Deer,
To tak' the prize he had nae fear,
But he got, "Hey, my mannie, here,"
    That day among the ploomen.

Jim Forbes thocht he'd tak' a prize,
A bonnie lass is mair his size,
He'll stick to them if he is wise,
    An' syne he'll be a plooman.

The champion plooman stood the test,
But young Jim White cam' out the best;
And Davie Fife got some lang-faced
    That day among the ploomen.

The judges cam' frae far an' near,
To put them richt they had nae fear,
But some wad say their sicht was puir
    That day among the ploomen.

When singing this song the singer generally puts in the names of persons known to his audience. The names of the original competitors and prize-takers have accordingly been lost. The locus of the match has also been forgotten.

THE PRAISE OF PLOUGHMEN.

YE lads and lasses a' draw near,
I'm sure it will delight your ear,
And as for me I'll no be sweir
   To sing the praise o' ploughmen.
The very King that wears the crown,
The brethren of the sacred gown,
And Dukes and Lords of high renown,
  Depend upon the ploughmen.

      Oh, happy is the ploughman's joe
      To hear the ploughman cry, Hie, wo,
      And make his horse so straight to go,
        The gallant, merry ploughman.

The gardener he cries out wi' speed,
I'm sure I was the first man made,
And I was learned the gardener trade
   Before there was a ploughman.
Oh gardener, lad, it's true you say;
But how long gardener did you stay?
I'm sure it was just scarce a day
   Ere ye became a ploughman.

The blacksmith he says, I hear news,
Do I not make you iron ploughs,
And fit the coulter for it's use,
   Or there would be nae ploughmen?
Oh, blacksmith, we must all allow
That you can mak' an iron plough,
But you would ne'er got that to do
   If it were not for the ploughmen.

The mason he cries, Ho, ho, fie,
Do I not build your castles high
The wind and rain for to defy,
   Far better than the ploughman?
Oh, mason, ye may build a house,
And fit it for its proper use,
But from the King unto the mouse
   Depends upon the ploughmen.

The miller he speaks out wi' glee—
Do I not sit at the mill e'e,
And grind the corn food for thee
    Far better than the ploughman?
Oh, miller, ye may haud your jaw,
And sit and look at your mill wa',
And see if dust frae it wad fa'
    If it were not for the ploughmen.

The souter he cries out, Hurrah,
Do I not make boots and shoes richt braw
For to defend baith frost and snaw.
    That's worn by the ploughmen?
You may mak' boots and shoes wi' speed,
Wi' last and leather, birse and thread,
But where's the meal for to mak' breid,
    If it were not for the ploughmen?

The tailor he cries out wi' haste—
I pray of this don't make a jest;
Oh, I can make coat, trews, and vest
    Far better than a ploughman.
Oh, tailor, ye may mak' braw clothes,
But where's the meal for to be brose?
Ye might close up baith mouth and nose,
    If it were not for the ploughmen.

Success the ploughmen's wages crown;
Let ploughmen's wages ne'er come down,
And plenty in Scotland aye abound,
    By the labour o' the ploughmen.
For the very King that wears the crown,
And the brethren o' the sacred gown,
And Dukes and Lords of high renown,
    Depend upon the ploughmen.

    Oh, happy is the ploughman's joe
    To hear the ploughman cry, Hie, wo,
    And make his horse so straight to go,
        The gallant, merry ploughman.

The late Mr. Gavin Greig, in his *Folk-song of the North-east*, states that "The Praise of Ploughmen" was written by John Anderson, Farmer, Upper Boyndlie, about the middle of the last century. It has, however, travelled far since then, as versions of it is to be found all over the country.

THE MILKING SONG.

Pbroo, pbroo! my bonnie cow!
 Pbroo, hawkie! ho, hawkie!
Ye ken the hand that's kind to you;
 Sae let the drappie go, hawkie.

Your caufie's sleepin' in the pen,
 Pbroo, hawkie! ho, hawkie!
He'll soon win to the pap again;
 Sae lat the drappie go, hawkie.
  Pbroo, pbroo, etc.

The stranger is come here to-day,
 Pbroo, hawkie! ho, hawkie!
We'll send him singin' on his way;
 Sae let the drappie go, hawkie.
  Pbroo, pbroo, etc.

The day is meeth and weary he,
 Pbroo, hawkie! ho, hawkie!
While cosy in the bield were ye;
 Sae let the drappie go, hawkie.
  Pbroo, pbroo, etc.

He'll bless your bouk when far away,
 Pbroo, hawkie! ho, hawkie!
And scaff and raff ye aye shall hae;
 Sae let the drappie go, hawkie.
  Pbroo, pbroo, etc.

Sic benison will sain ye still,
 Pbroo, hawkie! ho, hawkie!
Frae cantrip, elf, and quarter-ill;
 Sae let the drappie go, hawkie.
  Pbroo, pbroo, etc.

The stranger's blessing's lucky aye,
 Pbroo, hawkie! ho, hawkie!
We'll thrive, like hainet girss in May;
 Sae let the drappie go, hawkie.
  Pbroo, pbroo! my bonnie cow!
   Pbroo, hawkie! ho, hawkie!
  Ye ken the hand that's kind to you;
   Sae let the drappie go, hawkie.

THE QUERN-LILT; OR, GRINDING SONG.

THE cronach stills the dowie heart,
   The jurram stills the bairnie;
But the music for a hungry wame's
   The grinding o' the quernie.
     And loes me o' my little quernie!
     Grind the gradden, grind it:
     We'll a' get crowdie when it's done,
     And bannocks steeve to bind it.

The married man his joys may prize,
   The lover prize his arles;
But gin the quernie gang nae round,
   They baith will soon be sar'less.
     Sae loes me, etc.

The whisky gars the bark o' life
   Drive merrily and rarely;
But gradden is the ballast gars
   It steady gang, and fairly.
     Sae loes me, etc.

Though winter steeks the door wi' drift,
   And ower the ingle bings us,
Let but the little quernie gae,
   We're blythe, whatever dings us.
     Then loes me, etc.

And how it cheers the herd at e'en,
   And sets his heart-strings dirlin',
When, coming frae the hungry hill
   He hears the quernie birlin'.
     Then loes me, etc.

Though strut and strife, wi' young and auld,
   And flytin' but and ben be;
Let but the quernie play, they'll soon
   A' lown and fidgin'-fain be.
     Then loes me, etc.

The quern was a little hand mill used by crofters to grind their corn into meal.

The Milking Song and the Quern Song are imitations of the action-songs sung by the women when milking the cows and grinding the corn. They were both written by Robert Jamieson, the Morayshire poet. Jamieson is likely to have picked them up from the singing of the peasant women and improved them as to metre.

AULD LUCKIE OF BRUNTIES.

It's a' ye rovin' young men,
  Come listen unto me,
And dinna gang to Brunties' toon
  The lasses for to see;
Auld Luckie she's a wily ane,
  And she does watch the toon,
And ilka lad that she does catch
  She fines him half-a-crown.

'Twas on a Tuesday's evenin',
  As I was told by one,
A laddie went to see the girls,
  Wi' them to hae some fun;
Auld Luckie, growin' restless,
  She jumped out-owre her bed,
And there she found a young man
  Wi' her servant maid.

So quickly she did bolt the door,
  To keep it firm and fast;
And after five o'clock did ring
  The men appeared at last,
Cryin' for an open door,
  But Luckie she said " No,"
Ye'll need to change your road the day
  And to the entry go.

Oh, na, na, says the foreman,
  The brose they winna work,
If we go to your entry door
  We'll need the knife and fork;
But as it's only breakfast time
  We'll no be ill to please,
We'll just tak' tea or coffee,
  With butter, eggs, or cheese.

But if ye winna open the door,
  The keys o't ye can keep,
And we'll gang to our beds again
  And tak' anither sleep;

But one of them he steppit up
   And knockèd the door in—
" Good mornin'," cried the prisoner,
   But he was obliged to rin.

Auld Luckie she's a Christian,
   As ye do likely ken,
And she maun hae a regular hoose,
   Ay, baith but and ben.
But although she be a Christian,
   One thing she does forget,
And that's to gie her horses
   Their sufficient meat.

Sax bushels a week amongst the five,
   It's a' that they do get,
And sometimes in the evening
   They got a taste o' bait;
But it's composed of cauf and strae,
   And keeps them aye so thin,
The men they do declare to me
   The banes will cut the skin.

Fare-ye-weel, auld Luckie, noo,
   And fareweel evermore;
When ye gang up the narrow road
   Ye'll find a lockit door;
Ye'll need to change your course, I think,
   And gang where deevils dwell,
And there ye can quarrel and fight
   In a place we needna tell.

In some versions the last two lines are as follows:—
     And there she can quarrel and fight
     In the lowest rooms o' h—l.

MRS. GREIG OF S——.

'Twas at a certain fairm toon,
   By Deveron's banks and pleasant **border**,
A braw guidwife ca'd Mrs. Greig,
   Her servant girlies kept in order.

     Tow, row, row, etc.

Each night before she went to bed
  Their sleeping-place she searchèd over,
For fear some fellow there might hide,
  And in among them prove a rover.

The women they had tirèd been
  Of this attention which she gave them,
So to play a trick on her was keen,
  The auld guidman to get a share o't.

Martinmas being coming on,
  A suit of men's clothes was procured,
With that and straw they made a man,
  Which in below the bed they moored.

When Mrs. Greig cam' roon that night
  To guard them from all carnal danger,
In below the curtain pan
  The foot appeared of a stranger.

Come oot o' that, what do ye want?
  Ye needna think ye're frae me hidin';
But all that she could scold and rant,
  He gaed nae heed until her biddin'.

She told the women, they do say,
  To drag him oot where he was lyin',
And placed the auld man doon the stair,
  To cudgel him when from them flyin'.

They dragged him oot and threw him doon
  Where the auld man was for him ready;
And sae weel's he laid the cudgel on
  That baith the legs flew aff the body.

A court-martial was held next day,
  And a' the scattered bones collected;
The women they were put away,
  For this bit rig right sore corrected.

Now Mrs. Greig and her guidman
  I trust nae mair will lovers bother;
Nor yet the cudgel try again,
  Perhaps the same might slay some other.
        Tow, row, row, etc.

MILL OF BOYNDIE.
(MULLNABEENY.)

WHEN I was young and in my prime,
    Guid-fegs, like me there wisna mony;
I was the best man in the Boyne,
    And foreman lang at Mullnabeeny.
        Rare, O rare, O dear, O dear,
          Rora, Rora, Mullnabeeny;
        I was the best man in the Boyne,
          Ay, and foreman lang at Mullnabeeny.

When I engaged wi' Johnny Mull
    My fee was five pounds and a guinea,
It was to drive the foremost pair,
    Ay, and lead the mennies o' Mullnabeeny.

I had a hat upon my heid,
    It cost me mair than half-a-guinea,
Held a' the lasses in Brannan Fair
    Gazing at the foremost man o' Mullnabeeny.

Ho, flesher Rob, he's but a snob,
    Ha, fat's the mennies o' Mullnabeeny?
The bowes o' bere I carried there
    Wad hae killed the mennies o' Mullnabeeny.

Oh, for back at twenty-one,
    Hip, hurrah for Mullnabeeny!
To ca' blin' Joe the game's but low,
    Besides the hash o' Mullnabeeny.

When this auld hat o' mine was new
    It cost me mair than half-a-guinea,
Mair than fifty years ago
    When at the hash o' Mullnabeeny.
        Rare, O rare, O dear, O dear,
          Rora, Rora, Mullnabeeny;
        I was the best man in the Boyne,
          Ay, and foreman lang at Mullnabeeny.

About seventy years ago there was for a time twenty pairs of horses at the farm of Milne of Boyndie, pronounced Mullnabeeny by the natives of the place. It is situated in the parish of Boyndie, near Banff, and in a district known of old as the Boyne.

Brannan Fair is the name of the feeing market at Banff.

ARLIN'S FINE BRAES.

I'VE travelled this country both early and late,
And among the lasses I've had mony a lang sit,
Comin' hame in the mornin' when I should hae been at ease,
When I was a ploughboy on Arlin's fine braes.

The first thing I did when I gaed to yon toon
Was to corn my horses and rub them weel doon;
Syne awa to the bothy and shift aff my claes
And get out a-rovin' on Arlin's fine braes.

It's mony's the nicht I hae gane to yon toon,
And mony's the nicht I hae watched the loon
Sit darnin' his stockin's or mendin' his claes,
When I was a ploughboy on Arlin's fine braes.

Amang the bonnie lasses I hae sat by the fire,
Sometimes in the barn, sometimes in the byre,
Chattin' a' the nicht wi' them when I should been at ease,
When I gaed rovin, on Arlin's fine braes.

When I go to their window so gently I kneel,
The girlies when they hear me they spring to their heel,
They spring to their heel and they get on their claes,
Says, " Here's the wild rover frae Arlin's fine braes."

Oh, a' the day lang as I gae in the yoke
My mind is containing some roving exploit,
Expecting good prospect when I should be at ease,
When I was a ploughboy on Arlin's fine braes.

At meal times my mistress aften yoked upon me,
Says, " Laddie, ye'd be better gin ye'd lat them a' be,
Ye will mind on my words when ye come to auld age,
For ye'll nae aye be a ploughboy on Arlin's fine braes."

It's mony a fair maid I've caused for to sigh,
Says, " Where is the laddie that he never comes nigh?
I'll awa to my bed and lie down at my ease,
Since yon hard-hearted ploughboy has left Arlin's fine braes."

Come, all ye rovin' ploughboys, tak' a warnin' frae me,
Never follow young women whatever they be,
For they will entice you when they get on braw claes,
And set ye a-rovin' on Arlin's fine braes.

In some districts of the North-east of Scotland " The Carse o' Pomaize "
is substituted for " Arlin's Fine Braes."

SOWENS FOR SAP AT OOR NEW TAP.

THE foremost man o' oor New Tap
  He works a stallion fine,
The Lion they do call him,
  The Lion is his name.
The little one that goes to him
  She's swift and spunky too—
Sowens for sap at oor New Tap,
  Ye'll find it winna do.

The second pair at oor New Tap
  They are counted the best,
If he forgets to clean them,
  He will be sore opprest;
If on their legs a speck be found
  There'll be a Waterloo—
Sowens for sap at oor New Tap,
  Ye'll find it winna do.

The third pair at oor New Tap,
  The one of them's a bay;
The little one that goes on him
  He's true and trusty aye;
Likewise the man that works them
  He's a cut below his broo—
Sowens for sap at oor New Tap,
  Ye'll find it winna do.

Likewise we hae an orra man,
  He says he comes frae Perth,
He is the drollest shaver
  That ever lived on earth;
There's never a day wi' Sandy
  But there's a Waterloo—
Sowens for sap at oor New Tap,
  Ye'll find it winna do.

Likewise we hae an orra woman
  For waiting on oor nowte,
Ye widna see the like o' her
  The country roun' aboot;
For she does wear her leggin's,
  And snap her brose, I troo—
Sowens for sap at oor New Tap,
  Ye'll find it winna do.

THE WOODS OF RICKARTON.

Come, all ye jolly ploughman lads,
　And listen to my rhyme;
The praises of your bonnie glen
　I would be fain to sing.

For I dearly lo'e the heather hills,
　And lasses leal and true,
That lo'e the bonnie laddie
　That ca's the cairt and plough.

The bonnie woods o' Rickarton
　I love to wander through,
To hear the blackbird whistle,
　And the cushie curdle-doo.

To see the burnie winding clear,
　The cowslips spring so sweet;
And to see the bonnie lassie
　That I've trysted there to meet.

We ploughman lads are hardy chiels,
　We're clean as well as clad;
We like to please our masters,
　And see our horses fed;

But we dearly lo'e the girlies,
　And meet them on the sly,
And get a kindly crack wi' them
　At the milking o' the kye.

For ilka Jockie has a Jean,
　A Bawbie or a Nell;
I hae a lass I dearly lo'e,
　Though her name I winna tell.

But it winna be yon dandy lass
　That'll wile my heart awa',
She's foul and clorty at her wark,
　Though Sunday she gangs braw.

She wadna marry a ploughman lad,
   'Cause she has a puckle gear;
But if it wasna for her father's cash
   There's few wad gang to see her.

But she need not be so mighty prood,
   And cast her head so high,
For there's no ae lad in a' the glen
   But would gae pass her by.

But she'll maybe get some farmer's son
   Mair suiting to her mind;
And I hope she'll soon get married
   If she so feel inclined.

But he's very welcome to her,
   And her muckle tocher too;
He's free to wear out my auld shoon
   Since I hae gotten new.

Now the harvest it is over,
   And winter's coming on,
The lang dark nichts will soon he here,
   And I'll get wanton fun

Among the lasses in the glen,
   They're all so trig and neat;
But we winna cross the Cowie
   For fear our feet get weet.

Success to the farmer,
   And much prosperity;
And health unto the ploughboy
   That works for meat and fee.

I wish the lassie happiness,
   May she ne'er hae to rue,
That marries the bonnie laddie
   That gangs whistling at the plough.

THE BRAES O' BROO.

GET up, get up, ye lazy loons,
    Get up, and waur them a', man,
For the braes o' Broo are ill to ploo,
    They're roch and reesky a', man.

    But the plooman laddie's my delight,
        The plooman laddie lo'es me;
    When a' the lave gang to their bed
        The plooman comes and sees me.

The braes o' Broo they're ill to toil,
    They're roch and reesky a', man,
And they haena left but ae auld horse
    To toil and tear them a', man.
    But the plooman laddie's, etc.

Oh, he's taen up his owsen gaud,
    And it sets him weel to ca', man,
He's laid it owre the owsen bow,
    Says, " Scurry, come awa', man.
    But the plooman laddie's, etc.

It's I will wash the plooman's hose,
    And dry them owre the door, man;
I'll maybe be the plooman's wife,
    I've been his lass before, man.
    For the plooman laddie's, etc.

It's I will wash the plooman's hose,
    And I will brush his sheen, man,
I'll maybe be the plooman's wife
    Or a' thae days be deen, man.
    For the plooman laddie's, etc.

This appears to be the original verses of a very old bothy-song which no doubt belongs to the days of the wooden plough and the shearing hook. The late Gavin Greig, M.A., of New Deer, picked up in that district a version with the following modern verses incorporated into it:—

    What think ye o' oor ploomen noo,
        Wi' their high-cuttin' ploos an' a , man?
    But it wasna sae ance in a day,
        When the wooden ploo ploo'd a', man.
        But the plooman laddie's, etc.

What think ye o' oor farmers noo,
  Wi' their binders ane and a', man?
But it wisna sae ance in a day,
  When the plooman sheared it a', man.
    But the plooman laddie's, etc.

What think ye o' the farmers noo,
  Wi' their thrashin' mulls and a', man?
But it wisna sae in their mithers' day,
  When the ploomen threesh it a', man.
    But the plooman laddie's, etc.

What think ye o' oor lasses noo,
  Wi' their bicycles sae braw, man?
But it wisna sae ance in a day,
  When shanks' mear did it a', man.
    But the plooman laddie's, etc.

THE MILL O' LOUR.

WE a' agreed at Martinmas,
  At Mill o' Lour to dwell,
They said it was a very fine place
  But it turned out not so well.

    Ah riddel doo, ill-dum, da-dee,
    Ah riddel doo, ill-dum, da-day.

The Lour mill's a heavy mill,
  And unco ill to ca';
Tho' we yoke a' the horses in
  She'll hardly draw ava.

Sandy works the foremost pair,
  They are a pair o' blues;
Altho' ye had them at your wale
  Ye wadna ken which to choose.

Jamie works the second pair,
  A black ane and a broon;
There's no a cannier, trustier pair
  In a' the country roun'.

Jess comes in ahint the lave,
  She's ca'd the orra mare;
In winter when we're sheuchin' neeps
  She rins like ony hare.

Note.—A version of this Bothy Song appears in Ford's *Vagabond Songs and Ballads*.

HARROWING TIME.

Air.—" Drumdelgie."

CAULD winter it is noo awa,
  And spring has come again;
And the cauld, dry winds o' March month
  Has driven awa the rain,

Has driven awa the dreary rain,
  Likewise the frost and snaw;
So our foreman in the mornin'
  He's ordered out to saw.

The rest o' us merry ploughboys
  We a' maun follow fast;
We're told by our hard master
  There is no time to rest.

We're told that we must be a-yoke
  Each mornin' sharp by five;
And quickly owre and owre the rigs
  Our horses we maun drive.

We drive them on to twelve o'clock,
  Syne home to dinner go;
And before the end of one short hour
  The farmer cries, " Hillo!"

Till the farmer cries, " Hillo, boys,
  It's time to yoke again,
See that ye get it harrowed oot,
  For fear that it comes rain."

So on we drive until the sun
  Ahint yon hill does hide;
And syne we loose our horses tired,
  And homewards we do ride.

Then homewards we do ride fu' keen
  To get our horses fed;
We kaim them weel, baith back and heel,
  Their tails and manes we redd.

When that is done we supper get,
  And after that we hie
Awa' to see our pretty girls,
  A-milkin' o' their kye.

Each one to see his sweetheart,
    And pree her cherry mou',
Then tak' a daffin' 'oor or twa,
    Shak' hands and bid adieu.

So now I mean to end my song,
    And I will end wi' this—
May the ploughman get mair wages,
    That is my earnest wish.

That is my heartfelt wish, I say,
    It is the ploughman's due;
For he sustains both rich and poor
    By the handling o' the plough.

NEWMILL.

It was to Newmill, ayont the hills,
    Last term I did fee,
To Maister B——, a farmer there,
    His servant for to be.

I hadna been a week come hame
    When I could plainly see
The tables they were rather bare,
    And they did not suit me.

The breid was thick, the brose was thin,
    The broth they were like bree;
I chased the barley roun' the plate,
    And a' I got was three.

So unsuccessful was my search,
    My spoon I did throw doon;
The knife and fork were seldom' seen
    But in the carpet room.

Our humble cot, as you may see,
    It stands both bleak and bare;
And the hen-house it stands west a wee
    For to complete the square.

And Maister Langnecks is a man
    Who can baith cheat and lee,
And tries to put his servants off
    Without their penny fee.

And he wad sell his chaff an' strae,
    The black silk goons to buy;
He wad sell the water in his dam,
    If ony ane wad buy.

Three hundred stones of hay we cut,
    And drank three quarts o' beer;
Two and sixpence was the cost,
    Our medicine wasna dear.

Our mistress she the silk goons wore,
    As true as I do say,
And orders to the maister gave
    To give us every day.

When we were to the barn sent,
    To raip and draw the strae,
She's at the keyhole o' the door
    To hear what we might say.

And when her daughters were with us,
    She did regard them right,
And always kept her eye on them
    Till twelve o'clock at night.

Ae day my horse did lose a shoe
    While grazing on the lay,
And I was put to seek the same
    The feck o' one whole day.

Wi' blessed hand and happy fit,
    The shoe I then did find,
And safely to my maister brought
    To ease his troubled mind.

Now fareweel, Maister Langnecks,
    And to your daughters three;
But the turkey-hen that lives her lane,
    I think I'll lat her be.

So fareweel, Maister Langnecks,
    Nae langer will I bide;
But I will steer my course again
    Back to bonnie Deeside.

From a literary standpoint "Newmill" is pure doggerel, but the description of the food supplied by Mr. B. to his servants, as described in the third verse, is excellent.

BETWEEN STANEHIVE AND LAURENCEKIRK.

BETWEEN Stanehive and Laurencekirk
  Last term I did fee,
'Twas wi' a wealthy farmer,
  His foreman for to be.
To work his twa best horses
  Was what I had to do,
A task that I could manage weel
  Both in the cart and ploo.

I worked my horses carefully,
  And did my master please,
Excepting to some rants o' fun
  That did his temper tease;
Until the month o' January,
  As you may weel believe,
For courtin' wi' the servin' girl
  We both did get our leave.

One night into the stable,
  By tryst I met her there,
On purpose for to have some fun,
  And guid advice to gie 'er;
Our master hearing o' the same,
  To the stable he cam' o'er;
And he did give us both our leave
  Out o' the stable door.

But it's not upon my master
  That I lay all the blame,
It is the maiden o' the place,
  That high respected dame.
Since no sweetheart to her did come,
  It grieved her sore to see
The happy moments that were spent
  Between my love and me.

Come, all ye jolly ploughboys
  That want to mend the fau't;
Be sure it is the maiden first
  That ye maun court and daut;

For if ye court the servant first,
   And gang the maiden by,
Ye may be sure the term for you
   Is quickly drawin' nigh.

Surely the times are gettin' hard
   When courtin's ca'ed a crime;
For it has been practised noo
   Guid ken's for hoo lang time;
But yon big toon aboon the road,
   It is forbidden there;
And for feein' wi' yon farmer
   I bid you a' beware.

CAMELOUN.

It's Tarvis pairish that I come fae,
And to tell ye that I am some wae,
For there's a lang road I maun gae,
   To the Fyvie lands in the mornin'.

At Cameloun I did arrive,
A pair o' horses for to drive,
And ilka mornin' up at five,
   And ca' the fan in the mornin'.

At first when I to Camel's cam',
They a' cried oot, "Here's oor new man!"
And to gaze at me they a' began
   In the Fyvie lands in the mornin'.

I hadna weel begun to sleep
When the foreman he began to creep,
And oot o' his bed he sprang to his feet—
   Cries, "Losh boys, rise, for it's mornin'."

To ca' the fan they set me tee,
Which I began richt cannily,
And took a look fu they wad dee
   In the Fyvie lands in the mornin'.

The winnyin' bein' past and the fan by set,
The foreman cries, "We maun hae some meat,"
At the head o' the table he's ta'en his seat,
  Says, "Ate, boys, ate, for it's mornin'."

" Ye'll yoke your horse as fast as ye may,"
The foreman unto me did say;
" And ye'll get a plough oot owre the brae
  That'll please ye weel in the mornin'."

I hadna lang been at the plough
When I began to couck and spue;
The nicht afore I'd been some fou,
  Sae I had a dowie mornin'.

We hae a bailie[1] stout and stark,
It sets him weel to work his wark,
Out owre his heid he draws a sark,
  As lang's himsel' in the mornin'.

Oor kitchie cook she's nae great dale,
I think I wad dee as weel mysel',
For she maks oor breid as green as kail
  In the Fyvie lands in the mornin'.

Oor dairymaid she is some shy
At the bailie lad as he gangs by,
When she gae's oot to milk her kye
  By grey daylicht in the mornin'.

Fyvie pairish is lang and wide,
Fyvie pairish is fu' o' pride;
But in this same corner I'll nae langer bide,
  Gin I had Whitsunday mornin'.

And noo I've tauld ye clear and fair
Aboot the Fyvie lands sae rare;
An' gin ony ane after me enquire,
Ye can tell them I left in the mornin'.

[1] Cattleman.

ELLON FAIR.

'Twas in the merry month of May
When flowers had clad the landscape gay,
To Ellon Fair I bent my way
    With hopes to find amusement.

A scrankie chiel to me cam' near,
An' quickly he began to speir
If I wad for the neist half-year
    Engage to be his servant.

" I'll need you as an orra loon;
Four poun' ten I will lay down
To you, when Martinmas comes roon
    To close out our engagement.

" Five shillings more will be your due,
If you to me prove just and true;
But that will be referred to you
    By my good will and pleasure."

An' to a tent he then set sail,
And bade me follow at his tail;
And he called for a glass o' ale
    Therein to keep us sober.

Said he, " A saxpence noo, my loon,
I freely will to you lay down,
Thrippence for ale I will pay soon,
    And thrippence buys my fairin'."

When I went hame to my new place,
And at the table showed my face,
It's to the brose they said nae grace—
    The time was unco precious.

Although our usage was but scant,
Of wark we never kent nae want;
And aye to carry on the rant
    The farmer cried, " Come on, lads."

An' when the hairst it did come roun',
It's to a scythe I hid to boun';
Likewise to draw the rake aroun',
    To keep the fields in order.

THE HAIRST.

Air.—" The Miller o' Drone."

I SEE the reapers in the field, for hairst is come again,
An' O, how sweet fa's on the ear their sang among the grain!
I like to hear the sound o' waves that lash our rock-girt shore,
They are the type of liberty as Wallace was of yore;
I like to hear the tars' ye-ho! I like the fact'ry's hum,
But nae a sound doth please me like what saith, " The hairst is
        come."

> The hairst is come, the hairst is come,
>   An' sweet's the reaper's strain;
> Let ilka heart rejoice and sing,
>   " The hairst is here again."

The bonnie yellow waving grain, our precious staff o' bread;
Tak' it awa, an' whaur are we?—amo' the famish'd dead;
We wouldna hear ae soun' o' mirth at noon, at nicht, nor morn,
Nor hear the railway's whistle scream were it nae for the corn;
The souters couldna mak' our sheen, nor sailors plough the main,
Nor printer bodies print the news gin't wer'na for the grain.

> That the grain's the strength, the staff o' life,
>   Is evident an' plain;
> Let ilka heart rejoice and sing,
>   " The hairst is here again."

Ye fields o' bonny waving grain, I like to hear your sang,
It speaks o' meat to man and beast—to plenty doth belang;
Lang may our ain dear fatherland frae famine be preserved,
An' may her sons to all that's great an' good be will'd an' nerv'd.
May our beloved Victoria o'er us hae lang to reign,
An' feel delighted as she views our crops o' gowden grain.

> The hairst is come; the blades are sharp,
>   And reapers mow the grain,
> An' we with thankfu' hearts will sing,
>   " The hairst is here again."

This fine song was written in 1859 by Mr. James Davidson, of New
Pitsligo, Aberdeenshire. Davidson, who was for some time on the staff of
the *Banffshire Journal*, published at Aberdeen, in 1861, a small volume of
poems chiefly in the Buchan dialect.

K

THE LOTHIAN HAIRST.

On August twelfth from Aberdeen
　We sailed upon the *Prince*,
And landed safe at Clifford's fields,
　Our harvest to commence.

For six lang weeks the country roun'
　Frae toon to toon we went,
And I took richt weel wi' the Lothian fare,
　An' aye was weel content.

Our master, William Mathieson,
　From sweet Deeside he came;
Our foreman came from the same place,
　An' Logan was his name.

I followed Logan on the point,
　Sae weel's he laid it down,
And sae boldly as he's led our squad
　O'er mony's the thistley toon.

My mate and I could get nae chance
　For Logan's watchful eye,
And wi' the lads we got nae sport,
　For Logan was sae sly.

He cleared our bothy every night
　Before he went to sleep,
And never left behind him one,
　But strict the rules did keep.

And when we come to Aberdeen
　He weel deserves a spree,
For the herding o' us a' sae weel
　From the Lothian lads we're free.

Farewell M'Kenzie, Reid, and Rose,
　And all your jovial crew,
An' Logan, Jock, and Chapman, Pratt,
　And Royal Stuart too.

We'll fill a glass and drink it round
　Before the boat will start,
And may we safely reach the shore,
　And all in friendship part.

JOHNNIE SANGSTER.

O a' the seasons o' the year,
  When we maun work the sairest—
The harvest is the foremost time,
  And yet it is the rarest.
We rise as seen as mornin' licht,
  Nae craters can be blyther,
We buckle on oor finger-steels
  And follod oot the scyther.

    For you, Johnnie, you, Johnnie,
      You, Johnnie Sangster—
    I'll trim the gavel o' my sheaf[1]
      For ye're the gallant bandster.

A mornin' piece to line oor cheek
  Afore that we gae forder,
Wi' clouds o' blue tobacco reek,
  We then set oot in order.

[1] Shafe.

The sheaves are risin' thick and fast,
  And Johnnie he maun bind them;
The busy group, for fear they stick,
  Can scarcely look behind them.
    For you, Johnnie, etc.

I'll gie ye bands that winna slip,
  I'll pleat them weel and thraw them,
I'm sure they winna tine the grip,
  Hooever weel ye draw them.
I'll lay my leg oot ower the sheaf,
  And draw the band sae handy.
Wi' ilka strae as straucht's a rash,
  And that will be the dandy.
    For you, Johnnie, etc.

If e'er it chance to be my lot
  To get a gallant bandster,
I'll gar him wear a gentle coat,
  And bring him gowd in handfu's.
But Johnnie he can please himsel',
  I wadna wish him blinket;
Sae aifter he has brewed his ale
  He can sit doon and drink it.
    For you, Johnnie, etc.

A dainty cowie in the byre,
  For butter and for cheeses;
A grumphie, feedin' in the sty,
  Wad keep the hoose in greases;
A bonnie ewie in the bucht
  Wad help to creesh the ladle,
And we'll get ruffs o' cannie woo'
  Wad help to theek the cradle.
    For you, Johnnie, etc.

"Johnnie Sangster"—both words and music—were sent to me by Mr. Gavin Greig, M.A., ex-President of the Buchan Field Club, Whitehill, New Deer, who writes regarding it as follows:—"I cannot be sure that the words are complete. They have been taken down as sung in this district. The song is said to be the composition of William Scott, who belonged to Fetterangus, in the parish of Old Deer, and was born in 1785. Scott was a herd laddie to begin with. He subsequently went to Aberdeen to learn tailoring, from thence to London, but returned to Aberdeen. He afterwards visited America, returning to Old Deer, where he died at a pretty advanced age. Published poems, chiefly in the Buchan dialect, in Aberdeen in 1832."

THE GALLANT SHEARERS.

Adam's wine[1] and heather bells,
Comes rattlin' ower yon gloomy hills,
There's corn rigs in yonder fields,
    And autumn brings the shearing.

    O, bonnie lassie, will ye gang
    And shear wi' me the hale day lang,
    And love will cheer us as we gang
        To join yon band o' shearers?

For blythe and lichtsome is the toil,
Yer bonnie een my care beguile,
We'll meet together 'yont the stile,
    And join yon band o' shearers.
    O, bonnie lassie, etc.

And if the thistle it be strong,
I fear 'twill jag thy milk-white hand,
But with my hook I'll cut it down,
    When we join yon band o' shearers.
    O, bonnie lassie, etc.

And if the weather it be hot,
I'll cast my waistcoat and my coat,
And shear wi' you among the lot
    When we join yon band o' shearers.
    O, bonnie lassie, etc.

And if the weather it be dry
They'll say there's love 'tween you and I,
So we'll slyly pass each other by
    When we join yon band o' shearers.
    O, bonnie lassie, etc.

And when the harvest days are done,
And slowly sets the wintry sun,
Ye'll be my ain till life is run
    Nae mair to join the shearers.
    O, bonnie lassie, etc.

[1] Name given by country folk to rain and to water generally.

THE BOGEND HAIRST.

Air.—" Linten, Lowrin."

I SHEARED my first hairst at Bogend,
  Down by the fit o' Bennachie;
An' sair I wrought and sair I focht,
  But I won my penny fee.
    Linten, lowrin, linten lowrin,
      Lintin, lowrin, lowrin lee,
    I'll gang back the gait I cam',
      An' a better bairn I will be.

O, Rhynie's wark is ill to work,
  An' Rhynie's wages are but sma',
An' Rhynie's laws are double strict,
  An' that's what grieves me maist ava'.
    Linten, lowrin, etc.

O, Rhynie is a Hielan' place,
  It doesna suit a Lawland loon;
An' Rhynie is a cauld clayhole,
  It is nae like my father's toon.[1]
    Linten, lowrin, etc.

[1] Farm.

This is another Aberdeenshire harvest song. About the beginning of the last century a Buchan farmer's son, having quarrelled with his father, left his home and engaged as a harvest-hand at the farm of Bogend, in Rhynie, Strathbogie, but the change does not seem to have been for the better.

THE BAND O' SHEARERS.

'TWAS on an August afternoon,
When folk could spy the harvest moon,
The lads and lasses gathered roun'
  To talk about the shearing.
I whisper'd Jean if she wad gang,
And shear wi' me the hale day lang,
And join wi' me a merry thrang—
  A jolly band o' shearers.
    So, bonnie lassie, will ye gang,
      And shear wi' me the hale day lang,
    And love will cheer us as we gang
      To join the band o' shearers?

And should the weather be ower hot
I'll cast my gravat and my coat,
An' help my lass to shear her lot,
    Amang the band o' shearers.
So, bonnie lassie, will ye gang
And shear wi' me the hale day lang,
I'll cheer ye wi' a hearty sang,
    Amang the band o' shearers?

And should the thistles be ower strong,
Thy bonnie feet or hands to wrong,
I'll swear they'll no be standing long
    To hurt the lassie shearing.
And when our daily task is done,
We'll wander by the rising moon,
And string our hearts to love's sweet tune,
    When comin' frae the shearing.

THE HERDIE.

Oh, for the innocent days I hae seen,
When a' my young thoughts they were happy and keen,
When up in the mornin' I raise frae my bed,
And got my fu' sairin' o' milk and o' bread.
Then on wi' my plaidie and up wi' my tree ·
And out to the leas I gaed singing 'wi' glee—
Sometimes a wee bonnet to keep my head dry,
And moggans to wear on my leggies forby.

Then frae the fauld I drave out my nowte,
So merry as they gaed friskin' about,
They licked their sleek sides as they fed on the sward
When I lived the life of a jovial young herd.
When wee Jenny used to be keepin' the kye,
Oh, wha were sae happy as Jenny and I?
We gaed down to the burnie on yon hallow green,
And puddled till we were baith wet to the e'en.

Yet fan I min' fu she priend up her cottie
To catch the quick minnen that swam through the pottie,
And that I the better might help her to ca',
I took aff my breekies and flang them awa.
When baith had been tired and dubbed to the chin,
We halted to dry our wee duds in the sun,
To the sunshinie side o' the dykie we'd flit
And tummle owre goudie frae the head to the fit.

We spread down our plaidies to mak' oursels beds,
And biggit wee houses to cover our heads;
Gin they were but happit, jocosely and sly,
Lat onything licht on our tails that cam' by.
Awa to the ring-fowlie then we would haste,
And try to surprise the wee thing on its nest;
The sweet bonnie eggies, so speckled and braw,
We'd gaze at a filie and then rin awa.

Thus hae we played through a long simmer's day,
We thocht on nae ill, and we dreaded no wae;
Till ance the bricht sun fell a-hiding his nose,
And then we gaed hame to get our kail-brose.
A dish o' guid brose wi' the kail and the says
A herdie was needin' jist aff o' the leas;
The kail and the says and the drappie o' ream
Wad set me a-sleepin' as seen's they were deen.

Then aff to my bed I was packet wi' speed,
My feet they were crazy and sleepie my head;
Awa to the chamer we had then to jog,
I and my constant bed-fellow, the dog.
The bed for its sleepers was naething unmeet,
Tho' aft it afforded but strae and a sheet;
And lang ere the mornin' the sheet sled awa
And left the bare hide to enjoy the straw.

Then in the mornin' the men had a lark,
To tell hoo the bed-strae my hippies did mark;
And fat was the skith? for I sleepit as soun'
As gin I had lien on the saftest o' down.
Then were the days when I never had care,
But brown as a tod, and as wild as a hare,
I scoured through the heather, and kissed the sweet bells,
And pu'd the wild roses that grew in the vales.

THE HAIRST O' RETTIE.

I HAE seen the hairst o' Rettie,
  Ay, and twa-three on the throne;
I've heard for sax and seven weeks
  The hairsters girn and groan.
But a covie Willie Rae,
  In a monthie and a day,
Mak's a' the jolly hairster lads
  Gae singing down the brae.

A monthie and a day, my lads,
  The like was never seen;
It beats to sticks the fastest strips
  O' Victory's new machine.
A Speedwell now brings up the rear,
  A Victory clears the way;
And twenty acres daily yelds
  Nor stands to Willie Rae.

He drives them roun' and roun' the fields
  At sic an awfu' rate;
He steers them canny out and in
  At mony's the kittle gate;
And wiles them safely owre the clods
  To mony's the hidden hole;
But he comes by no mischanter
  If you leave him wi' the pole.

He sharps their teeth to gar them bite,
  Then taps them on the jaws;
And when he finds them dully like,
  He brawly kens the cause.
A boltie here, a pinnie there,
  A little out o' tune,
He shortly stops their wild career
  And brings the slushet down.

He whittles aff at corners,
  Mak's crookit bitties straught;
And sees that man and beast alike
  Are equal in the draught;

And a' the sheavies lyin' straught,
  And nane o' them agley;
For he'll count wi' ony dominie
  Frae the Deveron to the Spey.

He's no made up o' mony words,
  Nor kent to puff and lee;
But just as keen a little chap
  As ever you did see.
If you be in search of harvest work
  Upon a market day,
Tak' my advice, be there in time,
  And look for Willie Rae

Now we hae gotten't in about,
  And a' oor thingies ticht,
We gather roun' the festive board
  To spend a jolly nicht.
Wi' Scottish song and mutton broth
  To drive all cares away,
We'll drink success to Rettie,
  And adieu to Willie Rae.

Come, all ye jolly Rettie chaps,
  A ringin' cheer to a';
A band o' better workin' chaps
  A gaffer never saw.
So eager aye to play their part,
  And ready for the brae;
'Twas you that made the boatie row,
  'Twas steered by Willie Ray.

THE HARVEST HOME.

Come, ye jolly lads and lasses,
  Ranting round in pleasure's ring,
Join wi' me, tak' up the chorus,
  And wi' mirth and glee we'll sing.

    Blythe and merry we hae been,
      Blythe and merry let us be;
    Mony a merry nicht we've seen,
      And mony mair we hope to see.

We come nae here for wardly gear,
　Nae warldly motive did us draw;
But we came here to fit the fleer,[1]
　And dance till we were like to fa'.

Noo, minstrels, screw your fiddles up,
　And see if they be richt in tune,
And gie us " Donald kissed Katie
　Comin' through the camowine."

Wha wad see the bonnie lasses,
　A' sae handsome, trig, and braw;
Them to please wha wad refeese[2]
　To want their sleep an hour or twa?

The craps, secure frae wind and rain,
　Stand in the stackyard snug and dry;
Boreas' blasts may rage in vain,
　We'll whistle while it's going by.

Now the harvest wark is owre,
　The fields are bare, the yards are fu',
And we unto the ploo repair,
　And for another crap pursue.

He that first does weary here,
　A dozin fleep we will him ca';
But he that's hinmost in the fleer,
　We'll judge him chief among us a'.

Now we're a' here sae happy met,
　Floating around in pleasure's stream,
We winna flit till Phœbus' licht
　Be shining out wi' morning beam.

　　Blythe and merry we hae been,
　　　Blythe and merry let us be;
　　Mony a merry nicht we've seen,
　　　And mony mair we hope to see.

---

[1] Floor.　　[2] Refuse.

THE HERD LADDIE'S LAMENT.

A WEE laddie sat wi' the tear in his e'e
A-herding his kye on a bleak whinny lea,
An' aye as he spak' his bit heartie got fou,
For his tale it was waefu', though nane the less true.

" My feet," said the laddie, " are hacket an' sair,
An' my shune and my stockings they winna repair,
An' I've nae money left to buy new anes wi'
That my feet might be hale on this bleak whinny lea.

Though it rains and the win' blaws bitter and caul',
I've nae cloak about me to keep out the caul',
An' my duddies, though drippin', they ne'er get a dry,
For there's nae fire allow'd in the laft where I lie.

A hoosie I bigget wi' divots and stanes,
Whaurin I took shelter frae caul' win's an' rains;
Some wild, idle laddies, wha thocht it fine fun,
Fell foul o't an' ca'd it a' flat wi' the grun'.

The claes I hae on me are a' worn dune,
They're maist as far through as my stockings an' shune:
An' ae leg o' my breekies is aff by the knee,
An' can bring me nae bield on this bleak whinny lea.

I weary fu' sair an' the days appear lang
When I min' on the playmates that I ran amang,
An' wi' them fu' sunner again I wad be
Than herding thae kye on this bleak whinny lea.

The folk that I'm servin' are scrimpin' an' bare,
An' there's few o' their dainties that come to my share,
But the grun' o' my stamack that aften I feel
Gars their aul' mouldy bannocks aye taste unco weel.

When I look to their bairns, sae weel are they dress'd,
Sae weel they're taen care o' an' served wi' the best,
I wonder a naked, bit loonie like me
Can outlive the caul' blasts that I get on this lea.

Though I ettle my best to please when I can,
I'm sair cuff'd about by baith maister an' man;
Cou'd they feel for an orphan, they'd aye feel for me,
A wee, duddy loon on this bleak whinny lea.

THE BRAW SERVANT LASSES.

Ye decent auld women, I'll sing you a song,
The wit o' the auld and the pride o' the young;
They're a' grown sae gaudy, as sure as my life,
Ye'll scarce ken the servant lass by the guidwife.
    Wi' my twigie fala falaldidee da,
    Wi' my twigie fala falaldidee dee.

It's no farmers' daughters, nor tradesmen's indeed,
For which I intend to sing my new creed;
It's our servant lasses, they're a' grown sae braw,
They outstrip their mistress by far and awa.
    Wi' my twigie, etc.

Between six and seven young miss goes to school,
Before you can tell if she's wise or a fool,
And there she must learn to read and to write,
Till she's fit for a lawyer or something sic like.
    Wi' my twigie, etc.

When schooling is over to service she goes,
For the greed of high wages as you may suppose;
And the first of it goes for a white muslin goon,
And a bonnet wad keep the moonlicht frae a toon.
    Wi' my twigie, etc.

She curls up her hair like a waterdog's tail,
Rowed up in a paper as roun' as a snail;
Wi' that and the veil hangin' down owre her e'en
There's never ae wrinkle ava to be seen.
    Wi' my twigie, etc.

And down frae the bonnet there hings a bit silk,
Like what my auld grannie had for synin' her milk;
I own it is useful the beauty to grace,
For it hides a' the wrinkles that is in her face.
    Wi' my twigie, etc.

And noo she's rigged out like a ship in full sail,
Wi' sax-seven flounces aboot her goon tail;
The very first Sunday the buckle goes on,
Says the ane to the ither, " Jock, wha is she yon?"
    Wi' my twigie, etc.

For Sunday aboot she goes to the church,
But what she hears there she winna mind much,
The text and the Psalms she'll no mind upon,
But she'll mind very weel what her neighbours had on.
    Wi' my twigie, etc.

At balls and at weddin's she'll rant and she'll rove,
At every new meetin' she'll get a new love;
But wi' her gallavantin', ere three years gae roon,
Her pride that was up it gets a tak' doon.
    Wi' my twigie, etc.

When some o' her sweethearts kens something is wrang,
Into the same country they'll no tarry lang,
But rin aff to America, oh! sic a trick!
And missie, poor thing, gets the whip-shaft to lick.
    Wi' my twigie, etc.

And now she's confined like a cow on the grass,
The bonnet's laid by wi' the hail gaudy dress;
The cradle she rocks, while the wee one does roar,
And she greets for the thing that she lauched at afore.
    Wi' my twigie, etc.

I am an auld bachelor, sixty and three,
I made up this sangie to keep me in glee;
I made up this sangie for the fun o' the thing;
But my throat's growin' sair, and I'm no fit to sing.
    Wi' my twigie, etc.

DARRAHILL.

Air.—" The Barnyards o' Delgaty."

When I engaged to Darrahill,
    'Twas low down in a Buchan fair,
The wark that I did tak' in han',
    It was to work his second pair.

Darras[1] bade me seek a fee,
    And I the same did sune lay on;
He said the wages are too high,
    But I'll gie you the sax poun' ten.

Darras took me to a tent,
    And Darras he called for a dram;
He put the shillin' in my han',
    Says, "Lad, come hame as sune's ye can."

When I gaed hame to Darrahill
    To work the wark I took in han',
The horse they werena very guid,
    And the harness werena worth a hang.

Darras' horse were very poor,
    They got their corn ance a day,
And ither twice got neeps and cauf,
    To gar them nab their pickle strae.

In the mornin' we got brose,
    As mony's we could belly in;
Willie Buchan made the brose,
    And, faith, he didna mak' them thin.

Anither thing I did remark,
    We never got a drap o' ale;
But I'll gae back to Yokieshill,
    And there I canna tell the tale.

Darras was a kerrious[2] chiel,
    And that I kent when I gaed hame,
For deil a word o' sense he spak',
    But aye the ither, "Like ye ken."

He sent me owre to Smiddy burn
    To ploo upon yon staney knowe;
'Twas but the wark I took in han',
    But sair, sair did I rue.

The Buchan fairs are drawin' near,
    And doon to them it's we will steer,
In hope to find some better place,
    For ony waur we dinna fear.

[1] In the North-east of Scotland a farmer is never called by his own name but always after his farm.   [2] Curious.

JOCK HAWK'S ADVENTURES IN GLASGOW.

ONE night I into Glasga went,
　To spend my penny fee,
'Twas then a girl gave consent
　To bear me company.

I said I was a stranger,
　And Glasga did not know;
She said there was no danger
　If I wi' her would go.

She linked her arm into mine,
　And we walked down the street,
And I never dreaded any harm,
　Tho' hundreds we did meet.

But as we did pass through a crowd,
　I heard a whisper say—
"D'ye see Jock Hawk, he's got a Miss,
　But he'll repent that play!"

We walked down Jamaica Street,
　And through the Broomielaw,
Where the organ lads played rich and sweet,
　And fiddlers ane or twa.

We then into a tavern went,
　Where I called for some gin,
And the lads and lassies a' looked up
　And laughed as we came in.

I scarce had got the gin poured out,
　When in came half a score
O' sailor lads and girls so nice,
　I never saw before

I handed each a glass o' gin,
　And they drank it up richt free;
And ilka ane aye drank success
　To my bonnie young lass and me.

The spree kept up wi' mirth and song
　Till it was growin' clear,
And then a knock cam' to the door—
　"All hands on deck appear!"

Some o' them snatched a parting kiss,
    And other said "Good-bye,"
And the hindmost ane, as he passed out,
    Said, "Jock, ye've a' to pey."

They've ta'en frae me my watch and chain,
    My spleuchan[1] and my knife;
I wonder that they did not tak'
    My little spunk[2] o' life.

They've stripped me o' my braw new coat,
    My waistcoat and my shune.
And for my hat, I never saw't
    Since first I called the gin.

Now hame frae Glasga I'd to gae
    Baith naked and quite bare,
And back again I widna gang
    To get a spree nae mair.

[1] Tobacco pouch.   [2] Spark.

This is a real Bothy Song, which no doubt describes a Glasgow incident of a time prior to the passing of the Forbes Mackenzie Act. It was sung all over the country in farm kitchens and at feeing markets some forty or fifty years ago.

WHEN THE DAY'S ON THE TURN.

THO' the house be couth and warm,
    And aye a blazing fire,
The lang nichts o' winter
    Mak's everybody tire;
Mak's every ane to tire,
    An' to fret an' to mourn,
And naething will content them
    Till the day be on the turn.

The milkmaid in the evening
    Gaes lichtly wi' her pail;
The cotter sits contented
    O'er the lingle o' his flail;
The guidwife she is fond to say,
    When scourin' oot the churn,
We'll a' get fouth o' butter
    When the day's on the turn.

A PLOUGHMAN LAD FOR ME.

WHERE first I saw my Jockie
  Was at Huntly[1] feeing fair,
Wi' his rosy cheeks and dimpled chin,
  And bonnie curly hair.
When he looked at me so slyly
  Wi' his bonnie e'en o' blue,
I found my heart from me depart
  To the lad that hauds the plough.

    So a ploughman lad for me,
    For he's aye so frank and free;
    At kirk or fair none can compare
    Wi' my ploughman lad so free.

The ploughman lad's a jolly lad,
  He spends his money free,
And when he meets a bonnie lass
  He tak's her on his knee.
He puts his arms around her neck,
  And prees her bonnie mou',
Wi' kisses sweet he does her treat,
  The lad that hauds the plough.

    So the ploughman lad for me,
    And there's nane so blythe as he,
    Though my minnie and dad should baith gang mad,
    A ploughman's bride I'll be.

So briskly every morning
  To the fields he does repair,
To plough and sow and reap and mow,
  It is his constant care,
While the feathered, warbling songsters
  Round him sing the whole day through.
Thus every day is passed so gay
  By the lad that hauds the plough.

    So the ploughman lad for me,
    For the blythe blink o' his e'e,
    It is bright, baith morn and night,
    A ploughman's bride I'll be.

I'm but a country servant lass,
  And have but little gear,
But I would not wed a lord nor duke
  Wi' ten thousand pounds a year.

Give me a humble country cot,
  Wi' plenty wark to do;
Wi' my heart's delight in my arms at night,
  Young Jock that hauds the plough.
    So a ploughman lad for me,
    And I hope, before I dee,
    To milk my cow while he hauds the plough,
    For a ploughman's bride I'll be.

1 When rendering the first verse the singer usually puts in the name of the
town in which he or she is best acquainted.

YE'RE NOO ON BOGIESIDE.

Assist me, all ye muses,
  For to compose a song,
'Tis of a tyrant farmer
  Near Gartly did belong;
An' while we were his servants
  Ofttimes to us he said—
" Come, drive them on some smarter,
  Ye're noo on Bogieside."

We did drive on his horses
  Till they were out o' breath;
They were fitter for the tannerie
  Than for to be in graith.
For want o' corn they did lie hard
  And he with us did chide,
And he swore we had neglected them
  Upon sweet Bogieside.

His father's growing auld now,
  And he gars him herd the sheep;
And by the names he ca's him,
  He mak's his mither weep.
Sic ugly names he ca's him,
  I couldna' weel abide,
And he a gallant farmer
  Upon sweet Bogieside.
    .   .   .   .   .

But gin that bonnie day were come,
  The twenty-saxt o' May,
We'll pit oor packs upon our backs,
  And we'll pad on our way.

WATTY'S WOOING.

WATTY Wylie was a grieve and served at Whinnyknowe,
And he had gien his promise to marry Bessie Lowe;
He hoxed her, and coaxed her, and vowed she was his dear—
He was to marry Bessie at the fa' o' the year:
  Siller's aye sae scarce then,
   An' things are a' sae dear,
  It's a kittle time to marry
   At the fa' o' the year.

The simmer wore awa, an' the hairst was gathered in,
To get her hoose a' plenished bonnie Bessie did begin;
Ae nicht in steppit Watty, he had jist come 'yont to speir
If she'd put aff the wadden to the spring o' the year:
  For siller's awfu' scarce,
   An' things are a' sae dear,
  I think we'd better wait
   Till the spring o' the year.

The spring sune slippit by, the fields were ploughed and sawn,
But glaikit Watty ne'er cam' near to offer Bess his han';
But sent a trustie cronie wi' a letter till his dear,
Spierin' gin she'd wait till the autumn o' the year:
  For siller's awfu' scarce,
   An' things are a' sae dear,
  I think we shouldna marry
   At this time o' the year.

Noo, Bessie she was wrathfu', as a jilted lass should be,
Quo' she, the fause, deceivin' loon will never marry me;
The next time he comes 'yont the gate I'll meet him wi' a
  sneer,
An' I'll get anither joe before the fa' o' the year:
  Tho' he be scant o' siller,
   I winna heed his gear,
  If I get a lad to lo'e me
   A' the days o' the year.

The chiel that brocht the letter, he was buirdly, he was braw,
An' Bessie's smiles an' Bessie's wiles clean stole his heart awa;
He pappit on his bended knees and loodly he did swear
He'd marry bonnie Bessie ony day o' the year:

Tho' siller's awfu' scarce,
    An' things are a' sae dear,
True love mak's peace an' plenty
    A' the days o' the year.

There's no a wife in a' the lan' like bonnie Bessie Lowe,
In Scotland there's nae sadder man than Wat o'
    Whinnyknowe;
The auld folks mock his wooin', the young anes joke an' jeer,
He vows he'll leave the fairm at the close o' the year:

    By trusting to a freen',
        He lost his Bessie dear,
    He'll ne'er coort ony mair,
        Tho' he lives a thousan' year.

This is a west country farm song. It was written in the early " seventies "
of the last century by William Penman who died in the Kinning Park
District of Glasgow in 1877, in the thirtieth year of his age. Born in the
country, " Rhyming Willie " as he was called, was brought by his parents
to Glasgow in early boyhood. Although he received part of his education
and spent his early manhood in Glasgow, city life never appealed to him.
He was a keen angler and spent all his leisure time either at trout-fishing
or rambling through the country.

TIPPERTY'S JEAN.

Air.—" The Laird o' Cockpen."

In a wee thacket hoosie, far doon i' the glen,
There lived a young lassie, the plague o' the men;
Sae dainty, sae genty, sae canty and keen,
The wale o' the parish was Tipperty's Jean.

The minister smiled till her braid o' the kirk,
The dominie winkit wi' mony a smirk,
An' douce lookin' elders on Saturday e'en
Could crack about naething but Tipperty's Jean.

Auld Lowrie, the laird, wi' his hat in his hand,
Says will ye tak' me wi' my siller an' land?
Mony thanks to ye, laird, but it's sinfu' gin ane
Sud marry their grandad, quo' Tipperty's Jean.

The doctor grew dowie and maist like to dee,
Sae wowf gat the lawyer he bade folks agree;
An' Rob o' the Milltown and Tam o' the Green
Maist tint their scant wits aboot Tipperty's Jean.

The lasses gaed wanderin' their lanes i' the loan,
The auld folks were girnin' wi' mony a groan;
The warld's seerly gyte, sirs, there's never been seen
Sic wark as they haud aboot Tipperty's Jean.

Nae dellin' was deen, nae thrashin', nae ploughin',
The wark a' gaed wrang, sae thrang war they wooin',
Sic ridin', sic racin', there never was seen,
The chiels were sae daft aboot Tipperty's Jean.

They happit aboot her like craws on a rig,
A' fechtin', or fleechin', or crackin' fell big;
Gae wa', sirs, to Freuchie, for brawly it's seen
It's siller yer wooin', quo' Tipperty's Jean.

Sin' auld Uncle Davie cam' back owre the sea,
And left sic a hantle o' siller to me,
I'm deaved wi' yer wooin', frae mornin' till e'en,
The deil tak' sic wooers, quo' Tipperty's Jean.

Oh, wae on the siller! it's turned me an' Johnny,
Though scanty o' wealth, yet he's kindly an' bonnie;
Gin he wad but seek me this very guid e'en,
He'd no tine his errand, quo' Tipperty's Jean.

Puir Johnny o'erheard her, his heart like to brack,
He cuist his arms aroun' her an' gaed her a smack:
Wull ye be my dawtie? she blinkit fu' keen,
Yer welcome to tak' me, quo' Tipperty's Jean.

An' there was a waddin', sic vivers and drinks,
Sic fiddlin' an' pipin', sic dancin' an' jinks;
The haggis e'en hotched to the piper it's lane,
It's a' weel that ends weel, quo' Tipperty's Jean.

The minister danced i' the barn wi' the bride;
The elders cried, Fiddlers play up " DELVIN SIDE ";
The dominie sang like a mavis at e'en:
Here's a health to guid lasses like Tipperty's Jean.

This fine song was written by Dr. Patrick Buchan, the eldest son of
Peter Buchan, the famous ballad collector. Dr. Buchan was born in 1814
and died in 1881.

LESCRAIGIE.

MEND up your peats, pretty Peggie,
    And gar a' your coals burn clear;
Put clean sheets to your bed, Peggie,
    For the fair-haired laddie will be here.

He winna lie in the kitchen,
    Neither will he in the ha',
But he'll lie in your bed, Peggie,
    And you in his airms twa.

For when ye come into the kitchen,
    Ye're happy among us a';
But when ye gang into the parlour,
    Ye lat the tears doonfa'.

I'm gaun to yon toon, Peggie,
    And will I the baker laddie tell?
Will I tell him to send you a letter,
    Or will he come himsel'?

O, haud ye your tongue, Sandy Fraser,
    And dinna ye taunt me;
For how could the baker laddie mind me
    When he kens I am promised to thee?

It's my back is sair, Sandy Fraser,
    And sair, sair is my side,
And I maun awa frae Lescraigie,
    For I'm nae langer able to bide.

Gin I had this sair hairst shorn,
    And a' wrocht that I've ta'en in hand,
I winna bide langer at Lescraigie,
    Nor yet into Fyvie's land.

Noo she's got that sair hairst shorn,
    That sair hairst that she'd ta'en in hand;
And noo she has marriet Sandy Fraser
    And awa wi' him she's gane.

Lescraigie is a farm in the parish of Fyvie, Aberdeenshire. The song
goes back to the time of the shearing-hook.

PART III.

Songs relating to
Soldiers, Sailors, War and Adventure

PART III.

Songs Relating to Soldiers, Sailors, War and Adventure.

———

"THE GALLANT NINETY-TWA."

BRAVE Ninety-Twa, I've read your story,
A valour tale of fadeless glory
   For brave auld Scotia braw.
Won by her mountain sons o' fame,
You've laurel-wreathed auld Scotland's name,
   Brave, gallant Ninety-Twa.

Reared 'mong these glens 'mid which I stand,
The brave, heroic Gordons grand,
  Wi' stern and dauntless front.
On mony a rude and bloody field,
Where thousands from their bayonets reeled,
  Bore fiercest battle's brunt.

True kilted heroes o' the North,
Weel may auld Scotia praise your worth,
  An' cheer your noble arms;
She lo'es her kilted sodgers a',
But nane mair than the Ninety-Twa,
  Her martial ardour warms.

Frae Maya's Pass an' dark Pyr'nees,
Your cheers cam' on the hameward breeze,
  To mony a Highland glen.
An' there around the auld peat fires
Your brithers brave and hoary sires,
  A' hardy, stalwart men,

Looked sternly up wi' pridefu' mien,
Ne'er shamed to claim you as their ain,
  When battle news cam' hame.
An' aft the reeky rafters rang
Wi' warlike pibroch, loud and lang,
  To cheer your martial fame.

The lads o' Avon an' the Spey,
O' Deveronside and Bogie gay,
  An' glens by Dee and Don,
Hae won your noble tartans braw,
And raised the Gordons' wild hurrah
  On fields right stoutly won.

Red Waterloo, beyond a' praise,
Your valour there burst to a blaze,
  In bayonet charges free,
An' when the Grey's, wi' warlike cry,
O' Scotland's name, went cheering by,
  You joined the wild melee.

The veteran Frenchmen, thousands deep,
Fled 'fore your charge like stricken sheep,
  Your bayonets redly shone,
While wild the grand auld pibroch blew,
The French retreat from Waterloo,
  An' British victory won.

Through dark Majuba's blunder sore
Ye bore your dauntless mien of yore,
   An' only bowed to death.
Had but the Boers braved your steel
They'd had another tale to tell,
   A tale o' wae and skaith.

March proudly on, brave Ninety-Twa,
The gallant Gordons, leal and braw,
   The bravest of the brave;
We know the record o' your fame,
An' lang may Scotland lo'e your name,
   An' you her honour prove.

Frae oor green glens fu' many a son
O' brave auld kilted Caledon
   'S gane forth to ne'er return.
An' while your famous deeds we hail,
Loud let the wailing pibroch tell
   For those who fell we mourn.

They fell amidst the bloody fray,
On many a fierce and fateful day,
   By ball and bayonet keen;
But 'midst these northern glens o' oors
We'll keep their fame thro' coming years
   Untarnished, fresh, an' green.

THE BATTLE OF BAROSSA.

ON the second day of February, from Cadiz we set sail,
Which many a gallant hero had reason to bewail;
And straight from Gibralter our gallant ship did steer,
And on the twenty-first, my boys, we landed at Algiers.

The next port we arrived at was called the Reef o' Bay,
And waiting for the Spaniards in a convent there we lay;
As soon as they arrived we marched both night and day,
Expecting soon our foes to meet to show them British play.

Our general he told to us the hardships we would bear,
Still hoping British heroes would conquer everywhere;
O'er hills and lofty mountains our army marched along,
Although our number it was small our courage it was strong.

Some watchful eye soon spied the foe, and to our general flew,
Which wounded sore his tender heart and tears of sorrow drew;
" Oh! cursèd is my fate," he cried, " upon this very day,
That Britain must deplore her fate, by Spaniards led astray."

Our gallant General Graham, not knowing their design,
Resolved that British heroes should not be left behind;
So we drew up into a wood, not knowing any snare,
Where the enemy in ambush lay, enclosing on our rear.

The Spaniards said they'd take the front their country for to
     free,
And let bold Britain take the rear, that glorious day to see;
But when Barossa's plains appeared, we never saw them more,
Their column drew behind a wood along some hidden shore.

" Wheel to the right about, brave boys, and give to them three
     cheers,
Extend your rifles in the front, keep aye the front rank clear,
And look into Trafalgar Bay where Nelson fought before,
When'er you hear the bugle sound, then Britons clear the shore."

Like lions we advancèd, our laurels for to gain,
Disdaining every danger though thousands there were slain;
Both fire and smoke convulsed the air, and thunder shook the
     sky,
But soon we closed upon their rear and caused the French to fly.

" Well done, brave boys," our general cries, " our number is but
     small,
But worse than that, it grieves my heart, to see our heroes fall."
Three generals left behind, their guns and eagles low;
But Britons cheered, and cheered again, and after did pursue.

The Ninety-Second and Eighty-First, they formed a hollow
     square
All in the dead-time o' the night to keep their wounded there,
To hear their sighs and mournful cries would grieve your hearts
     full sore,
But Britain still protects them along yon petrean shore.

Come, now, fill up a bumper, although it gives you pain,
And drink to those who nobly fought along Barossa's plain,
Likewise to every soldier who acted on the field,
Although we fought them four to one, we fought till they did
     yield.

Now we're returning home again, we'll make the alehouse ring,
We'll drink to them that we love best, likewise to George our
    King;
And may we ever guard our Isle, and plenty keep in store,
And we'll repay the wife, or lass, that welcomed us ashore.

THE MUIR OF CULLODEN.

I'LL sing of my country, its deep glens and fountains,
Its woods and its bowers, and its steep-rising mountains;
I'll sing of its battles renownèd in story,
That crownèd our sires with immortal glory:
    I'll sing of its battles renownèd in story,
    That crownèd our sires in immortal glory.

On the sixteenth of April, I'll ever remember,
The night it was dark, dark as December;
The moon showed its beams, something awful foreboding,
And lulled were the streams as they rolled by Culloden:
    The moon showed its beams, etc.

As we lay under arms our chiefs were debating;
Some thought they would fight, and some for retreating;
But Lochiel, and Lord Drummond, and young Lewis Gordon
Drew their swords and they swore they would die on Culloden:
    But Lochiel, Lord Drummond, and young Lewis Gordon, etc.

The war-pipes did play, and the fierce charge was sounding,
The high Highland hills with their echoes rebounding;
Had our whole clans but charged, the same as at Flodden,
The day would have been ours on the Muir of Culloden:
    Had our whole clans but charged, etc.

The Gordons, Macgregors, and the Macdonalds,
The Camerons, Macphersons, and the Clan Ronalds
Rushed fierce to the charge, while down thousands were trodden,
Determined to conquer or die at Culloden:
    Rushed fierce to the charge, etc.

Nae mair the pipes play Prince Charlie's a-coming;
Nae mair the hurrah, and the Southrons are running,
And now for our Prince every Scot's heart was throbbin',
And cauld lies our lads on the Muir of Culloden;
    And now for our Prince every Scot's heart was sobbin',
    Crying, " Cauld lies the the lads on the Muir of Culloden."

YOUNG JAMIE FOYERS.

KEY F. {:d .r | m :m :m | m .r :d :m .r | r .d :l :l, | l, :— }

{:l .t | d' :t :l | s .l :d' :t .l | l .s :m :r | m :— }

{:l .t | d' :t :l | s .l :d' :t .l | l .s :m :r | m :— }

{:m .l | l :s :l | m :r .d :t, .l, | t, :l, :t, | l, :— ‖

FAR distant, far distant, lies Scotia, the brave!
No tombstone memorial to hallow his grave;
His bones now lie scattered on the rude soil of Spain,
For young Jamie Foyers in battle was slain.

From the Perthshire Militia to serve in the line,
The brave Forty-Second we sailed for to join;
To Wellington's army we did volunteer,
Along with young Foyers that bold halberdier.

That night when we landed the bugle did sound,
The General gave orders to form on the ground,
To storm Burgos Castle before break of day,
And young Jamie Foyers to lead on the way.

But mounting the ladder for scaling the wall
By a shot from a French gun young Foyers did fall:
He leaned his right arm upon his left breast,
And young Jamie Foyers his comrades addressed:

" For you, Robert Percy, that stands a campaign,
If goodnes should send to auld Scotland again,
You will tell my old father, if yet his heart warms,
That young Jamie Foyers expired in your arms.

" But if a few moments in Campsie I were
My mother and sisters my sorrow would share;
Now, alas! my poor mother, for long may she mourn,
Her son, Jamie Foyers, will never return.

" Oh! if I had a drink of Baker Brown's well,
My thirst it would quench, and my fever would quell ";
But life's purple current was ebbing so fast,
And young Jamie Foyers soon breathed his last.

They took for his winding-sheet his ain tartan plaid,
And in the cold grave his body was laid;
With hearts full of sorrow they covered his clay,
And muttering " Poor Foyers!" marched slowly away.

His father and mother and sisters will mourn,
But Foyers, the brave hero, will never return;
His friends and his comrades lament for the brave
Since young Jamie Foyers is laid in his grave.

The bugle may sound and the war drum may rattle,
No more will they raise this young hero to battle;
He fell from the ladder like a hero so brave,
And rare Jamie Foyers is lying in his grave.

THE BONNET O' BLUE.

It was down in Greenwillow, a town in Yorkshire,
I lived in great splendour, and free from all care;
I lived in great splendour, had sweethearts not a few,
Till wounded by a bonnie boy and his bonnet o' blue.

There is come a troop of soldiers of whom you shall hear,
From Scotland to Kingston, abroad for to steer;
And there is one among them I wish I never knew,
He's a bonnie Scotch laddie, wears a bonnet o' blue.

His cheeks are like roses, his eyes are like sloes,
He is handsome and proper wherever he goes;
Likewise he's good natured and comely to view,
He's a bonnie Scotch laddie wi' his bonnet o' blue.

When I go to my bed I can find no rest,
The thought o' my laddie still runs in my breast;
The thought of my lover still runs in my view,
He's a bonnie Scotch lad, wears a bonnet o' blue.

It was early one morning I rose from my bed,
I called upon Sally, my own waiting maid,
To dress me as fine as her two hands would do,
For to go and see my lad and his bonnet o' blue.

I was instantly dressed, and quickly I came;
I stood with great patience to hear my love's name,
Charlie Stuart is his name, and I love him most true,
Once a prince of that name wore a bonnet o' blue.

When I came to the regiment they were on parade,
I stood with great pleasure to hear what was said,
His name's Charlie Stuart, and I love him most true,
He's a bonnie young lad wi' his bonnet o' blue.

My love he passed me wi' his gun in his hand,
I strove to speak to him, but a' was in vain;
I strove to speak to him but the faster he flew,
And my heart it went wi' him and his bonnet o' blue.

I said, "My dear laddie, I'll buy your discharge,
I will free you from the soldiers and set you at large;
I will free you from the army if your heart will be true,
And you'll never wear a stain on your bonnet so blue."

He said, "My dear lady, you would buy my discharge,
You would free me from the soldiers and set me at large;
You would free me from the army if my heart it was true,
But I'll never wear a stain on my bonnet so blue.

" I have a dear lassie in my ain countrie,
I would not forsake her for her povertie;
I would not forsake her for her heart it is true,
And I'll never wear a stain on my bonnet so blue."

I will send for a limner to London or Hull,
I'll have my love's picture, I'll have it in full,
And in my bed-chamber so closely I'll view
My bonnie Scotch lad and his bonnet o' blue.

THE HIGHLAND MAID.

Air.—" The Harp that once through Tara's Halls."

AGAIN the laverock seeks the sky,
    And warbles dimly seen;
And simmer views wi' sunny joy
    Her gowany robe o' green.
But, ah! the simmer's blythe return,
    In flowery pride array'd,
Nae mair can cheer this heart forlorn,
    Or charm the Highland Maid.

My true love fell by Charlie's side,
    Wi' mony a clansman dear,
That fatal day—oh, wae betide
    The cruel Southron's spear!
His bonnet blue is fallen now,
    And bluidy is the plaid
That aften on the mountain's brow
    Has wrapt his Highland Maid.

My father's shieling on the hill
    Is dowie now and sad;
The breezes whisper round me still,
    I've lost my Highland lad.
Upon Culloden's fatal heath
    He spake to me, they said,
And faltered wi' his dying breath,
    "Adieu, my Highland Maid."

The weary nicht for rest I seek,
    The langsome day I mourn;
The smile upon my withered cheek
    Can never mair return.
But soon beneath the sod I'll lie
    In yonder lonely glade;
Then haply some may weep an' sigh—
    "Adieu, sweet Highland Maid."

This is one of the most pathetic Jacobite songs. It was written by
William Blair, who was born in Dunfermline in 1880.

THE BANKS O' THE NILE.

HARK! hark! the drums do beat, my love, and I must haste
    away,
The bugles sweetly sound, and no longer can I stay;
We are called up to Portsmouth, many a lang, lang mile,
All for to be embarked for the Banks of the Nile.

Oh, Billy, dearest Billy, will you leave me here to mourn?
Will you leave me here to curse the day that ever I was born?
For the parting with my Billy is like parting with my life;
Oh, stay at home, my Billy—make me your lawful wife.

I'll put on my velveteens and go along with you,
I'll volunteer my services, and go to Egypt too;
I'll fight beneath your banner, love, kind fortune yet may smile,
And I'll be your loyal comrade on the Banks of the Nile.

Oh, no, my dearest Nancy, sure that will never do,
For Government has ordered no women there to go;
For Government has ordered—the King he doth command—
And I am bound on oath, my love, to serve on foreign land.

Your waist is rather slender, your complexion is too fine,
Your constitution is too weak to stand the hot campaign;
The sultry suns of Egypt your precious health would spoil,
And the hot sandy deserts on the banks of the Nile.

Oh, cursèd, cursèd be the day that e'er the wars began,
For they've ta'en out of Scotland many a pretty man;
They've ta'en from us our Lifeguards, protectors of our isle,
And their bodies feed the worms on the Banks of the Nile.

Let a hundred days be darkened, and let maidens give a sigh,
It would melt the very elements to hear the wounded cry;
Let a hundred days be brightened, and let maidens give a smile,
But remember Abercrombie on the Banks of the Nile.

The Abercrombie referred to in the last verse of this song was Sir Ralph
Abercrombie, K.B., a celebrated British General, born at Menstrie,
Clackmannanshire, in 1734. He commanded the expedition sent against the
French in Egypt in 1801. Early in March of that year he landed forces
·in the Bay of Aboukir. successfully encountering the troops that opposed
him. On the 21st of the same month the whole French army attacked his
lines, but were completely defeated.

Abercrombie, like the gallant Wolfe at Quebec, was mortally wounded at
the glad moment of victory, and died about a week after.

THE PLAINS OF WATERLOO.

On the sixteenth day of June, my boys,
  In Flanders, where we lay,
Our bugles did the alarm sound
  Before the break of day;
The British, Belgians, Brunswickers,
  And Hanoverians, too,
Marched forward on that morning
  For the plains of Waterloo.

By a forced march we did advance
  Till three that afternoon,
Each British heart with ardour burned
  To pull the tyrant down.
At Quatre Bras we met the French,
  Their form to us was new;
For in steel armour they were clad
  On the plains of Waterloo.

Between the hours of three and four
  The action did begin,
When many a one her husband lost,
  And mother lost her son;
Till orders from our general,
  And the plan we did pursue—
We retired in files for full six miles
  For the plains of Waterloo.

On the seventeenth both armies kept their ground,
  But scarce a shot was fired;
The French did boast of victory
  Because we had retired.
This noble act of generalship
  Them from their strongholds drew;
Then we'd some share by fighting fair
  On the plains of Waterloo.

On the eighteenth, in the morning,
  Both armies did advance,
On this side stood brave Albion's sons,
  On that the pride of France.
The fate of Europe in his hands,
  Each man his sabre drew,
And death or victory was the word
  On the plains of Waterloo.

Napoleon to his men did say,
    Before the fight began:
" My heroes, if we lose this day,
    Our nation is undone;
The Prussians we've already beat,
    We'll beat the British too,
And display victorious eagles
    On the plains of Waterloo."

But our brave hero Wellington
    To us no speech did make:
We were Peninsula heroes,
    And oft had made them quake;
At Vittoria, Salamanca,
    Tolouse, and Burgos too,
They beheld their former conquerors
    That day at Waterloo.

In bright array Britannia stood
    And viewed her sons that day;
Then to her much loved hero went,
    And thus to him did say:
" If you the wreath of laurel wrest
    From yon usurper's brow,
Through ages all you shall be called
    The Prince of Waterloo."

All on our right they did begin,
    Prince Jerome led the van,
With Imperial Guards and Cuirassiers,
    Thought none could them withstand:
But our British steel soon made them reel,
    Though our numbers were but few;
Prisoners we made, but more lay dead
    On the plains of Waterloo.

Next to our left their course they bent,
    With disappointed rage;
The Belgian line fought for a time,
    But it could not stand the charge;
Till Caledon took up the drone
    And loud her chanter blew,
Played Marshal Ney a new Strathspey
    To the tune of Waterloo.

The tune had not been half played out
  Till the French had danced their fill,
Twenty thousand of her bravest troops
  Upon the field lay still;
Ten thousand prisoners we had ta'en,
  With Imperial Eagles too,
And British victory was proclaimed
  On the plains of Waterloo.

Here's a health to our Prince Regent,
  And long may he govern;
Likewise the Duke of Wellington,
  That noble son of Erin.
Three years are added to our time,
  With pay and pension too;
And now we are recorded
  As " The Men of Waterloo."

Half-a-century ago a version of this ballad was sung in the Feeing Markets
of the North-east of Scotland, which finished up thus:—

    Here's a health to Queen Victoria,
      In peace lang may she reign;
    Likewise the Duke of Wellington,
      That noble son of Erin.
    For though he was a Tory knave,
      His courage aye was true,
    He displayed both skill and valor too
      That day at Waterloo.

THE BONNY BUNCH OF ROSES.

By the margin of the ocean
  One morning in the month of June,
The feathered warbling songsters
  Their notes so sweetly sang in tune;
There I spied a female,
  Seemingly in great grief and woe,
Conversing with young Bonaparte
  Concerning the bonny bunch of roses, O.

O then, said young Napoleon,
  And grasped his mother's hand,
Do, mother, pray have patience
  Until I'm able to command.

I will raise a terrible army,
  And through tremendous danger go,
And in spite of all the universe
  I will gain the bonny bunch of roses, O.

When first you saw great Bonaparte
  You fell upon your bended knee,
And asked your father's life of him,
  He granted it most manfully;
It was then he took an army,
  And over the frozen realms did go;
He said, I'll conquer Moscow,
  Then go to the bonny bunch of roses, O.

He took three hundred thousand men,
  And likewise kings to join the throng;
He was so well provided,
  Enough to sweep the world along;
But when he came to Moscow,
  Near overpowered by driven snow,
All Moscow was a-blazing,
  Then he lost the bonny bunch of roses, O.

Now, son, ne'er speak so venturesome,
  For England is the heart of oak;
England, Ireland, and Scotland,
  Their unity has ne'er been broke;
And, son, look at your father,
  In St. Helena his body lies low,
And you'll soon follow after,
  So beware of the bonny bunch of roses, O.

O, mother, adieu for ever,
  Now I'm on my dying bed;
Had I lived I might have been clever,
  But now I bow my youthful head;
But while our bones do moulder,
  And weeping willows o'er us grow,
The deeds of brave Napoleon
  Will sing the bonny bunch of roses, O.

Reprinted from an old "Broadside."

THE DAY OF WATERLOO.

Air.—" Scots Wha Hae Wi' Wallace Bled."

REVOLVING time has brought the day
That beams with glory's brightest ray,
In history's page or poet's lay—
    The day of Waterloo.

Each British heart with ardour burns
As this resplendent day returns,
While humbled France in secret mourns
    The day of Waterloo.

Then lift the brimful goblet high,
While rapture beams in every eye,
Let shouts of triumph rend the sky,
    In toast of Waterloo:

To all who can the honour claim,
From Wellington's immortal name
To the humblest son of martial fame
    Who fought at Waterloo.

Then fill the wine cup yet again,
But altered be the joyous strain,
To those the cup now silent drain
    Who fell at Waterloo.

Soft sigh ye breezes o'er the grave,
Where rest the relics of the brave,
And sweetest flowerets o'er them wave,
    Who sleep at Waterloo.

From their ensanguined, honoured bed
The olive rears its peaceful head,
Nursed by the sacred blood they shed
    At glorious Waterloo.

In freedom's sacred cause to die,
In victory's embrace to lie;
Who would not breathe his latest sigh,
    Like those at Waterloo?

A few years ago Mr. Jonathan Gauld, Edinburgh, sent to me for perusal a manuscript book of Scottish songs by different authors, which he had purchased at a second-hand bookstall in that city. The book bore the date 1816 on the cover. and 1817 at the end. In this book I found the above song, and a footnote set forth that it was written in 1817 by Lieutenant Skinner, of the 92nd Regiment (the Gordon Highlanders). The song is worthy of a place in any collection.

THE BONNIE LASS O' FYVIE.

GREEN grows the birks on sweet Ythanside,
   And low lies the bonnie Lewes o' Fyvie,
In Fyvie there's bonnie, in Fyvie there's braw,
   In Fyvie there's bonnie lasses mony.

There cam' a troop o' Irish Dragoons,
   And they were quartered in Fyvie;
And their captain's fa'en in love wi' a very pretty maid
   That was by a' ca'ed pretty Peggie.

"Come down the stairs, pretty Peggy," he said,
   "Come down the stairs, pretty Peggy;
Come down the stairs and comb back your yellow hair,
   Tak' fareweel o' your mammy and your daddie.

" I'll gie you ribbons for your bonnie, yellow hair,
   And I'll gie beads o' the amber;
I'll gie ye silken petticoats wi' flounces to the knee,
   If ye'll convoy me to my chamber."

" I hae got ribbons for my bonnie, yellow hair,
   An' I hae got beads o' the amber;
An' I hae got petticoats befitting my degree,
   An' I'd scorn to be seen in your chamber."

" What would your mammy think if she heard the guineas clink,
   And saw hautboys playin' before ye?
What would your mammy think if she heard the guineas clink,
   And kent ye had married a sodger?"

" Little would my mammy think though she heard the guineas
     clink,
   And saw hautboys playin' before me;
Little would she think though she heard the guineas clink,
   If I followed a sodger laddie."

" A single sodger's wife, love, ye'll never be,
   For ye'll be the captain's lady,
And I'll mak' my men stand wi' their hats in their hand
   And bow in the presence of Peggy.

"There's mony a bonnie lass between this and Inverness,
 An' there's mony a bonnie lass in the Gerry;
There's mony a bonnie lass in the Howe of Auchterless—
 But the flower o' them a's into Fyvie."

But the colonel he cried, "Come, mount, boys, mount!"
 The captain he cried, "Let us tarry,
Oh, gang nae awa this day yet or twa,
 Till we see if the bonnie lass will marry."

"I've gien you my answer, kind sir," she said,
 "And ye needna ask me any further;
I do not intend to go to a foreign land,
 And I'd scorn to follow a sodger."

Then out it spak' the drum-major's wife,
 "Oh, dear, but ye are saucy;
There's mony a bonnier lass than you
 Has followed a sodger laddie.

"But gin I were on my high horse set,
 And riding to Old England,
I would ne'er turn my horse head about
 For a' your Fyvie women."

Early next morning they a' marched away,
 And, O, but the captain was sorry;
But the drums they did beat by the bonnie Bog o' Gight,
 An' the band played "The Bonnie Lewes o' Fyvie."

The band it did play, and the troops marched away,
 Until they were far, far away from Fyvie,
But ay as they played, the captain he said,
 "Bonnie lassie, I'm gaun to leave you."

Lang, lang ere they wan to Auld Meldrum toon,
 They got their captain to carry;
And lang ere they wan to bonnie Aberdeen,
 They got their captain to bury.

He was ca'ed Captain Ward, and he died on the guard,
 He died for the love o' pretty Peggy,
And he said, "When I'm gone, you'll let it be known,
 That I died for the bonnie lass o' Fyvie."

THE ENNISKILLEN DRAGOON.

A BEAUTIFUL damsel of fame and renown,
A rich merchant's daughter of Monaghan town—
As she rode by the barracks this beautiful maid
Stopped her coach to see the dragoons on parade.

They were all dressed up neat like gentlemen's sons,
With bright, shining swords and carbine guns;
With silver mounted pistols she observed them full soon,
Because that she loved an Enniskillen dragoon.

Yon bright son of Mars who stands on the right,
Whose armour does shine like the bright stars of night;
Oh, William, dearest William, you've enlisted full soon,
To serve as a Royal Enniskillen Dragoon.

Oh, Flora, dearest Flora, your pardon I crave,
For now and for ever I am but a slave;
Your parents insult you both morning and noon,
For fear you should wed an Enniskillen Dragoon.

Oh, William, dearest William, do mind what you say,
For children their parents are bound to obey;
But when you leave Ireland they will soon change their tune,
And say, "The Lord be with your Enniskillen Dragoon."

Farewell, Enniskillen, farewell for a while,
And all round the borders of Erin's green isle;
And when the wars are over you'll return in full bloom,
And you'll be made welcome, Enniskillen Dragoon.

Now the wars are over, and William's returned at last,
Our regiment lay at Dublin, and William got a pass;
Next Sunday they were married, and William was the groom,
And now she enjoys her Enniskillen Dragoon.

This is another Irish song which has become very popular in Scotland.

THE RECRUITING SERGEANT.

As we were a-walking along the seaside,
Who did we meet but Sergeant M'Bride;
We determined to have a bit bathe in the tide,
    It was on a fine summer's morning.

As we were a-walking along the sea sand
Who did we meet but Corporal Brand,
And a little wee drummer called Arthur M'Dand,
   Going to the fair in the morning.

" It's now, my brave fellows, if you want to enlist,
It's five golden guineas I'll clap in your fist;
Besides, there's five shillings to kick up a dust
   As you go to the fair in the morning.

" It's then you will always go decent and clean,
While all other fellows go dirty and mean;
While all other fellows go dirty and mean,
   And sup their burgoo in the morning."

" Och, you need not be talking about your fine pay,
For all you have got is one shilling a day;
And, as for your debt, the drums pay your way
   As you march through the town in the morning.

" And you need not be talking about your fine clothes,
For you've just got the loan of them, as I do suppose;
And you dare not sell them in spite of your nose,
   Or you would get flogged in the morning."

" I'm blest," says the sergeant, " if I'll take more of that
From any coxcomb or cowfeeding brat,
And if you tip me any more of your chat
   I will run you through in the morning."

But before they had time to pull our their blades
Our whacking shillalahs came over their heads,
And we did teach them that we were the blades
   To dampen their rage in the morning.

As for the wee drummer, we diddled his pow,
And made a football of his rowdidedow;
And into the tide we did make him to row;
   Then we bade them a' good-morning.

This is another Bothy favourite which was brought to this country by the
Irish harvesters of a century ago.

IT FELL ABOUT THE MARTINMAS TIME.

It fell about the Martinmas time,
  When the snow lay on the Borders,
There cam' a troop o' soldiers here
  To tak' up their winter's quarters.

    To my right falal di reedle, al al de dal,
    To my right falal di riddle air-O.

They rode up and they rode down,
  And they rode owre the Borders,
And there they met a weel-faur'd maid
  And she was a farmer's daughter.

It's money we maun hae, fair maid,
  Oh, money we maun hae all, O;
Money frae me ye canna get,
  For I hae got none at all, O.

Money frae me ye canna get,
  For I'm but a poor man's wife, O;
My children live a little forby
  A very sober life, O.

Gin ye be but a poor man's wife,
  Oh, why go ye so rare, O,
Wi' rings upon your white fingers
  And garlands in your hair, O?

My husband is a gardener fine,
  That makes me go so rare, O,
Wi' rings upon my white fingers
  And garlands in my hair, O.

But they made her swear a solemn oath,
  Wi' the saut tear in her e'e, O,
That she wad call at their quarter-gates
  When no one did her see, O.

As she was walking up and down
  And thinking of her vow, O,
How she could these young men beguile
  And prove a maiden true, O.

She went to a barber's shop,
  To a barber's shop went she, O,
And she made him cut her bonnie yellow hair
  A little above her e'e, O.

She's gone to a tailor's shop,
  In men's clothing dressèd, O,
Wi' a pair of pistols by her side,
  And a very bonnie boy was she, O.

When she came to their quarter-gates,
  It's loud, loud did she call, O—
" There comes a troop o' soldiers here,
  And we maun hae quarters all, O."

The quarter-master he spoke out,
  And he gave her half-a-crown, O;
Says, " Tak' ye that, get lodgings for yoursel'
  For here there is nae room, O."

She drew nearer to the gates,
  And louder did she call, O—
" Room, ye, room, ye gentlemen,
  We maun hae lodgings all, O."

The quarter-master he spoke out,
  He gave her eighteen pence, O,
Says, " Go get lodgings for yoursel',
  This nicht there comes a wench, O."

She's taen the garters frae her legs,
  And the ribbons frae her hair, O;
And she's tied them to their gate-posts,
  For a token that she's been there, O.

She took a whistle from her side,
  She blew it loud and shrill, O—
" Ye are weel-willy o' your pence,
  But ye're nae for a maid at all, O."

But when they knew that it was her
  It's they wad have her in, O;
But she put the spurs to her horse's side
  And she went a maiden hame, O.

SWEET CALDER BURN: or BONNIE WOODHA'.

Doon by yon green bushes by Calder's clear stream,
Where I an' my Annie sae aften hae been,
The hours they flew past us, richt happy were we;
It was little she thocht that a soldier I'd be.

"Fare ye weel, Annie, for I maun away,
My country calls on me, so I must obey;
But if Heaven protects me until I return
I'll sport wi' my Annie by sweet Calder burn.

Here's to my auld father, his lips noo are cauld,
Likewise to my mither, she's noo getting auld;
When I was a wee thing an' played roun' her knee,
It was little she thocht that a soldier I'd be.

On the twentieth of August our regiment was lost,
And a shot frae our foes our lines came across,
I was struck on the forehead, the blood it ran doon,
I reel'd an' I stagger'd and fell to the groun'.

"Come here," cried the captain, "Come here with great speed,
I'm afraid by that bullet young Dinsmore is dead";
They poured out the water and brandy so free,
An' they turned me all over my wounds for to see.

If I had my Annie, she'd bind up my wounds,
One word from her sweet voice would soothe all the stounds,
Wi' God's will I'll get better, an' when I return
I will sport wi' my Annie near sweet Calder burn.

Aft-times when I weary I think o' lang syne,
When I was a collier and wrought in the mine,
An' the tears they do trickle an' doon they do fa',
Like the dew on the gowans at bonnie Woodha'.

Noo, freen's and relations, ye see what I've got
For gaun wi' the laddie that wears the red coat;
But I maun awa noo, an' dress mysel' braw,
To wed wi' young Dinsmore o' bonnie Woodha'.

THE SOLDIER MAID.

When I was a maid, at the age of sweet sixteen,
From my parents I did run away a soldier to become;
I 'listed in the army and a soldier I became,
And they learned me to play upon the rub-a-dub-a-dum.

    With my nice cap and feathers, if you only me had seen,
    You would have said and sworn that a young man I had been;
    With my gentle waist so slender, and my fingers long and
        small,
    I could play upon the rub-a-dub the best among them all.

Oh, many was the prank that I played on the field,
And many was the young man his love to me revealed;
And so boldly as I fought though only a wench,
And many a prank I have seen played upon the French.

My officers they favoured me; for fear I would be slain
They sent me back to England for to recruit again;
They sent me up to London to keep guard in the tower,
'Twas that I remained for many a day and hour.

Many a night in the guard-room I have lain,
I never was afraid to lie down with the men;
At the putting-off my clothes, I oft times gave a smile,
To think that I lay with soldier-men, and a maid all the while.

I had not been in London a year but only three,
When a beautiful young lady she fell in love with me;
'Twas then that I told her that I was a maid;
She went to my officer and my secret she betrayed.

My officers they sent for me to ask if it were true;
I told them that it was—what other could I do?
I told them that it was—with a smile to me they said,
" 'Tis a pity we should lose such a drummer as you've made.

" But for your gallant conduct at the seige of Valenciennes,
A bounty you shall get, my girl, and a pension from the King."
But should the war arise again, and the King in want of men,
I'll put on my regimentals and I'll fight for him again.

THE ARABY MAID.

Away on the wings of the wind she flies,
　Like a thing of life and light,
And she bounds beneath the eastern skies
　And the beauty of the eastern night.

Why so fast flies the bark through the ocean's foam,
　Why wings it so speedy a flight?
'Tis an Araby maid who hath left her home
　To fly with her Christian knight.

She hath left her sire and her native land,
　The land which from childhood she trod;
And hath sworn by the pledge of her beautiful hand
　To worship the Christian God.

Then away, away, oh swift be thy flight,
　It was death one moment's delay;
For behind there is many à blade gleaming bright,
　Then away, away, away.

They are safe in the land where love is divine,
　In the land of the free and the brave;
They have knelt at the foot of the holy shrine,
　Nought can sever them now but the grave.

THE BONNIE SHIP THE DIAMOND.

The Diamond is a ship, brave boys,
　For Davis Straits she's bound,
And the quay it is all garnished
　With pretty girls around.
Captain Gibbons gives command
　To sail the oceans high,
Where the sun it never sets, brave boys,
　Nor darkness dims the sky.

　　So be cheerful, my lads,
　　　Let your courage never fail,
　　While the bonnie ship the Diamond
　　　Goes a-fishing for the whale.

Along the quay at Aberdeen
  The girlies they do stand,
With their mantles all around them,
  And the salt tears running down.
Don't weep my pretty, fair maids,
  Though you be left behind;
For the rose will grow on Greenland's ice
  Before we change our mind.
    So be cheerful, etc

Oh, joyful will be the days
  When our Greenland lads come home;
For they are men of honour,
  Of bravery and renown.
They wear the trousers of the white,
  The jacket of the blue;
And when they come to Aberdeen
  They'll get sweethearts enew.
    So be cheerful, etc.

Oh, jovial will be the days
  When our Greenland lads come home;
For they are men of honour,
  Belonging to the town.
They'll make the cradles for to rock,
  The blankets for to wear;
And the girlies into Aberdeen
  Sing, " Hushie-ba, my dear."
    So be cheerful, etc.

Here's a health unto the Hercules,
  Another to the Jane,
Here's a health unto the Bon-Accord,
  The Diamond by her lane;
Here's a health unto the Bon Accord,
  The Diamond and her crew;
Here's a health unto each bonnie lass
  That's got a heart so true.

    So be cheerful, my lads,
      Let your courage never fail,
    While the bonnie ship the Diamond
      Goes a-fishing for the whale.

NAIRN RIVER BANKS.

It was in the merry month of June, delightful fresh and fair,
For fishing sport I rose in time to take the country air;
I was delighted for to hear the charming blackbird's song
When near to Nairn river banks I gently moved along.

Cheered with the warm summer sun I still kept on my walk,
When coming to a spreading tree I thought I heard some talk;
I turned me quickly round about to hear what words were said,
When in behind a bramble bush I spied a pretty maid.

Her fleecy flocks around her upon the grass they fed,
As she lay sore lamenting upon a primrose bed;
And as she issued forth her grief the little birds they sang
Upon a tree whose branches out o'er the river hang.

The reason of her grieving I understood quite plain,
The lad that gained her tender heart had now gone off to Spain;
'Twas three long years since he had gone, which grieved her
        heart full sore,
And aye she cried, " I fear my love, O, he'll return no more."

But as she thus was grieving there came a little boy
Who had a letter in his hand which turned her grief to joy;
She soon did know her lover's write, and opened it with speed,
And, thinking no one to be near, she thus began to read:

" Dear Kitty, from the coast of Spain this letter I have sent
With my dear wounded comrades that to Great Britain went;
I send you this to let you know that I'm alive and well,
And hope to see fair Scotland yet, but when I cannot tell.

" Each day and night we're in the fight our enemies to subdue,
And when the deadly bullets fly I often think of you,
And on the happy days we had among the grass so green,
By Nairn river's bonnie banks so happy we have been.

" Although I be far off from you, and here must take my lot,
I love you still, and always will, my dear, you're not forgot;
And though I trample o'er the dead, as oft times I must do,
Bright in my mind I still can find your image in my view.

"Grieve not for me, my darling love, though I far distant be,
I hope all danger to surpass and to return to thee;
And if kind Providence preserve, who guides the flying ball,
Tho' dangers rise I will be safe when thousands round me fall.

"Like brethren with the Spanish troops undaunted we advance,
While we with victory and success keep down the pride of
    France;
Long have we been engaged here, but never yet did yield,
While brave Lord Wellington and us could keep the bloody field.

"Like midges on a summer's day the French around us lie,
But with our British bayonets we'll make them fight or fly;
We'll make tnem fight or fly, he says, and drive them out of
    Spain,
That war may cease and bring us peace, and send us home again.

"Soon may that happy day arrive to make us both complete,
When near to Nairn river's banks in happiness we'll meet,
When we'll be joined in heart and hand as happy as before,
So loudly now the bugle sounds, and I can add no more."

This is a real Bothy Song, and one that would have delighted the heart of the late Robert Ford. Hitherto it appears to have escaped the notice of collectors, and has only been printed on broadsides, and sold at markets and fairs. It is a great favourite among country folks, and has been sung at harvest homes and merry meetings in the North of Scotland since the Peninsular War times, to which period it apparently belongs.

BILLY TAYLOR.

Billy Taylor, a brisk young sailor,
  Full of youth and beauty rare,
Well could he the mind discover
  Of a girlie that was fair.
    A th' day the ri dum dalderiddle.
    A the day the ri dum dee.

Four and twenty brisk young sailors,
  All to Billy's wedding dressed;
But before the bride was ready,
  Billy to the sea was pressed.

But the bride soon followed after,
  Under the name of Richard Carr,
Snow-white fingers, long and slender,
  A' clad o'er wi' pitch and tar.

A storm arose upon the ocean,
　She being there among the rest,
The wind blew off her silver buttons,
　Then appeared her snow-white breast.

Then the captain did behold her,
　Says, " What the world has brought you here?"
" It's for the sake of my true lover
　Whom you pressed the other year."

" If your true lover be on board,
　Come, pray tell to me his name ";
" Billy Taylor is my true lover,
　Whom you pressed from the Isle of Man."

" If Billy Taylor be your lover,
　He has proved to you untrue;
He's got married to another,
　Left you here alone to rue.

" If you rise early the next morning,
　Early by the break of day,
There you'll see young Billy Taylor
　Walking with his lady gay."

She rose early the next morning,
　Early by the break of day,
And there she spied young Billy Taylor
　Walking with his lady gay.

Sword and pistol she has ordered,
　They were brought at her command,
She has shot young Billy Taylor,
　Stabbed his wife at his right hand.

When the captain did behold her,
　And the deeds that she had done,
He has made her chief commander
　Over a ship and a hundred men.

　　A th' day the ri dum dalderiddle,
　　A the day the ri dum dee.

THE WHALERS' SONG.

Music by Mr. Jas. B. Allan, A.L.C.M., Glasgow.

KEY F (Lah is D). *Animato.*

AGAIN for Greenland we are bound,
　To leave you all behind,
With timbers firm, and hearts so warm
　We sail before the wind.

A blowing breeze came from the south,
　All sails all seemed asleep;
With three cheers more we leave the shore
　And float upon the deep.

We leave our sweethearts and our wives
　All weeping on the pier;
Cheer up, my dears, we'll soon return,
　'Tis only half a year!

With tarry dress we'll reach Stromness,
　We then shall go on shore;
With water less, and landsmen scarce,
　We soon shall take in more.

And now we've safely reached the ice,
　We soon shall crowd all sail;
Each boat well manned with a strong band
　For to pursue the whale.

Now dark and dreary grows the night,
　The stars begin to burn;
Our valiant crew, with hearts so true,
　Full ship we do return.

And now we're past the Orkney Isles,
　The pilot boat draws near;
We see our sweethearts and our wives
　All waiting on the pier.

And now in harbour safely moored,
  We next shall go on shore;
With plenty o' brass and a bonnie lass
  We'll make yon tavern roar.

To Greenland's frost we'll drink a toast,
  And those we love so dear;
And across the main to it again
  We'll take a trip next year.

In the "*Weekly Welcome*" of 27th March, 1908, I appealed to the readers for the words and music of some of the old whalers' songs which were so popular in Scotland half-a-century ago, and in response to my appeal several songs were sent in. The above song, which in my opinion was the best, was sent to me, together with a copy of the music, by a lady reader in Saltcoats. My correspondent informed me that she took down the song from the singing of an old gentleman whose grandmother used to sing it to him in his early childhood. The tune, which is a very pretty one, is identical with the one to which I heard the fisher girls sing the song in the seaport towns of North-eastern Scotland nearly forty years ago.

During the first sixty years of the last century whale-fishing was an important Scottish industry. One whaling vessel, *The Bonnie Ship the Diamond*, immortalised in song and story, sailed from Aberdeen; two or three whaling ships sailed from Fraserburgh; and a large fleet sailed from each of the ports of Dundee and Peterhead. The whalers left this country in the spring, and the voyage lasted about six months. The outward-bound vessels called at Stromness, took in water, and completed their crews from amongst the hardy Shetlanders.

I WILL SET MY SHIP IN ORDER.

I WILL set my ship in order,
  I will sail her upon the sea;
I'll sail far over yonder border
  To see if my lovie mind on me.

He sailed east and he sailed west,
  And he sailed far, far seeking lan',
Until he came to his true love's window,
  And rapped loudly and would be in.

"Oh, who is that at my bower-window,
  That raps so loudly and would be in?"
"It's I, it's I, your own true lover,
  Oh rise, oh rise, love, and let me in."

"It's few true lovers I have without,
  And as few lovers I have within;
Unless it be my true love, Johnnie,
  And I'm weel sure that ye're no him."

"Oh then, oh then, go and ask your father,
    And see if he'll let you marry me,
And if he says no, love, come back and tell me,
    For it's the last time I'll visit thee."

"My father's in his chamber writing,
    And setting down his merchandise;
And in his hand he holds a letter,
    And it speaks much to your dispraise."

"To my dispraise, love, to my dispraise?
    To my dispraise, love, how could it be?
For I never slighted nor yet denied you,
    Until this night ye've denied me.

"It's oh then, oh then, go and ask your mother,
    And see if she'll let you my bride be;
And if she denies then come back and tell me,
    And it will be the last time I'll trouble thee."

"My mother's in her chamber sleeping,
    And words of love she will not hear,
So ye may go, love, and court another,
    And whisper softly in her ear."

Then up she rose, put on her clothing,
    It was to let her true love in;
But ere she had the door unlocked
    His ship was sailing upon the main.

"Come back, come back, my true love, Johnnie,
    Come back, come back and speak to me."
"Oh, how can I come and speak wi' thee, love,
    When our ship is sailing upon the sea?

"The fish may fly, and the seas go dry,
    And the rocks may melt down wi' the sun;
The working men may forget their labour
    Before that I do return again."

She's turned herself right and round about,
    And she's flung herself into the sea,
Saying, "Farewell for aye, my true love, Johnnie,
    For ye'll never hae to come back to me."

YOUNG ALLAN.

A' THE young sailors o' merry Ardeen
    As they sat drinkin' wine,
They fell a-reesin' amang themsels
    At an unlucky time.

Some o' them reesed their horse, their horse,
    And some o' them reesed their hound;
But young Allan he reesed his bonnie new ship
    It cost him mony a pound.

Oot then spak' a little wee boy
    At the fit o' young Allan's knee—
" Ye lee, ye lee, young Allan," he said,
    " Sae loud as I hear ye lee.

" My father has a bonnie ship
    To-morrow it will sail wi' thee."
" What will the wager be, brave boys,
    What will the wager be?"

" Thirty pints o' guid red wine,
    And drunken it shall be;
There's no a ship in all the seas
    To-morrow will sail wi' me;

" Except the Duke o' Dermondee,
    Or the Rose o' Auchlingene,
The Black Snake o' the Leelangin—
    That three we winna tak' in."

They drank late, and they drank ear',
    And they drank Marsindene,
And they took farewell o' their ladies gay,
    And left their girls at hame.

They sailed up and they sailed doon,
    Through mony a stormy stream,
Till they saw the Duke o' the Dermondee,
    She sank and never was seen.

Young Allan he grat and he wrang his hands,
    And he didna ken hoo to dee;
For the winds blew loud, and the waves beat proud,
    And we'll a' be lost at sea.

" O, where will I get a bonnie boy
   To tak' my helm in hand,
Till I gang up to yon high topmast
   To look out for some dry land?

" He'll hae the ae half o' my gear,
   And the third part o' my lan',
And if we do get safe on shore,
   He'll wed my daughter Ann."

" Here am I, a bonnie wee boy,
   That'll tak' your helm in han',
Till ye gang up to yon high topmast
   To look out for some dry lan'.

" I'll hae the ae half o' your gear,
   And the third part o' your lan',
And if we do get safe on shore,
   I'll wed your daughter Ann."

" Come down, come down, my master dear,
   Ye see not what I see;
It's throch-and-through your bonnie new ship
   The green-wall seas do gae."

" Ye'll tak' four and twenty feather beds
   And busk the bonnie ship roun',
And ye'll tak' as much o' the canvas cloth
   As keep her safe and soun'.

" And where ye want an oaken spell,
   Ye'll beat the yellow gold in;
And where ye want an iron nail,
   Ye'll drive a silver pin."

They took four and twenty feather beds
   And buskit the bonnie ship roun',
And they took as much o' the canvas cloth
   As keepit her safe and soun'.

And where they wanted an oaken spell,
   They beat the yellow gold in;
And where they wanted an iron nail,
   They drove a silver pin.

The ship she hearkened to their voice,
　　To her helm answered she;
And she gane skippin' out owre the waves
　　As a bird gangs owre the lea.

The first kent shore that we cam' to
　　Was at the Rose o' Linn,
Wi' guns and swords they kept us out,
　　And they wadna let us in.

The next kent shore that we cam' to
　　Was bonnie Aberdeen;
Wi' dancin' and wi' harpin' loud,
　　They welcomed young Allan in.

The sailors they danced on the green
　　Wi' their new buckled sheen,
To see their bonnie ship back again
　　Through twenty ships and ane.

There were four and twenty bonnie ships,
　　They a' set sail frae hame,
But nane o' them cam' back again
　　But just young Allan his lane.

" Where is now the bonnie boy
　　That took my helm in han',
Till I went up yon high topmast
　　To look for some dry lan'?

" He'll hae the ae half o' my gear,
　　And the third part o' my lan',
And since we've now got safe on shore
　　He'll wed my daughter Ann."

" Here am I, the bonnie wee boy,
　　That took your helm in han',
Till ye gaed up yon high topmast
　　To look out for some dry lan'.

" I'll no hae the ae half o' your gear,
　　Nor the third part o' your lan';
But since we've now got safe on shore
　　I'll wed your daughter Ann."

THE DARK EYED-SAILOR.

KEY A. { .s₁ | d .,r :m .r .m :d .r | l₁ :— : .l₁,l₁ | d .,r :m :r d }

{| t₁ .l₁ :d :- .d | r .,s₁ :s₁ :f₁ .m₁ | l₁ .,t₁ :d :- .s₁,l₁ | t₁ .s₁ :m₁ .r₁ }

{ : .s₁,l₁ | d .,r :m .r :m ,r .d | t₁ :s₁ :l₁,s₁ .fe₁ | s₁ :— : . ||

THERE was a comely young lady fair,
She was walking out for to take the air,
She met a sailor down by the way,
So I paid attention, so I paid attention
   To hear what they would say.

Said William, "Lady, why roam alone?
The night is coming, and the day's near gone."
She said, while tears from her eyes did fall,
"It's a dark-eyed sailor, it's a dark-eyed sailor
   That's proving my downfall.

"'Tis three long years since he left the land,
I took a gold ring from off my hand;
We broke the token, here's part with me,
While the other's rolling, while the other's rolling
   At the bottom of the sea."

Said William, "Lady, drive him from your mind,
Some other sailor as good you'll find;
Love turns aside and soon cold does grow,
Like a winter's morning, like a winter's morning
   When lands are clothed with snow."

These words did Phœbe's fond heart inflame:
She said, "On me you shall play no game."
She drew a dagger, and then did cry—
"For my dark-eyed sailor, for my dark-eyed sailor
   A maid I'll live and die.

" His coal-black eyes and his curly hair,
His pleasing tongue did my heart ensnare;
Genteel he was, and no rake like you,
To advise a maiden, to advise a maiden
    To slight the jacket blue.

" But still," said Phœbe, " I'll ne'er disdain
A tarry sailor, but treat the same.
Go, drink his health, here's a piece of coin,
But my dark-eyed sailor, but my dark-eyed sailor
    Still claims this heart of mine."

Then half the ring did young William show;
She seemed distracted 'twixt joy and woe:
Says, " Welcome, William, I've got lands and gold,
For my dark-eyed sailor, for my dark-eyed sailor
    So manly, true, and bold."

Now in a village down by the sea
They're joined in wedlock, and well agree.
So, maids, be true when your love's away—
For a cloudy morning, for a cloudy morning
    Oft brings forth a pleasant day.

This favourite old ballad song has hitherto escaped the attention of the
ballad collector. The late Robert Ford informed me that he was unable to
recover a complete copy for his *Vagabond Songs and Ballads*. I have,
however, been more successful. A few weeks ago I appealed to the readers
of the *Weekly Welcome* for it, and I received copies which were almost
identical from each of Mrs. D. Gair, Newton of Arbirlot; Mrs. C. Binnie,
Carmyllie, Arbroath; and Mr. J Gauld, Edinburgh. Mr. J. B. Allan,
A.L.C.M., Glasgow, has noted down the music from the singing of one who
heard the song often sung in the Feeing Markets in the North of Scotland
between thirty and forty years ago, and has thus preserved a favourite tune
which would in all probability have been lost.

JACKY TAR.

Air.—" Jack Tar Hornpipe."

WHEN Jack had pulled the oar, and the boat had gone,
Left his lassie on the shore with her head hanging down,
The tears stood in her eyes, and her bosom heaving sighs,
Fareweel, my dear, she cries, with your trousers on.

Fareweel, said he, I go to sea, and you must stay behind,
But do not grieve, for while I live I ever will prove kind;
And when I come to land you must meet me on the strand,
And welcome Jacky Tar, with his trousers on.

Now peace is proclaimed, and the wars are all o'er,
The fleet is moor'd, and the sailors come ashore;
Now you may see her stand, with a glass in her hand,
To welcome Jack to land, with his trousers on.

While up on high she caught his eye with all her lovely charms,
Then quickly from aloft he came and took her in his arms;
Her hand he kindly pressed, as he held her round the waist;
And he kissed the bonnie lassie, with his trousers on.

O! where have you been since you left me?
Or what ills have you seen upon the raging sea?
I have mourned for your sake, till my heart was like to break,
For I thought I'd ne'er see Jack, with his trousers on.

And while you stayed I sigh'd and pray'd to Neptune and to
      Mars,
That they would prove kind and send you home from the wars:
And to my request they have pleased for to list,
And sent you home to my breast, with your trousers on.

I've sailed the seas for you to the Torrid Zone,
From the confines of Peru to Van Dieman's Land,
From the Bay of Baltimore to the coast of Labrador;
But now I'm safe on shore, with my trousers on.

I've faced the storms in many forms upon the raging main;
I've fought my foes with deadly blows, and many a hero slain;
I've heard the cannons roar, I've been rolled in blood and gore;
But now I'm safe on shore, with my trousers on.

I've been aloft when the winds they have blown,
And I've been aloft when the bombs were thrown;
But, like a sailor bold, I've now come from the hold
With my pockets full of gold and my trousers on.

And now no more from shore to shore I'll plough the raging
      seas,
But from the strife, as man and wife, we'll live in peace and
      ease.
To the church this couple hied, and the priest the knot has tied,
And the sailor kissed his bride, with his trousers on.

DICKY JOHNSTON; OR, THE ROVING SAILOR.

I AM a man of a roving mind,
 And oft-times cross'd the ocean,
And many a battle I've been in
 For honour and promotion.
Oh, many a battle I've been in,
 Some have been lost and some were won;
But now in jollity and fun,
 I am a roving sailor.

Oh, I will go no more to sea,
 My life would have no ransom;
But here on shore I'll range about
 And speak to girls that are handsome.
Oh, brother sailors, I'll here remain,
 Nor tempt the raging seas again;
But serve on shore in Venus' train
 And be a roving sailor.

For by the wars I've lost a limb,
 My name is Dicky Johnston;
And I've got leave from Venus Queen
 To court the girls that are handsome.
With my soft words and flattering tongue
 I'll court the girls both old and young;
I'll court them all, and marry none,
 And I'll still be a roving sailor.

This is a good specimen of the songs that were sung in the markets and Fairs throughout Scotland sixty years ago.

THE BRISK YOUNG SAILOR.

A LADY in her garden walking,
 A brisk young sailor cam' owre the lea,
And for to woo her he stepped up to her
 And said, " Fair maid, would you fancy me?"

" I'm not a maiden to woo nor marry,
 Nor yet a servant girl to fee;
I'm but a poor forsaken lover,
 Which makes the young men all scoff at me.

" It's seven years since I loved a sailor,
   And six of them since I did him see;
But other seven I'll wait upon him,
   An' he'll come back and marry me."

" I wonder how you could love a sailor,
   I wonder how you could love a slave;
For he may be married, or he may be drownèd,
   The wide ocean may have become his grave."

" If he be married I wish him pleasure;
   If he be drownèd I wish him rest;
But for his sake I will never marry,
   The reason why—'cause I loved him best."

" Oh, don't you see yon high castle,
   And how it glitters in the sun?
Will you forsake your poor single sailor,
   And come along with me and dine?"

" Oh, yes, I see yon high, high castle,
   And how it glitters in the sun;
But I'd rather drink one cup of water
   With my poor sailor when he comes home."

" Oh, what if I be your single sailor?
   Oh, what if I be the man you love?"
" Pull out the ring that was broke between us,
   And when I see it I will believe."

He put his hand into his pocket,
   His fingers they being long and small,
Pulled out the ring that was broke between them;
   And when she saw it she down did fall.

He took her up into his arms,
   And says, " My dear, you are none the worse,
For I have gained as much gold and silver,
   The raging ocean I'll no more cross."

And now this couple they've got married
   And she's become the young sailor's wife;
And now they live into London city,
   A happy couple, man and wife.

M

MY BONNIE SAILOR BOY.

IT's of a brisk young sailor lad,
    And he apprentice bound;
And she a merchant's daughter
    With fifty thousand pound.
They lov'd each other dearly,
    In sorrow and in joy;
Let him go where he will, he's my love still,
    He's my bonnie sailor boy.

'Twas in my father's garden,
    Beneath the willow tree,
He took me up all in his arms
    And kissed me tenderly.
Upon the ground we both sat down
    And talked of love and joy;
Let him say what he will, he's my love still,
    He's my bonnie sailor boy.

Her father he being near her,
    And heard what she did say,
He cried, "Unruly daughter,
    I'll send him far away;
On board a ship I'll have him pressed,
    I'll rob you of your joy";
Send him where ye will, he's my love still,
    He's my bonnie sailor boy.

A variant of this song appears in *Folk Song from Somerset* under the title of " The Handsome Lighter Boy."

THE LOWLANDS OF HOLLAND.
(SCOTTISH VERSION.)

THE lad that I had chosen
    Was to my heart's content,
The saut sea shall be frozen
    Before that I repent;
Repent me will I never,
    Until the day I dee,
Though the Lowlands o' Holland
    Hae twined my love and me.

My love lies on the saut sea,
   And I am on the side,
Enough to break a young thing's heart,
   Wha lately was a bride;
Wha lately was a bonnie bride,
   Wi' pleasure in her e'e,
But the Lowlands o' Holland
   Hae twined my love and me.

My love he built a bonnie ship,
   And set her on the sea,
Wi' seven score brave mariners
   To bear her companie;
Three score gaed to the bottom
   And three score died at sea,
And the Lowlands o' Holland
   Hae twined my love and me.

My love he built anither ship,
   And set her on the main:
He had but twenty mariners
   In a' to bring her hame.
But the weary wind began to rise,
   And the ship began to rout;
My love then and his bonnie ship
   Turned widdershins[1] about.

There shall nae coif come on my head,
   Nae kame come in my hair;
There will neither coal nor candle licht
   Shine in my bower nae mair;
Nor shall I hae anither love
   Until the day I dee;
I never loved a lad but ane,
   And he was drowned at sea.

O haud your tongue, my daughter dear,
   Be still, and be content;
There are mair lads in Galloway,
   Ye needna sair lament.
Oh! there is nane in Galloway,
   There's nane at a' for me,
For I never lo'ed a lad but ane,
   And he's drowned in the sea.

[1] In a direction contrary to the sun.

THE LOWLANDS OF HOLLAND.

(ENGLISH VERSION.)

THE first night I was married and laid in marriage-bed
There came a young sea captain and stood at my bedhead,
Saying—" Rise up, rise up, young Riley, and go along with me
To the Lowlands of Holland to fight and never flee."

" 'Tis but a day and half a night since I have wedded been;
How shall I go along with you and this my bridal e'en?
How shall I leave my bonnie bride a hagbut man to be
On the Lowlands of Holland to fight and never flee?"

" The maids of Germanie are kind and lavish of their love,
Their lips are like the rose in May; their eyes are of the dove;
And well they love young Englishmen who roam along with me
On the Lowlands of Holland to fight and never flee."

" Oh, tell me not of other maids, and this my bridal night;
'Twould break my heart to leave my love, my joy, my heart's
          delight;
Then kind and courteous captain, take some single man with
          thee
To the Lowlands of Holland to fight and never flee."

" My ship is in the harbour with her anchor at the prow,
And down the Humber comes the gale, I hear it piping now:
I may not go for other men to sail along with me
On the Lowlands of Holland to fight and never flee."

Then up and spake the bonnie bride in bed where that she lay—
" Oh, kind and courteous captain, do not press my love away;
Five hundred crowns to thee I'll give in gold and white monie
From the weary wars in Holland to set my husband free."

" It may not be, it cannot be," the cruel captain said.
" Were I to take a bribe from thee 'tis I would lose my head;
Our King must have brave warriors to send beyond the sea
On the Lowlands of Holland to fight and never flee."

Then up spake the bride's brother—" I have no kith nor kin,
Save yonder new-made wife that lies her bridal bed within;
Then I will go along with you, since better may not be,
On the Lowlands of Holland to fight and never flee."

"It may not be, it cannot be," the cruel captain cried;
"Full long I wooed sweet Marjorie, who still my suit denied.
I swore that she should rue the day she gave the scorn to me,
When the weary wars of Holland took her lover o'er the sea."

"Now draw thy sword, thou coward loon, and dearly thou shall
  rue."
"Upon them lads," the captain cried, "and bind the gallants
  two;
The play is played; our bonnie bark shall bear them o'er the sea,
On the Lowlands of Holland to fight and never flee."

THE ROCKS OF GIBRALTER.

THE first night I was married
 My sorrows did begin,
I being a widow's daughter,
 And loved a captain's son;
But now he's gone and left me,
 And ne'er return will he,
For the rocks of Gibralter lie
 Between my love and me.

The first night I was married,
 Laid on my marriage-bed,
There came a bold sea captain,
 Stood up at my bedside;
Says, Rise, arise young married man,
 And come along with me,
To the Rocks of Gibralter
 And face your enemy.

Oh, Holland it's a bonnie place,
 And bonnie lads are there;
The gates are all thrown open
 To welcome strangers in;
Of sugar-cane there's plenty,
 And fruit grows on the tree;
But the Rocks of Gibralter lie
 Between my love and me.

My father built a bonnie barque,
    And set her on the main,
With four and twenty mariners
    To bring her back again;
But the gallant ship struck on a rock
    The wind blew from the shore,
And we never saw the bonnie ship
    Nor my true-lover more.

My mother says unto me,
    What makes you to complain?
There's plenty other young men
    Can ease you o' your pain.
Oh yes, oh yes, there's plenty
    But none a match for me;
Since the Rocks of Gibralter lie
    Between my love and me.

There shall no coat go on my back,
    Nor comb go in my hair,
There'll neither coal nor candle light
    Shine in my chamber mair;
I'll never love another man
    Until the day I dee,
For the rocks of Gibralter
    Hae ta'en my love frae me.

SCARBOROUGH'S BANKS.

On Scarborough's banks a young damsel did dwell,
She loved a young sailor, she loved him right well;
He promised for to marry her when he did return,
But mark what misfortune there has him befallen.

As they were a-sailing, a-sailing on the sea,
Storms did arise and with them did not agree;
The moon was overclouded, and dreadful was the skies,
Which made these poor sailors to swim for their lives.

As they were a-swimming, a-swimming for their lives,
Some of them were young men, and some of them had wives:
But this poor unfortunate young man he happened to go down,
And, instead of getting married, he found a watery tomb.

As soon as the news came to Scarborough's shore,
She fell a-wringing of her hands and a-tearing of her hair;
Cries, " Oh, you cruel billows, cast my true love ashore,
So that I may kiss his pale lips once more."

As she was a-walking round Robin Hood's Bay,
She spied a drowned sailor, upon the sands he lay;
She stepped up to him, and amazed she did stand,
For she knew it was her own true love by the marks on his
        hand.

Now since I have found you your death I will deplore,
Now since I have found you, the lad whom I adore,
Both happy and contented I will lie down by your side,
So she kissed his cold lips, broken-hearted she died.

In Scarborough's churchyard this couple they were laid,
And written on their tombstone a warning was which said—
Come all ye pretty, fair maids, a warning take by me,
And never let your true love sail upon the raging sea.

This is an English folk-song which has found its way to the North-east of
Scotland, where it has been a great favourite for the past sixty years.

THE MERMAID.

On Friday night when we set sail,
    And our ship not far from land,
We there did espy a fair maid
    With a comb and a glass in her hand.

Chorus.

While the raging seas did roar,
    And the stormy winds did blow,
And we jolly sailor boys were up, up aloft,
    And the land lubbers lying down below, below, below,
    And the land lubbers lying down below.

Then spoke the captain of our gallant ship,
    Who at once did our peril see,
" I have married a wife into fair London town,
    And this night she a widow will be."
    Chorus.

Then us spoke the little cabin boy,
  And a fair-haired boy was he,
" I've a father and mother in fair Portsmouth town,
  And this night they will weep for me."
      Chorus.

Then three times round went our gallant ship,
  And three times round went she;
And three times round went our gallant ship,
  Then she sank to the bottom of the sea.
      Chorus.

This song is founded on two superstitions; first, that it is unlucky to put
to sea on a Friday, and second, that if a mermaid is seen by a sailor, he
and all with him are sure to be drowned. The song is very old and there
are several versions of it. There was an entirely different version sung by
the sea-faring folks of Macduff when I was living there upwards of forty
years ago, but I only remember one verse which was as follows:—

      The mermaid stands on the top of the cliff,
        With a bottle and a glass in her hand,
      Drink about, drink about, my brave sailor lads,
        For you'll never more see dry land.

PART IV.

(a) Songs of Home and Country
(b) Laments, Farewells, and Parting Songs.
(c) Convivial Songs

PART IV.

(a) Songs of Home and Country.

QUEEN VICTORIA'S WELCOME TO DEESIDE.

Air.—" The Lass o' Glenshee."

YE hills and ye mountains surrounding Balmoral,
  Ye groves and ye valleys, ye surely can tell,
Frae the mouth of the Dee to the fam'd Ballochbui,
  Where cannons and pibrochs made a' the woods yell?

The eighth of September will ne'er be forgotten,
  A merrier day we never hae seen,
We ran and we jumpit ower moorlands and mosses
  To bonnie Aboyne to welcome the Queen.

The Queen and her Consort and three bonnie bairnies
  Arrived at twelve on Charlestons' Green;
The blackbirds were singin', the church bells were ringin',
  The minstrels o' Tarland played " God save the Queen."

All in a sudden the royal coach started,
  Wi' four bonnie steeds 'maist the colour o' cream;
Though the Queen was a stranger, she was in nae danger,
  They a' wished her weel to her ain Hieland hame.

Lang! lang may she reign as the Queen o' our nation,
  Wi' health and contentment and wealth at her call;
Lang may she be spared to comfort her children,
  And spouse to Prince Albert, the Laird o' Birkhall.

IN PRAISE O' HUNTLY.

I'VE been abroad, I've been at hame,
An' mony's the footstep I hae gane;
Been at school ye weel ken that,
  But noo I've come to Huntly.

With Mr. Stephen I did agree
To work to him for meat and fee,
And win my breid richt honestly,
  Like others in the country.

But just as sure's the sun goes roun',
I fell in love wi' the girls o' the toon,
An' they ca'd me a clever loon,
  And bade me stay in Huntly.

The lasses a' were fond o' me,
I sang to haud them aye in glee,
But the ne'er a sang had I to gie
  But aye the praise o' Huntly.

Mrs. Stephen did me advise
To rove nae mair but to be wise,
And mak' my father's house my choice,
  And leave the toon o' Huntly.

But I tell't her that wadna dee,
My parents wadna look on me,
Which causes me to tak' a fee
  Near by the toon o' Huntly.

But the term cam' an' I was free,
I stepped about at liberty;
I gaed down by the back o' Bennachie
  To see the Buchan gentry.

I stepped about at liberty
Till Jock o' Rhynie fell in wi' me;
He speired if I wad tak' a fee
  And leave the Buchan gentry.

He said on me he'd not impose,
If I wad work but a pair o' horse,
An' stay aside the Tap o' Noth,
  As others in the country.

I'm no a child nor yet a bairn,
An' what I want I mean to learn;
I'll haud your ploo and saw your corn
    Wi' ony in your country.

When my parents saw I did engage,
At me they were in a great rage,
My clothing they kept for a pledge;
    Sent me awa quite empty.

But when they saw that I was gone,
And knew not whether I'd dee or drown,
My clothing after me came down,
    But sore they were to hunt me.

But, stop, an' I'll tell you ere a' be deen,
I'll be mair wiser than I hae been,
I'll read my Bible, and hain my sheen[1],
    An' gang nae mair on the country.

[1] Shoes.

THE HOWES O' KING-EDWARD.

Though lovely the land where in childhood I wandered,
    Though green are her valleys and clear are her streams,
Though the meadows and groves where I often have pondered
    Be fresh as they bloom'd in my young sunny dreams;
Though rich in the verdant profusion of nature
    The scenes of my first recollections I see,
Yet ah! there's a gloom overhangs every feature,
    And darkens the Howes o' King-Edward to me.

The path by the burn now grows green and neglected,
    The once social haunts of my bright schoolboy days;
But where are the comrades who there were collected,
    Companions and friends of my class or my plays?
Ah! some are far hence, distant oceans dividing,
    There's some with the soldiers, and some on the sea,
And some in the homeland, far scattered residing,
    That once made King-Edward so charming to me.

And yonder's the den where the birk and the thorn,
  The hazel, the brier, and the primroses grow;
And yonder the kirk, to antiquity worn,
  Scarce seen on the slope of the green sunny knowe;
And round its old walls, in their last mouldering slumbers,
  From toil and oppression for ever set free,
I sigh as I gaze on the ashes of numbers
  That once made King-Edward so cheering to me.

'Tis here, 'mong the wreck of unknown generations,
  Reposes the teacher I loved and revered;
The friends of my youth, and my aged relations
  That watched o'er my childhood with tenderest care.
Each voice I can hear in the soft passing breezes;
  Their forms seem to haunt every grave that I see;
But ah! they are not—and each fond feeling freezes,
  And cold seem the Howes o' King-Edward to me.

I turn to the spot of my youth's habitation,
  The home of my childhood—ah! where is it now?
The ploughshare has pass'd through its humble foundation,
  And nothing remains but the bare beaten knowe.
I wander a stranger where once my young notion
  Deemed no spot on earth half so lovely could be;
The dream of my fancy—my youth's fond devotion—
  O, changed are the Howes o' King-Edward to me!

A few scattered friends of my childhood may gladden
  And welcome me yet to my own native plains,
But scenes of the past come the present to sadden,
  Our losses or crosses, our cares or our pains,
Our earliest pleasures, our fond recollections,
  Our tender attachments and wild infant glee;
Compar'd with the present, how dark the reflection,
  And dull seem the Howes o' King-Edward to me!

William Cruickshanks, the author of the above verses, was born at Bauds of Montbletton, in the parish of Gamrie. His father, a gardener, died when the author was three years old. At seven he was removed to Mill of Fishery, King-Edward, where he was sent to school for three years. When ten, he went to farm service. At the age of twenty-four, he resolved to learn the business of a mole-catcher. While pursuing this vocation, he travelled through much of Scotland and England, thereby affording him opportunities of studying men and manners. Having finished his apprenticeship, he commenced business in Ellon; thence he removed to Bogbrae, Cruden, where he remained four years, and latterly to Kinknockie, Old Deer, at which place he resided until the time of his death. On Tuesday, 7th July, 1868, he was suddenly taken ill near Auchoch, Brucklay; and on the following morning he died.

BONNIE UDNY.

O Udny, bonnie Udny,
   At present adieu;
Wherever I wander
   I'll still think on you.

O'er hills and through valleys
   How often I've gone,
Through brambles and brushwood,
   Myself all alone.

Through hedges and ditches,
   On dark nights and clear,
I've wandered to Udny
   To meet with my dear.

It is not the journey
   That I have to go,
It is not the long road
   That vexes me so:

'Tis the leaving of Udny
   And loved ones behind;
O Udny, bonnie Udny,
   Ye're aye in my mind.

O Udny, bonnie Udny,
   Unnumbered thy charms,
The longer I see you
   The more my heart warms.

Let me back to Udny
   And her that loves me,
And I'll never forget them
   Until that I dee.

The young men from Udny
   Are all rovin' blades,
And they take great pleasure
   In courtin' fair maids:

They kiss them and clap them,
   And spend money free;
Of all gates in Scotland,
   Bonnie Udny for me.

We'll drink and be merry, lads,
    We'll drink and gae hame;
If we stay ony langer
    We'll get a bad name:

We'll get a bad names, boys,
    And fill ourselves fou;
And the lang walks o' Udny
    They're a' to gang through.

THE HIGH ROCKS O' PENNAN.

CAULD blaws the wind o'er the high rocks o' Pennan,
    And deeply does murmer the white foaming sea,
That clearly does indicate winter is coming,
    And cauld is the winter it will be to me.

My Jamie's awa, my bonnie Scots callan',
    And his bonnie face nae mair I will see;
He's bound for America, owre the sea sailin',
    And left his dear native to winter and me.

Sair, sair was my heart to part wi' my laddie,
    For blythesome an joyous wi' him I hae been,
When herdin' together we waukit the plaidie,
    And licht as the lammies we skipt owre the green.

But now he is gone, and lonely he's left me,
    While I sit and sigh wi' the tear in my e'e;
Nae mair to his fond beating bosom he'll press me,
    Nae mair sweet kisses will he gie to me.

Nae mair will we herd the yowies thegither,
    Nae mair will we range the forest sae wide;
Nae mair will he pu' the bonnie blaeberries,
    And treat me wi' them while he sat by my side.

Nae mair will we climb up yon high healthy mountain
    To see that our flocks be free frae a' skaith;
Nae mair will we sit by the side o' yon fountain
    Sae close that ae plaidie aft happit us baith.

Sair, sair was my heart the day that my Jamie
    First tauld me he meant to cross the wide main;
Sair, sair did I urge him never to leave me,
    But stay here content in our ain native glen.

" Fain wad I obey," he said, " my dear lassie,
   But here we can mak' naething ava;
Frae mornin' till nicht we toil without ceasin'—
   The lairds and the taxes they still need it a'."

" The minister tells us," I said, " my dear laddie,
   And he is a man that I'm sure winna lee,
Oor laws are sae just, sae wholesome and easy,
   Nae nation on earth are sae happy as we."

" The minister is guid, we shanna dispute it,
   But that is a subject he weel may lat be;
Oor laws are severe, there's nae ane can doot it,
   And mony a ane grudges them as weel's me.

" For if we shoot but a hare or a muircock,
   Or mak' but a bushel or twa o' oor bere,
The gauger or gamekeeper they come to hear o't,
   There's on wi' a vengeance ye then may be seer.

" And then we are dragged to courts they call justice,
   But justice I'm sure is foreign to them;
For judge hoo they like, they're aye in the richt o't,
   The puir man aye maun be put in the blame.

" But I will awa to that blest land o' freedom,
   Where honest industry does meet its reward,
And what we can mak' we will aye get the guid o't,
   And nae mair be pestered wi' taxes and laird.

" I'll get a bit land, and I'll big a bit hoosie,
   To get a bit bield to my lassie and me;
And syne I'll come back and ye shall gae wi' me,
   And never till death we pairted will be.

" Sae dinna thing lang," he says, " my dear cratur,
   But min' o' the joys we will hae when we meet;
We'll gang to Mess John, and he'll link us thegither,
   And we'll seal the bargain wi' kisses sae sweet.

" Wi' freedom and liberty, peace and contentment,
   Oor lives will glide past like a smooth rinnin' stream;
Nae ill will molest you, if I can prevent it,
   Ye aye may depend upon me as a frien'."

BONNIE JEANIE SHAW.

I'M far awa frae Scotland,
  Nae lovin' voice is near,
I'm far frae a' my ain folk,
  The anes I lo'e sae dear;
But I'll leave this foreign land,
  Wi' its sights and scenes sae braw,
And I'll wander hame to Scotland,
  An' my bonnie Jeanie Shaw.

Chorus.

Gie me back the days
On the flow'ry Cathkin braes,
An' the bonnie lass
I lo'e the best o' a';
I would cross the ocean wide
Just to wander by the Clyde,
In the gloamin'
Wi' my bonnie Jeanie Shaw.

The auld hoose an' the auld folk
  Are ever in my view,
The burnie rinnin' merrily,
  I seem to see it noo;
But I miss the purple heather
  That blooms sae far awa',
An' I miss the loved ane o' my he'rt,
  My bonnie Jeanie Shaw.
    Chorus.

I dinna see the thistle,
  The wild deer on the hills;
I dinna hear the mavis,
  Its singing fairly fills
This he'rt o' mine wi' joy,
  So I'll up and gang awa
To my hame in dear auld Scotland
  An' my bonnie Jeanie Shaw.
    Chorus.

Words by Alexander Melville. Printed by permission of Messrs. Bayley & Ferguson, Music Sellers, 54 Queen Street, Glasgow.

THE TOWN O' ARBROATH.

ALTHOUGH far awa frae my ain native heather,
 And thousands o' miles across the blue sea,
At night, when I'm weary, my mind likes to wander
 To scenes of my childhood sae dear unto me.
The town o' Arbroath is my hame and my birth-place,
 It was there when at school wi' the rest o' the boys,
When lessons were over, we played to the gloamin',
 It was there that I tasted my life's sweetest joys.

　　Then here's to the sons o' the dear auld St. Thomas,
　　 The lasses sae comely, sae frank and sae free,
　　The auld Abbey ruins, the cliffs, and the commons,
　　 The town o' Arbroath will be aye dear to me.

It was here that my father and my mother baith taught me
 To act fair and honest, to be kindly and free,
And ne'er to forget that there's an eye aye abune me
 To watch o'er my actions where'er I may be. ·
It was there that I courted my ain bonnie Mary,
 Her cheek like the rose and her skin like the snow,
I proposed, she consented, wi' a kiss then we sealed it,
 A-down Seaton's den where the burnie doth flow.
　　Then here's to the sons, etc.

I've lived like an exile since I left auld St. Thomas,
 I've toiled day and night on a far distant shore,
But, like a true Scotsman, my work never failed me,
 And now I can boast I've got riches galore.
But the next ship that sails I'll sail for auld Scotland,
 And live in the hame that I left lang ago,
And when life's journey's over, I'll die there contented,
 And sleep my last sleep aneath the Roon O.
　　Then here's to the sons, etc.

Words by Charles Myles, Arbroath.　Printed by permission.

KELVIN'S PURLING STREAM.

THE summer time being in its prime,
 The weather calm and clear,
I left that town called Portadown
 Between me and my dear.

In Glasgow city I arrived,
  And to Woodside I came,
Where all alone I made my moan
    To Kelvin's purling stream.

Ye stream, said I, as I passed by,
  Give ear to what I say,
How can you roll, without control,
  Unto some foreign quay?
Your murmurs pain my bosom sore;
  Here stands an honest boy,
He'll ne'er prove false to the girl he loves
  Till Kelvin's stream runs dry.

There's many a pretty little fish,
  Swims in yon water clear;
There's many a long and a weary mile
  Between me and my dear;
There's many a flower grows in yon bower
  That would my fancy please,
But I'll ne'er forget the girl I love
  Who lives near Lurgan Braes.

PART IV.

(b) Laments, Farewells, and Parting Songs.

OH! GIN I WERE WHERE GAUDIE RINS.

Oh! gin I were where Gaudie rins, where Gaudie rins, where
    Gaudie rins,
  Oh! gin I were where Gaudie rins, at the fit o' Bennachie;
Oh! I should ne'er come back again, come back again, come back
    again,
  Oh! I should ne'er come back again, your Lowland lads to see.

I never had but twa right lads, but twa richt lads, but twa richt
    lads,
  I never had but twa richt lads that dearly loved me.
The teen was killed in Lourin Fair[1], in Lourin Fair, in Lourin
    Fair,
  The teen[2] was killed in Lourin Fair, and the tither drowned
    in Dee.

[1] Laurence Fair.   [2] One.

Had they gien my lovie[3] man for man, man for man, man for
  man,
  Had they gien my lovie man for man, or yet a man for three,
He wudna hae lien[4] so low th' day, so low th' day, so low th'
  day,
  He wudna hae lien so low th' day at the foot o' yon arn tree.

But they crooded[5] in so thick on him, so thick on him, so thick
  on him,
  They crooded in so thick on him he cudna fecht nor flee;
And wisna that a dowie day, a dowie day, a dowie day,
  And wisna that a dowie day, a dowie day for me?

The Dee was flowin' frae bank tae bank, frae bank tae bank,
  frae bank tae bank,
  The Dee was flowin' frae bank tae bank when my lovie dreed
  his dree—
And wisna that a dowie day, a dowie day, a dowie day,
  And wisna that a dowie day, a dowie day for me?

He bought for me a braw new goon[6], a braw new goon, a braw
  new goon,
  He bought for me a braw new goon and ribbons to busk it wi'!
And I bought him the linen fine, the linen fine, the linen fine,
  And I bought for him the linen fine, his winding sheet to be.

And now this twice I've been a bride, I've been a bride, I've been
  a bride,
  And now this twice I've been a bride, but a wife I'll never be.
Oh! gin I were where Gaudie rins, where Gaudie rins, where
  Gaudie rins,
  Oh! gin I were where Gaudie rins, at the fit o' Bennachie.

---

[3] Lover.   [4] Lain.   [5] Crowded.   [6] Gown.

This old Aberdeenshire ballad, which probably belongs to the eighteenth
century, is one of the best known songs in the North of Scotland, and yet
it is rare to find a person who is able to repeat it from beginning to end.
It is sung to a bagpipe air of the same name. The "air" may be called
the anthem of the Aberdeenshire people, as at all social gatherings of the
natives of that county, in Glasgow and other large cities, the chairman and
guests march on to the platform to the strains of "Oh! Gin I Were Where
Gaudie Rins."

FAREWELL TO ALVAH'S WOODS AND BRAES.

FAREWELL to Alvah's woods and braes,
 The place of my nativity,
And all along yon pleasant strand
 That marks a Scotsman's countrie.

Some cheerful evenings I have spent
 Some happy seasons I have seen;
Adieu, ye bonnie Deveron's banks,
 I'll never more see you again!

Some happy evenings I have spent,
 About your crystal strands alane,
Until one summer's night we met
 To crown our joys in yonder glen.

The silver glances of the moon
 They ofttimes have conducted me
Through dreary paths and midnight gloom,
 Where fancy ofttimes courted me.

Oh, Alvah it's a bonnie place,
 And Duff-House walks surpasses a';
Fareweel, ye bonnie Deveron's banks,
 For I maun gang and leave ye a'.

When I think on Colinard's parks,
 The trysting-place where we did meet,
Far, far beyond the rolling main
 I'll often think on them and weep.

My ship she lies in readiness,
 My loving friends I'll bid good-bye;
And I'll give you a parting kiss
 And thank you for your last convoy.

When I am dead, laid in my grave,
 And none but strangers around me a',
None will be there to shed a tear
 When I am buried far awa.

He turned him right and round about
 His ain sweetheart to bid adieu;
Then with melting heart, right mournfully,
 He sailed from our Scottish shore.

Lieutenant John Fordyce of the Glasgow Police Force, informs me that in
the neighbourhood of Banff, when he was a boy, this song was known as
" The Poacher's Fareweel."

THE EMIGRANT'S FAREWELL TO DONSIDE.

KEY C. *Dorian mode.*

Come, all my old comrades, once more let us join,
Let us join all our voices to muse on langsyne;
Let us drink and be merry, from sorrow refrain,
For we may and may never meet all here again.

The time is now approaching that I must away,
So I leave my best wishes with all you that stay,
May good fortune attend you who happy live here,
For away to America my course I must steer.

Ye powers above bless us with a sweet, pleasant gale,
To be free and safe guarded while we're under sail;
Bring us safe to the harbour o'er the proud raging waves,
Let us trust in His mercy who can sink us or save's.

Ye hills and low valleys of Donside, farewell,
For if ever I return there is none here can tell;
Farewell to your lasses of every degree,
Long in vain will I wish for your sweet company.

Farewell to the jewel, to you I love best,
For you and your beauty excel all the rest;
But if you prove constant, as constant can be,
Wherever I go, love, my heart is with thee.

Long may you be merry while I'm very sad,
When I think of the pleasures that you and I've had;
When I mind on the times that you've sat on my knee
There were none in this world more happy than we.

The time has now arrived that I must away,
Cold winter is over, sweet summer draws nigh.
There is an old proverb, I believe it is true,
That " true love is more precious than the wealth of Peru."

Farewell to all sorrows, drink it round with a glass,
Drink a health to each lad and his sweet, smiling lass;
Drink a health to each lover whose loved one is true—
Here's good health, peace, and plenty, so farewell and adieu.

This song was sung at a social gathering at Corriehoul, Corgarff, Aberdeenshire, in 1836, by a Mr. Charles Michie, prior to his emigrating to America. His friends long believed it to have been composed by himself, but Mr. Jonathan Gauld, Edinburgh, who sent it to me by special request, informs me that he has discovered it is much older than Michie's time, and that he simply altered some of the verses to suit his own case.

Mr. Gavin Greig, M.A., ex-President Buchan Field Club, kindly arranged the music for me.

The following version of the song was picked up by Mr. Gauld from the singing of a Bathgate lady, and she in turn learned it from her grand-mother, who was also a native of Bathgate.

BATHGATE VERSION.

Come, friends and acquaintances, once more let us join,
And raise our sweet voices in chorus wi' mine.
Let us drink and be merry, from sorrow refrain,
For we may and may never meet all here again.

Chorus.
For we may and may never meet all here again.

I ance had a lassie, I liket her weel,
For modesty and beauty none could her excel.
When she looked in my face as she sat on my knee,
There were none in this world more happy than we.

The time is fast approaching when I must away,
Farewell to my comrades, wherever you be;
And wherever I wander, by land and by sea,
I'll never forget all your kindness to me.

THE IRISH EMIGRANT'S LAMENT.

KEY F. {:l.,t,|d :r |m :-.r,d | r.d :t,.l,| s, :l, | d :r |m :s.m | 1 :-|-}

{:d'.l | s :1 |m.r :d.m | r.d :t,.l,| s, :l.,t,| d .r :m | r.d :1, | 1, :-|-||

Och! while I live I'll never forget
　　The troubles of that day,
When bound into a foreign land
　　Our ship got under way.

My friends I left at Belfast town,
　　My love at Carrick shore,
And I gave to poor old Ireland
　　My blessing o'er and o'er.

Och! well I knew, as off we sailed,
　　What my hard fate would be;
For, gazing on my country's hills
　　They seemed to fly from me.

I watched them as we sailed away
　　Until my eyes grew sore,
And I felt that I was doomed to walk
　　The Shamrock sod no more.

They say I'm now in freedom's land,
　　Where all men masters be;
But were I in my winding-sheet
　　There's none to care for me.

I must, to eat the stranger's bread,
　　Abide the stranger's scorn,
Who taunts me with thy dear loved name,
　　Sweet isle, where I was born.

Och! where—och! where's the careless heart
　　I once could call my own?
It bade a long farewell to me
　　The day I left Tyrone.

Not all the wealth by hardship won
    Beyond the Western main,
Thy pleasures, my own absent home,
    Can bring to me again.

This song was writen by William Kennedy, one of the Whistle-Binkie group of poets. Kennedy is the only one of this famous group regarding which no information appears in the first volume of the Whistle-Binkie series, and the only thing I have been able to learn regarding him is that he was a great friend of William Motherwell, and was also for some time British Consul at Texas, U.S.A.

TOCHINEAL.

COME a' my young lads, ye'll mak haste and be ready,
    For May twenty-saxt will be here in a crack;
An' we ane and a', but the man in the smiddy,
    Maun leave Tochineal, nae mair to come back.

Awa to the West we maun a' gang thegither,
    The men, wives and wee anes, wi' true herts and leal;
An' our wives they will a' be in a sad swither
    On that awfu' day that we leave Tochineal.

Aucht wives in a hoose wi' a brick separation,
    I never ance thocht it wad dee very weel,
For their tongues were sae rid for to gie provocation,
    There cou'd be nae contentment at auld Tochineal.

There were Jamie and Sandy, and Archie and Watty,
    There were Walker and Taylor, and Forbes and Kemp;
We were aucht jolly lads, but we're jist something chatty
    When ance we get in the wee drappie o' drink.

We're aul' and we're wracket, to work we'd nae scruple,
    Our joints they are stiff and that we do feel;
They're no like our wives' tongues, for faith, they're richt
        supple
    When they think we've been drinking the pure Tochineal.
            .   .   .   .   .   .

But what is a' this but a blether o' nonsense,
    There's nane o's been there yet that grievance to feel;
But there's ae thing I'll say, without hurtin' my conscience,
    The bye-word will be this is nae Tochineal.

THE PARTING OF BURNS AND HIGHLAND MARY.

Key D. {.t₁ | r   :f .,s |1   :t .d' | t   :d' .t |d' .s :m .l₁,l₁ }

{| r   :f .,s |1   :t .,d' | r¹   :d' .t |1   :-.1 | f .1 :s .f | s   :f .,m }

{| r   :m .f | s .m :d .,1 | r¹   :d' .t | 1 .s :f .,r | m   :r .,m | r :-. ||

In green Caledonia there ne'er were twa lovers
    Sae enraptured and happy in each other's arms,
As Burns, the sweet bard, and his dear Highland Mary,
    And fondly and sweetly he sang o' her charms.

And lang will his sang, sae enchanting and bonnie,
    Be heard wi' delight on his ain native plains;
And lang will the name o' his dear Highland Mary
    Be sacred to love in his heart-melting strains.

Oh, 'twas a May day, and the flowers o' the summer
    Were blooming in wilderness, a' lovely and fair,
When our twa lovers met in a grove o' green bowers
    Which grew on the banks o' the clear, winding Ayr.

And, O! to them baith 'twas a meeting fu' tender,
    As it was the last ane for a while they would hae;
Sae in love's purest raptures they feasted together,
    Till the red setting sun show'd the close o' the day.

" Oh Mary, dear Mary," exclaimed her fond lover,
    " Ye carry my heart to the Highlands wi' thee;
Every burnie and bank, every grove and green bower
    May talk o' the love o' my lassie and me.

" My life's sweetest treasure, my ain charming Mary,
    To you I'll be ever devoted and true;
For the heart that is beating so fast in this bosom
    Is a heart that can never love ony but you.

" O, dinna bide lang in the Highlands, my Mary,
   O, dinna bide lang in the Highlands frae me!
For I love thee sincerely, I love thee owre dearly,
   To be happy sae far, my dear Mary, frae thee."

" I winna bide lang, my dear lad, in the Highlands,
   I winna bide lang, for ye winna be there;
Altho' I hae friends I like weel in the Highlands,
   The ane I love best's on the banks o' the Ayr."

He kissed her red lips—they were sweeter than the roses—
   And he clasped her lily-white breast to his heart,
And his tears fell like dew-drops at e'en on her bosom
   When she said, " My fond lover, alas! we maun part."

" Then farewell," he said, and he flew frae his Mary;
   " Oh, farewell!" said Mary, she could say nae mair.
Oh, little they thought they had parted for ever
   When they parted that night on the banks o' the Ayr.

Yet the green summer saw but a few sunny mornings
   Till she, in the bloom of her beauty and pride,
Was laid in her grave like a bonnie young flower,
   In Greenock Kirkyard, on the banks o' the Clyde.

And Burns, the sweet bard o' his ain Caledonia,
   Lamented his Mary in mony a sad strain,
And sair did he weep for his dear Highland Mary,
   And ne'er did his heart love so deeply again.

Then bring me the lilies, and bring me the roses,
   And bring me the daisies that grow in the vale;
And bring me the dew o' a mid-summer's evening,
   And bring me the breath of the sweet-scented gale;

And bring me the sigh o' a fond lover's bosom,
   And bring me the tear o' a fond lover's e'e,
And I'll pour them a' down on thy grave, Highland Mary,
   For the sake o' thy Burns, wha dearly lo'ed thee.

It is safe to say that no song touching upon the life of our National Bard
—not even one of his own—ever attained the same degree of popularity
amongst country people as this one.

Mr. Walter Towers, Bonnybridge, Stirlingshire, informs me that the song
was written about sixty years ago by a West of Scotland police constable
named Thomson, who subsequently emigrated to Canada.

LAST PARTING OF BURNS AND BONNIE JEAN.

Air.—" The Braes o' Boyndlie," or " O, Open the Door."

COME near to me, Jean, come close to my side,
    Come kneel and pray wi' me, O,
That the widow's God may saften the road
    For my helpless bairns and thee, O.
My heart is now fu' o' love that's divine,
    Yet strong is my love for thee, O;
He who tempers the wind to the shorn lamb
    Will baith husband and father be, O.

My sun slowly sets this sweet summer eve,
    O' I'm loath to leave them and thee, O,
Yet I see through the gloom fast gatherin' roun'
    Kin' freens wha will succour gie, O.
She has come to his side as when first his young bride,
    Her arms aroun' him twine, O.
My true love, she cried, I richt fain wad hae died
    But maun bide wi' mine and thine, O.

She has clasped his cauld hand, and kissed his cauld lips,
    Mute grief is sair to dree, O;
Cut a lock from his hair on her widowed breast to wear,
    True love can never dee, O.
Late and ear' she'll toil and spin their daily bread to win,
    Though frugal it maun be, O;
An' his presence hoverin' near her patient soul will cheer,
    While she waits for Heaven's decree, O.

They hae laid him to rest in St. Michael's kirkyard,
    That martial, mournfu' train, O;
An' the wee birdies wild a requiem sing
    Aroun' his lowly headstane, O.
Now his name has a shrine in ilka true heart
    That kens the mither tongue, O,
And the glory and fame o' Scotia's sweet bard
    Will resound till the crack o' doom, O.

Written by the late Mrs. Elizabeth Rennie, Mill of Aden, Old Deer, Aberdeenshire, and printed by permission of her daughter, Mrs. Fred. Martin, St. Dunstan's, Mintlay.

JAMIE RAEBURN'S FAREWELL.

Key G. { .d .,r | m .,r :d .l, | d :l, .,s, | s, .r :r .,m | r :- .}

{ .s, | d .,r :f .m | s .m :r .d | m .,s :s .,l | s :- .}

{ .m ,m | f .,s :l .f | m ,s .- :s .m | f .m :r .d | r }

{ :s .,m | r .,m :d ,l,.- | d .,d :l, .,s, | s, .,l, :d .r | d :- .||

My name is Jamie Raeburn, in Glasgow I was born,
My place and habitation I'm forced to leave with scorn;
From my place and habitation I now must gang awa,
Far frae the bonnie hills and dales of Caledonia.

It was early one morning, just by the break of day,
We were 'wakened by the turnkey, who unto us did say—
"Arise, ye hapless convicts, arise ye ane and a',
This is the day ye are to stray from Caledonia."

We all arose, put on our clothes, our hearts were full of grief,
Our friends, who a' stood round the coach, could grant us no
    relief;
Our parents, wives, and sweethearts dear, their hearts were broke
    in twa
To see us leave the bonnie braes of Caledonia.

Farewell, my aged mother, I'm vexed for what I've done,
I hope none will cast up to you the race that I have run;
I hope God will protect you when I am far awa,
Far from the bonnie hills and dales of Caledonia.

Farewell, my honest father, you are the best of men,
And likewise my own sweetheart, it's Catherine is her name;
Nae mair we'll walk by Clyde's clear stream or by the
    Broomielaw,
For I must leave the hills and dales of Caledonia.

If we ne'er meet on earth again, I hope we'll meet above,
Where hallelujahs will be sung to Him who reigns in love;
Nae earthly judge shall judge us then, but He who rules us a',
Farewell to a' the hills and dales of Caledonia.

MISS FORBES' FAREWELL TO BANFF.

FAREWELL ye fields an' meadows green!
    The blest retreat of peace and love;
Aft have I silent stolen from hence
    With my young swain a while to rove.
Sweet was our walk, more sweet our talk,
    Among the beauties of the spring;
An' aft we'd lean us on a bank
    To hear the feathered warblers sing.

The azure sky, the hills around,
    Gave double beauty to the scene;
The lofty spires of Banff on view—
    On every side the waving grain.
The tales of love my Jamie told,
    In such a saft and moving strain,
Have so engaged my tender heart,
    I'm loath to leave the scene again.

But if the fates will be so kind
    As favour my return once more,
For to enjoy that peace of mind
    In those retreats I had before:
Now, farewell, Banff! the nimble steeds
    Do bear me hence—I must away;
Yet time, perhaps, may bring me back,
    To part 'no more from scenes so gay.

This song was composed by John Hamilton, who died in Edinburgh in
1814.

THE WARS O' GERMANIE.

O, wae be to the orders that marched my love awa,
And wae be to the cruel cause that gars my tears down fa',
O, wae be to the bluidy wars in Hie Germanie,
For they hae ta'en my luve and left a broken heart to me.

The drums beat in the mornin' afore the scriech o' day,
And the wee, wee fifes played loud and shrill, while yet the
    morn was gray;
The bonnie flags were a' unfurled, a gallant sight to see,
But waes me for my sodger lad that marched to Germanie.

O, lang, lang is the travel to the bonnie pier of Leith,
O, dreich it is to gang wi' the snawdrift in the teeth!
And, O, the cauld wind froze the tear that gathered in my e'e,
When I gaed there to see my luve embark for Germanie.

I looked over the braid blue sea sae lang as could be seen
A wee bit sail upon the ship my sodger lad was in;
But the wind was blawin' sair and snell, and the ship sailed
    speedilie,
And the waves and cruel war have twined my winsome luve
    frae me.

I never think o' dancin', I dinna try to spin,
But a' the day I speir what news kind neibour bodies bring.
I sometimes knit a stocking, if knitting it may be,
Syne for every loop that I cast on I am sure to let down three.

My father says I'm in a pet, my mither jeers at me,
And bans me for a dautit wean, in drots for aye to be,
But little weet they o' the cause that drumles sae my e'e;
O, they hae nae winsome luve like mine in the wars o' Germanie.

The above song by William Motherwell, the Glasgow poet, is a masterpiece.
About thirty years ago an American author wrote regarding it:—" I know
of only one song which surpasses this, if it does surpass it, and that is
'Auld Robin Gray,' which is less purely poetical in expression, but rather
more in keeping throughout with the simple homely character of the
imaginary singer. To be able to touch the heart is not given to many poets,
great or small. It was given in the eighteenth century to Lady Anne
Lindsay, and in the nineteenth century to William Motherwell."

N

IN LOW GERMANIE.

As I sailed past green Jura's isle,
  Among the waters lone,
I heard a voice, a sweet, low voice,
  Atween a sigh and moan.
With ae babe at her bosom, and
  Another at her knee,
A mother wail'd the bloody wars
  In Low Germanie.

Oh, wae unto these cruel wars
  That ever they began,
For they have swept my native isle
  Of many a pretty man;
For first they took my brethren twain.
  They wiled my love frae me;
Woe, woe unto the cruel wars
  In Low Germanie!

I saw him when he sail'd away,
  And furrow'd far the brine,
And down his foes came to the shore
  In many a glittering line.
The war steeds rush'd among the waves,
  The guns came flashing free,
But could nae keep my gallant love
  Frae Low Germanie.

Oh, say, ye maidens, have ye seen
  When swells the battle cry,
A stately youth with bonnet blue
  And feather floating high;
An eye that flashes fierce for all,
  But ever mild to me?
Oh, that's the lad that loves me best
  In Low Germanie!

I sit upon the high green land,
  Where mute the waters lie,
And think I see my true love sail
  Atween the sea and sky.

With ae babe at my bosom, and
  Another at my knee,
I sorrow for my soldier lad
  In Low Germanie.

This is one of Allan Cunningham's songs, and was once popular all over
Scotland, but it is now seldom heard except in the cotter's house or ploughmen's bothy.

THE NABOB.

Air.—" The Traveller's Return."

WHEN silent time, wi' lightly feet,
  Had trod on thirty years,
I sought again my native land
  Wi' mony hopes and fears.
Wha kens gin the dear friends I left
  May still continue mine?
Or gin I e'er again shall taste
  The joys I left langsyne.

As I drew near my ancient pile
  My heart beat a' the way;
Ilk place I pass'd seem'd yet to speak
  O' some dear former day.
Those days that follow'd me afar,
  Those happy days o' mine,
Whilk made me think the present joys
  A' naething to langsyne.

The ivy'd tower now met my eye,
  Where minstrels used to blaw;
Nae friend stepped forth wi' open hand,
  Nae weel-kenn'd face I saw;
Till Donald totter'd to the door,
  Wham I left in his prime,
And he grat to see the lad return
  He bore about langsyne.

I ran to ilka dear friend's room,
  As if to find them there,
I knew where ilka ane used to sit,
  And hang o'er mony a chair.

Till soft remembrance threw a veil
   Across those een o' mine,
I clos'd the door and sobb'd aloud,
   To think on auld langsyne.

Some pensy chiels, a new sprung race,
   Wad next their welcome pay,
Wha shudder'd at my Gothic wa's,
   And wished my groves away;
" Cut, cut," they cried, "those aged elms,
   Lay low yon mournfu' pine,"
Na, na, our fathers' names grow there,
   Memorials o' langsyne.

To wean me frae these waefu' thoughts
   They took me to the town,
But sair on ilka weel-kenn'd face
   I missed the youthfu' bloom;
At halls they pointed to a nymph
   Wham a' declared divine,
But sure her mother's blushing cheeks
   Were fairer far langsyne.

In vain I sought in music's sound
   To find that magic art,
Which oft in Scotland's ancient lays
   Has thrill'd through a' my heart;
The sang had mony an artfu' turn,
   My ear confessed 'twas fine,
But miss'd the simple melody
   I listened to langsyne.

Ye sons to comrades o' my youth,
   Forgie an auld man's spleen,
Wha 'midst your gayest scenes still mourns
   The days he ance has seen.
When time has past, and seasons fled,
   Your hearts will feel like mine,
And aye the sang will maist delight
   That minds ye o' langsyne.

The writer of this song was Miss Susanna Blamire, who was born at Cardew Hall, Cumberland, in 1747, and died at Carlisle in 1794.

ADIEU TO BOGIE SIDE.

Assist me all ye muses!
　My downcast spirits raise,
And join me in full chorus
　To sing sweet Huntly's praise.

I leave the girl behind me
　Whose joy is all my pride,
And bid farewell to Huntly,
　And adieu to Bogie side.

Companions of my youth, farewell!
　I bid you all adieu!
The pleasure of an evening walk
　I'll share no more with you.

Where'er I chance to wander
　In foreign regions wide,
My heart will be in Huntly,
　And on sweet Bogie side.

But now we must be parted,
　And fate with us divide;
So I'll bid farewell to Huntly,
　And adieu to Bogie side.

How heartsome I have wandered
　To see the gowan spring,
All in the merry month of May,
　And hear the linties sing,

When wearied with my fishing-rod,
　And when at eventide,
I've laid me down to rest awhile
　Upon sweet Bogie side.

Farewell, ye lovely meadows!
　Of you I'll often talk;
Likewise the hawthorn bushes
　That grace the gravel walk.

The pleasures I've enjoyed in you
　They on my heart will bide,
When I am far from Huntly,
　And far from Bogie side.

Or down the road to Huntly Lodge,
　With pleasant steps I roved,
Almost inspired with rapture
　By the sweet girl I loved,

Who joined me in her rambles,
　And who chose me for her guide,
Upon the walks of Deveron banks
　And on sweet Bogie side.

Providence protect the girl
　To whom I send these lines,
And keep her free from danger,
　Who has this heart of mine!

Bless her with contentment,
　And keep her free from pride,
Till I return to Huntly,
　And to sweet Bogie side!

WE PART, MY LOVE, TO MEET NAE MAIR.

WE part, my love, to meet nae mair,
　'Tis cruel fate's decree;
And a' the waes o' bleak despair
　This widowed heart maun dree.

But thy lo'ed form, where'er I rove,
　I'll still in fancy see,
And mind our hours o' youthfu' love
　Till I am doomed to dee.

When a' the warl' in sleep were laid,
　And last thou met wi' me,
The sighs we breathed, and tears we shed,
　For aye shall sacred be.

When death, frae worl'y waes and cares
　This labouring breast shall free,
My dearest bliss, in happier spheres,
　Shall be to meet wi' thee.

Anonymous.　Written about September, 1817.

FAREWELL TAMINTOUL.

FAREWELL Tamintoul! for the hour's come at last
When I can only think of thy joys in the past,
For destiny bears me away from the glen
Where dwell bonnie lasses and true-hearted men.

What though in their spite petty minds have decried thee,
And said with a sneer they could never abide thee!
I am sure that in this I shall not be alone
When I say I am certain the fault was their own.

As for me I can say, with my hand on my heart,
I'm as loath as can be from Strathavon to part;
Its hills and its streams and its valleys shall be
Ever dear as the home of my childhood to me.

I have found hospitality, kindness, and truth
To be deeply engraved on the hearts of its youth,
And I know you can always with safety depend
On them aye standing true in the cause o' a friend.

I shall always remember with happiness deep,
Craighalky, Knocklochy, and Ailnaic so steep,
The clear winding Avon, the fair Ellan-no,
And the birk-covered braes that surround Delnabo.

Strathavon, farewell! though I cannot remain,
I trust that thy vale I may visit again;
How that will delight me, words fail me to tell,
But soon may the day come—Strathavon, farewell!

Noted down from the singing of Alexander M'Donald, a native of Glenlivet, in the summer of 1881, and printed by permission of Messrs. John Heywood, Limited, Deansgate, Manchester.

THE TRUMPET SOUNDS AT BURRELDALES;
OR, THE TROOPER AND THE MAID.

THE trumpet sounds at Burreldales,
    Says, "Man and horse mak' ready,"
The drums do beat at Staneman hill—
    "Lads, leave your mam and daddie."
The fifes do play at Cromlet banks—
    "Lads, leave the Lewes o' Fyvie,"
The trooper to the fair maid said—
    "O lassie, I maun lea' you."

" O, when will we twa meet again?
   Or when will ye me marry?"
" When heather knaps grow siller taps,
   I winna longer tarry."
" O, when will we twa meet again?
   Or when will ye me marry?"
" When heather cows grow owsen bows,
   I winna langer tarry."

" O, when will we twa meet again?
   Or when will ye me marry?"
" When cockle shells grow siller bells,
   I winna langer tarry."
" O, when will we twa meet again?
   Or when will ye me marry?"
" When apple trees grow in the seas,
   I winna langer tarry."

" O, when will we twa meet again?
   Or when will ye me marry?"
" When fishes fly and seas gang dry,
   I winna langer tarry."
" O, when will we twa meet again?
   Or when will ye me marry?"
" When frost and snaw will warm us a',
   I winna langer tarry."

THE EXILED CROFTER'S LAMENT.

WE'RE awa, we're awa frae the auld countrie,
To a far awa land, far ower the sea,
Where strange folks will greet us, an' strange sichts appear,
But our herts will aye cling to the Heilan's sae dear.

In the wee crofter's gardens the deer will be browsing,
The Cockneys the grouse on the hills will be rousing;
But nae crofters' families appear on the scene,
They are chased ower the ocean that sportsmen may reign.

In the dreams o' the nicht the peat reek I smell,
In fancy I see the sweet nodding bluebell,
The bloom o' the heather, and I hear the wild bee;
But the Heilan's o' Scotland nae mair I shall see.

These verses were sent to me a few years ago by Mr. Allan D. Bailey,
Ardrossan, who states that they were copied from a chapbook of Scottish
songs published at Montreal in 1812.

CONVIVIAL SONGS.

PART IV.

(c) Convivial Songs.

O JOHNNIE, MY MAN.

"O Johnnie, my man, do ye no' think on risin'?
The day is far spent, and the nicht's comin' on;
Ye're siller's near dune, and the stoup's toom before ye,
So rise up, my Johnnie, and come awa hame."

"Wha's that at the door that speakin' so kindly?"
"'Tis the voice of your wifie, ca'd Jeanie by name."
"Come in by, my dearie, and sit down beside me,
It's time enough yet for to gang awa hame."

"Don't ye mind on the time when we first fell a-courting?
We had naething but love then to trouble our mind;
We spent a' our time 'mang the sweet-scented roses,
And I ne'er thocht it lang then to gang awa hame."

"O, weel dae I mind on the time that ye speak o',
And weel dae I mind on yon sweet flowery glen;
But thae days are a' past, and will never return, love,
Sae sit down beside me, and I'll soon gang hame."

" Don't ye mind on your bairns, they're a' at hame greetin'?
    There's nae meal in the barrel to fill their wee wames;
While ye sit here drinkin', and leave me lamentin',
    O, rise up, my Johnnie, and come awa hame."

Then Johnnie rose up, and he banged the door open,
    Saying, " Cursed be the tavern that ere let me in!
And cursed be the whisky that's made me sae frisky!
    O, fare ye weel, whisky, for I'm awa hame.

" And, Jeanie, my dear, your advice will be taken,
    I'll leave aff the drinkin' and follow thee hame,
Live sober and wisely, and aye be respected,
    Nae mair in the ale-house I'll sit down at e'en."

Noo Johnnie gaes out on a fine simmer's evening
    Wi' his wife and his bairnies fu' trig and fu' bien,
Though no' long before that in rags they were rinnin',
    While Johnnie sat drinkin' in the ale-house at e'en.

Contented and crouse he sits by his ain fireside,
    And Jeanie, a happier wife there is nane;
Nae mair to the ale-house at nicht he does wander,
    But he's happy wi' Jeanie and the bairnies at hame.

This was a favourite street song all over Scotland in the sixties and the seventies. A version of it appears in Robert Ford's *Vagabond Songs and Ballads*, but Ford was unable to obtain the air to which it was sung. I have, however, been more fortunate.

THERE'S WHISKY IN THE JAR.

I AM a young fellow that never yet was daunted,
And sometimes had money, but seldom it was wanted,
For robbing for gold it was my only folly,
And paying for good liquor to treat deceitful Molly.
    Musha-a-ring a-ding a-day, right fal de daddie O,
    There's whisky in the jar.

As I was going over Calvert Mountain,
I met with Captain Evan, his money he was counting,
First I drew my pistols, then I drew my rapier,
Saying, " Stand and deliver, for I'm your money-taker."
    Musha-a-ring a-ding a-day, etc.

Oh, when I got his money it was a pretty penny,
I put it in my pocket and took it home to Molly,
When she swore by what was good that she never would deceive
    me,
But the devil's in the women, for they never can be easy.

  Musha-a-ring a-ding a-day, etc.

Being both wet and weary I went to Molly's chamber,
I went to Molly's chamber for to have a slumber;
Then she flew unto my pistols and she loaded them with water,
It was then that I was taken like a lamb unto the slaughter.

  Musha-a-ring a-ding a-day, etc.

It was the next morning between six and seven,
I was surrounded by policemen, along with Captain Evan,
I fired off my pistols, but I was mistaken,
For splash went the water, and a prisoner I was taken.

  Musha-a-ring a-ding a-day, etc.

There's some take delight in fishing and fowling,
And others take delight in hearing cannons roaring,
But I take delight in being brisk and jolly,
And in paying for good liquor to treat deceitful Molly.

  Musha-a-ring a-ding a-day, etc.

I have got two brothers, and they are in the army,
One is in Cork, and the other's in Killarney.
If I had them here to-night, oh! wouldn't I make them jolly!
I would rather have them here than you, deceitful Molly.

  Musha-a-ring a-ding a-day, etc.

It was early next morning I was up and loudly calling,
And up against the cell door the turnkey he was bawling,
When I up with my shackles and I knocked the turnkey down,
And I made my escape out of sweet Phillipstown.

  Musha-a-ring a-ding a-day, etc.

  This is another thoroughly Irish song which has long been popular in rural
Scotland. It seems to have been introduced into this country by Irish
shearers about the beginning of the last century.

A WEE DRAPPIE O'T.

O, life is a journey we a' hae to gang,
And care is a burden we carry alang—
Though heavy be our burden, and poverty our lot,
We are happy wi' our freen's o'er a wee drappie o't.

    O'er a wee drappie o't, o'er a wee drappie o't,
      When we a' meet thegither o'er a wee drappie o't.

Our cares come daily on us, like the waves alang the shore,
This wee bit blink o' pleasure is very quickly o'er.
Death may come quite unawares and hurry us frae the spot:
While we can, let's a' be happy o'er a wee drappie o't.

    O'er a wee drappie o't, etc.

View the birk in winter, sae leafless and sae bare,
Resembles a man wi' a burden o' care—
But view the birk in summer wi' its green verdant coat,
Rejoicing like a man o'er a wee drappie o't.

    O'er a wee drappie o't, etc.

Job, in his lamentations, said that man was made to mourn,
That there was little pleasure 'tween the cradle and the urn;
But in these meditations he surely had forgot
The pleasure man enjoys o'er a wee drappie o't.

    O'er a wee drappie o't, etc.

Since we've a' met thegither o'er a dram and a sang,
Since we've a' met thegither by special command,
Free frae ambition and every wicked plot,
We'll be happy while we may o'er a wee drappie o't.

    O'er a wee drappie o't, etc.

The wee drappie o't can dee naebody ill,
But the big drap is sure to plunder and kill;
He only is wise who can husband a groat,
And never buy mair than a wee drappie o't.

    O'er a wee drappie o't, etc.

Wi' a wee drappie o't we a' can agree,
Takin' a big drap mak's a' wisdom flee—
And he wha wad wear an honest man's coat,
Must never tak' mair than a wee drappie o't.

    O'er a wee drappie o't, etc.

Here's unto them that's far, far away,
And may we never forget them that are cold in the clay,
And here's to every loving freen', may he always have a groat,
And be happy wi' his comrades o'er a wee drappie o't.

O'er a wee drappie o't, etc.

Additional verses.

Here's a health unto the memory o' Burns that's awa
To the land o' the leal, don't abuse him ava;
And a' our loving comrades, they should never be forgot
When we a' meet together o'er a wee drappie o't.

O'er a wee drappie o't, etc.

When we're a' met together wi' a glass into our hand,
When we're a' met together we're a jolly little band;
When we're a' met together, and we're free wi' a groat,
Then we'll aye sit and tipple o'er a wee drappie o't.

O'er a wee drappie o't, etc.

SAE WILL WE YET.

Air.—" The Wearing o' the Green."

SIT ye down here, my cronies, and gie us your crack;
Let the win' tak' the care o' this life on its back.
Our hearts to despondency we never will submit,
For we've aye been provided for, and sae will we yet.

And sae will we yet, and sae will we yet,
For we've aye been provided for, and sae will we yet.

Let the miser delight in the hoarding of pelf,
Since he has not the soul to enjoy it himself;
Since the bounty of Providence is new every day,
As we journey through life, let us live by the way.

Let us live by the way, let us live by the way,
As we journey through life, let us live by the way.

Then bring us a tankard o' nappy gude ale,
For to comfort our hearts and enliven the tale;
We'll aye be the happier the langer we sit,
For we've drank together mony a time, and sae will we yet.

And sae will we yet, and sae will we yet,
We've drank together mony a time, and sae will we yet.

Success to the farmer, and prosper his plough,
Reward his eident toiling a' the year through!
Our seed-time and harvest we ever will get,
And we've lippen'd aye to Providence, and sae will we yet.

    And sae will we yet, and sae will we yet,
    We've lippen'd aye to Providence, and sae will we yet.

Long live the King, and happy may he be,
And success to his forces by land and by sea!
His enemies to triumph we never will permit,
Britain's aye been victorious, and sae will we yet.

    And sae will we yet, and sae will we yet,
    Britain's aye been victorious, and sae will we yet.

Let the glass keep its course and go merrily roun';
For the sun has to rise, though the moon it goes down;
Till the house be rinnin' roun' about its time enough to flit;
When we fell we aye got up again, and sae will we yet.

    And sae will we yet, and sae will we yet,
    When we fell we aye got up again, and sae will we yet.

Written by Walter Watson, who was born at Chryston, near Glasgow, in
1780, and died at Kirkintilloch in 1854.

THE CALTON WEAVER.

I AM a weaver, a Calton weaver,
    An' I'm a rash and a rovin' blade;
I've got some money in my pocket,
    An' I go and try the rovin' trade.

As I gaed doon thro' Glasgow city
    Nancy Whisky I chanced to smell,
So I gaed in and sat doon beside her,
    For it's seven years since I loved her well.

The more I kissed her the more I loved her,
    The more I kissed her the more she smiled,
Till Nancy Whisky, O Nancy Whisky,
    Till Nancy Whisky had me beguiled.

'Twas very early the next morning,
    Finding myself in a strange bed,
I went to rise but I was not able,
    For Nancy's charms they held my head.

I called the landlady to the parlour,
　And asked her what was to pay;
Thirty shillings is the reckoning,
　So pay me quickly and go away.

It's I pulled out a purse with money,
　And to her the reckoning I did pay down;
I paid to her thirty shillings,
　And all that remained was a single crown.

As I gaed down thro' Glasgow city
　Nancy Whisky I chanced to smell;
I gaed in and drank four and sixpence,
　And a' 'twas left was a crooked scale.[1]

Do I regard one single sixpence,
　Or will I lay it up in store?
I'll go back and hae anither gill,
　It will help me home to work for more.

Then I'll go back to my old master,
　So merrily I'll mak' the shuttle fly;
For I'll mak' mair at the Calton weaving
　Than ever I did in a roving way.

So, come all ye weavers, ye Calton weavers,
　Come all ye weavers where e'er ye be;
Beware of Whisky, Nancy Whisky,
　She'll ruin you as she ruined me .

[1] Sixpence.

The old burgh of Calton, now part of the city of Glasgow, was famous for its weavers. Indeed, weaving seems to have been the chief industry there during the first quarter of the last century.

GUID NICHT, AN' JOY BE WI' YOU A'.

Guid nicht, an' joy be wi' you a',
　Since it is sae that I maun gang;
Short seem'd the gate to come—but ah!
　To gang again is weary lang.

Sic joyous nichts come nae sae thrang
  That I sae soon sou'd haste awa,
But since it's sae that I maun gae,
  Guid nicht, and joy be wi' you a'.

This nicht I ween we've had the heart
  To gar auld time tak' to his feet;
That mak's us a' fu laith to part,
  And aye mair fain again to meet.
To dree the winter's drift an' weet,
  For sic a nicht is nocht ava,
For hours the minutes o' the sweet—
  Guid night, an' joy be wi' you a'.

Our bald-pow'd daddies here we've seen
  In younkers' revels fidging fain;
Our gray-hair'd grannies here hae been
  Like daffin' hizzies young again.
To mony a merry, auld Scots strain,
  We've deftly passed the time awa,
We met in mirth, we part in pain,
  Guid nicht, an' joy be wi' you a'.

My nimble steed neighs at the yett;
  My shoulders roun' the plaid I throw;
I've clapt the spur upon my buit,
  The guid braid bonnet on my brow;
The nicht is wearin' late I trow—
  My hame lies mony a mile awa;
The mair's the need to mount and go,
  Guid nicht, an' joy be wi' you a'.

Bring me the deoch an doruis gill,
  'Twill licht a bouat in my e'e;
Tho' mirk nae fear that I gang will
  Drink doubly an' I'll doubly see.
Young lads an' lasses, tent ye me,
  As hame ye daunder twa an' twa,
Love guide your gait—blin' tho' he be—
  Guid nicht, an' joy be wi' you a'.

Words by John Imlah. Music by James B. Allan, A.L.C.M., L.T.S.C.

THE BEGGAR MAN.

A BEGGAR man cam' owre yon lea,
An' mony a fine tale he tauld me,
Seeking out for charity,
  Will ye lodge a beggar man?
    La lal-tee too roo a ree.

The nicht was cauld, the carl was wat,
An' down ayont the ingle he sat;
Then he threw the meal-pock aff o' his back
  An' aye as he ranted and sang
    La lal-tee too roo a ree.

If I were black as I am white
As the snaw that lies on yonder dyke,
I'd dress mysel' some beggar-like
  An' awa wi' you I would gang.
    La lal-tee too roo a ree.

O lassie, O lassie, you're far too young,
An' you haena the cant o' the begging tongue;
Ye haena the cant o' the beggin' tongue,
  An' wi' me ye canna gang.
    La lal-tee too roo a ree.

I'll bend my back an' bow my knee,
And I'll put a black patch on my e'e,
An' for a beggar they'll tak' me,
  Syne awa wi' you I'll gang.
    La lal-tee too roo a ree.

'Twas then the twa made up the plot
To rise twa hours before the auld folk;
Sae gently as they slipped the lock
 An' through the fields they ran.
   La lal-tee too roo a ree.

Early neist mornin' the auld wife arose,
An' at her leisure put on her clothes,
Syne to the servant's bed she goes
 To speir for the silly, puir man.
   La lal-tee too roo a ree.

She gaed to the bed where the beggar lay;
The strae was cauld and he was away;
She clapped her hands, cried, "Walladay,
 Is there ony o' our gude gear gane?"
   La lal-tee too roo a ree.

Some ran to the coffer, some ran to the kist,
But nocht was stolen that could be mist;
She danced her lane, cried, "Praise be the blest,
 I've lodged an honest auld man."
   La lal-tee too roo a ree.

Since naething's awa that we can learn,
The kye are to milk an' the milk is to kirn;
Gae but the house, lass, an' wauken my bairn,
 An' bid her come speedily ben.
   La lal-tee too roo a ree.

The servant gaed where the dochter lay;
The sheets were cauld and she was away;
An' fast to the gudewife she did say,
 She's awa wi' the auld beggar man.
   La lal-tee too roo a ree.

O fye gar ride, O fye gar rin,
An' haste ye find thae traitors again;
For she'll be burnt and he'll be slain,
 The wearifu' auld beggar man.
   La lal-tee too roo a ree.

Some rode on horseback and some ran on foot,
A' but the auld wife, and she wasna fit;
But she hobbled about frae hip to hip,
    An' aye as she cursed and she bann'd.
      La lal-tee too roo a ree.

Meanwhile, far out owre yon lea,
Fu' snug in a glen where nane could see,
The twa wi' kindly sport and glee
    Frae a new cheese cut a whang.
      La lal-tee too roo a ree.

When years had passed some twa or three,
The same beggar carl cam' owre yon lea,
Saying, gudewife for your courtsie
    Will you lodge a silly, puir man?
      La lal-tee too roo a ree.

A beggar, a beggar, I'll ne'er lodge again,
I hadna a dochter but ane o' my ain,
An' awa wi' a beggar man she's gane
    An' I dinna ken whence nor where.
      La lal-tee too roo a ree.

O, yonder she's comin' owre yon lea,
Wi' mony a fine tale unto thee;
An' she's got a baby on her knee
    An' anither comin' hame.
      La lal-tee too roo a ree.

O yonder she's comin' to your bower,
In silk an' satin wi' mony a flower;
She's held up her hands, and she's blest the hour
    That she followed the beggar man.
      La lal-tee too roo a ree.

There are several versions of this well-known ballad, but the one here printed is the most common in the bothies and farm kitchens in the North of Scotland. I have given it in preference to the others, as the words are specially adapted to the old bothy air, to which they are set. I heard the song first sung to this air at a Sunday school soiree in the parish of New Byth, Aberdeenshire, upwards of forty years ago. This song itself is attributed to King James V., and is supposed to celebrate one of His Majesty's own adventures in clandestine love-making.

PART V.

(a) Miscellaneous Songs

(b) Ballads

PART V.

(a) Miscellaneous Songs.

TO THE BEGGIN' I WILL GO.

O' a' the trades that man can try
    The beggin' is the best,
For when a beggar's weary
    He can sit down and rest.
      To the beggin' I will go, will go,
      To the beggin' I will go.

First I maun get a meal-pock
    Made o' the leather reed,
And it will haud twa firlots,
    Wi' room for beef and breid.

Afore that I do gang awa
    I'll lat my beard grow strang,
And for my nails I winna pare,
    For beggars wear them lang.

I'll gang to some greasy cook
    And buy frae her a hat,
Wi' twa-three inches o' a rim,
    A' glitterin' owre wi' fat.

Syne I'll gang to a turner,
    And gar him mak' a dish;
And it maun haud three chappins,
    For I cudna dee wi' less.

I'll gang seek my quarters
    Before that it drows dark,
Jist when the guidman's sitten doon
    And new-hame frae his wark.

Syne I'll tak' out my muckle dish
    And stap it fu' o' meal,
And say, "Guidwife, gin ye gie me bree
    I winna seek your kail."

And maybe the guidman will say,
  " Puirman, put up your meal,
Your welcome to your brose the nicht,
  Likewise your breid and kail.":

If there's a wedding in the toon,
  I'll airt me to be there,
And pour my kindest benison
  Upon the winsome pair.

And some will gie me breid and beef,
  And some will gie me cheese,
And I'll slip out among the folk
  And gather bawbees.
      To the beggin' I will go, will go,
      To the beggin' I will go.

THE BEGGAR'S DAWTIE.

'Twas in the merry month of June,
When woods and valleys a' grew green,
And gentle ladies walk their lane
  In a fine summer's morning.

Down in yon glen I spied a swain,
A shepherd's crook into his han',
He was driving yowes oot owre the knowes,
  He's a bonnie weel-faur'd laddie.

" O, shepherd lad, what is your trade?
What occupation are you bred?
Or what's the way ye win your bread
  When herding you give over?"

" It's makin' spin'les is my trade,
And fittin' sticks for them wha need,
And I'm a beggar to my trade—
  So, lassie, can ye lo'e me?"

" I love ye just as manifold
As Jesse loved the cups of gold,
And as Jacob loved Rachel of old—
  Sae dearly as I lo'e ye."

" It's ye'll cast aff your robes o' red,
And ye'll put on a beggar's weed,
And ye'll follow me and beg your breid,
  And be a beggar's dawtie."

" It's I'll cast aff my robes o' red,
And I'll put on a beggar's weed,
And I'll follow you and I'll beg my breid
    And be a beggar's dawtie."

When they cam' to yon burgh town
The lassie blushed and she looked down;
They bocht a loaf and they baith sat down,
    And the lassie ate wi' her laddie.

But when they cam' to yon high, high hill,
Where sheep and oxen eat their fill,
She set her down, and she wept her will
    For the following o' her laddie.

" It's ye'll cast aff your beggin' weed,
And ye'll put on your robes o' red,
And I'll hie ye back the road ye cam',
    For I canna bide your weeping."

" I winna cast aff my beggin' weed,
Nor will I put on my robes o' red,
But I'll follow you, love, and I'll beg my breid,
    And I'll be the beggar's dawtie."

But when they cam' to yonder gate,
He rappit loud, sae loud at it;
Says she, " My dear, we'll be fautit
    For rappin' here sae loudly."

There were four-and-twenty gentlemen
Cam' out to welcome the beggar in,
And as mony ladies gay cam' ben
    To welcome his bonnie lassie.

It's atween the kitchen and the ha'
He lat his clooty cloak downfa',
And he shone like red gowd owre them a',
    The Gaberlunzie laddie.

His brither Jock cam' ben the ha',
He leuch till he was like to fa'—
" I wish that we'd been beggars a'
    For sic a bonnie lassie."

" Yestreen I was the beggar's bride,
This nicht I will lie by his side;
I've come to good by my misguide,
    I'm now the young Knight's lady."

THE POACHERS.

Come all ye gallant poachers that ramble void of care,
That walk out on a moonlight night, with your dog, your gun,
      and snare;
The harmless hare and pheasant you have at your command,
Not thinking on your last career upon Van Dieman's Land.

'Twas poor Tom Brown from Glasgow, Jack Williams, and
      poor Joe,
We were three daring poachers, the country well did know;
At night we were trepanned by the keepers in the sand,
And for fourteen years transported unto Van Dieman's Land.

The first day that we landed upon this fatal shore
The planters they came round us, full twenty score or more,
They rank'd us up like horses, and sold us out of hand,
And yok'd us up to ploughs, my boys, to plough Van Dieman's
      Land.

The houses that we dwell in here are built of clod and clay;
With rotten straw for bedding, we dare not say them nay;
Our cots are fenced with fire, and we slumber when we can,
And we fight the wolves and tigers which infest Van Dieman's
      Land.

At night, when soundly sleeping, I had a pleasant dream,
With my sweetheart I was courting down by a purling stream;
Through Scotland I was roving, with her at my command—
But I awoke downhearted upon Van Dieman's Land.

There cam' a lass from sweet Dundee, Jean Stewart it was her
    name,
For fourteen years transported, as you may know the same.
Our captain bought her freedom, and married her offhand,
And she gives us a' good usage here, upon Van Dieman's Land.

Although the poor of Scotland do labour and do toil,
They're robbed of every blessing and produce of the soil;
Your proud, imperious landlords, if we break their command,
They'll send you to the British hulks, or to Van Dieman's Land.

So all you gallant poachers give ear unto my song,
It is a bit of good advice, although it is not long,
Throw by your dogs and snares, for to you I speak plain,
For if you knew our hardships you would never poach again.

ILKA BLADE O' GRASS KEPS ITS AIN DRAP O' DEW.

WHAT is't that gars ye hang your heid and quit the cheery sun?
What gars ye think o' dark afore the canty day is done?
The nicht will come owre sune, alas! an' find ye no half thro',
Yet ilka blade o' grass keps its ain drap o' dew.

The man that tak's ill fortune's dunts nor greets because they're
    sair,
That's glad, though meat is hard to win, he's water aye an' air,
He trows if things are bad the day, the morn may smile anew,
For ilka blade o' grass keps its ain drap o' dew.

He's but a fule that thinks that ill can never come his gate,
And he that waits for ill to come will no hae lang to wait,
But lat it come, it canna bide, the stout heart wrastles through,
And ilka blade o' grass keps its ain drap o' dew.

THE SMUGGLERS' SONG.

WHEN the blink o' the day is fading fast
  By the glade and the warlock knowe,
And the weary sun is far in the wast,
  Like a big red furnace lowe;
O, that is the hour for to flash the oar
  On the breast of the deep, deep sea;
Though we've perils afloat, we are merry on the shore,
  Then the moonlight night for me.
    Then the moonlight night for me, etc.

The German may brag, but we'll sneer at his boast—
  He may fume in his palace ha';
We will ride out the storm on our ain Carrick coast,
  And we'll fling a' his threats to the wa';
While he snores on his cushions, we will ride on the billow,
  Like the bird o' the ocean free;
Wi' the waves foamin' white, an' the deck for my pillow,
  O, the moonlight night for me.
    O, the moonlight night for me, etc.

Give the daylight to those wha wad bask in its blaze—
  Wha exault when their virtues are seen;
But the good deeds we do 'neath the moon's yellow rays
  Pass oft as they never had been;
Yet merrily we'll carol in our light peerless bark,
  As she skips o'er the brine wi' glee,
And we'll help where it's needed, though we work in the dark—
  Then the moonlight night for me.
    Then the moonlight night for me, etc.

There's mony a sweet lassie that will wish us gude speed,
  As we steer by the twinkling star;
An' as lang as we've their blessin' ne'er a danger we'll heed,
  Though we're racked by the tempests afar.
Wi' the lace for the lady and the gin for the laird,
  We'll return ere the sun's on the lea;
Then here's to the King an' to auld Lucky Baird—
  O, the moonlight night for me.
    O, the moonlight night for me, etc.

This song was published in the *Ayrshire Wreath* in 1844.

ERIN-GO-BRAGH.

My name's Duncan Campbell, from the shire of Argyle,
I've travell'd this country for many a mile,
I've travell'd through England, through Ireland an' a',
And the name I go under's bold Erin-go-Bragh.

One night in auld Reekie, as I walked down the street,
A saucy policeman I chanced for to meet,
He glowered in my face, and he gave me some jaw,
And says—" When came ye over from Erin-go-Bragh?"

" I'm not a Paddy, though Ireland I've seen,
Nor am I a Paddy, though in Ireland I've been,
But though I was a Paddy, that's nothing ava,
There's many a bold hero from Erin-go-Bragh."

" I know you're a Pat by the cut of your hair,
But you all turn Scotch as soon as you come here,
You've left your own country for breaking the law,
We are seizing all stragglers from Erin-go-Bragh."

" Well, though I were a Pat, and you knew it were true,
Or were I the devil—pray, what's that to you?
If it were not for that baton you have in your paw,
I would show you a game played in Erin-go-Bragh."

Then a switch of blackthorn that I held in my fist,
Across his big body I made it to twist;
And the blood from his napper I quickly did draw,
And paid him stock and interest for Erin-go-Bragh.

The people came round like a flock of wild geese,
Crying, " Stop that great rascal, he's killed the police ";
And for every friend I had, I'm sure he had twa,
It was very tight times with bold Erin-go-Bragh.

But I came to a wee boat that sails on the Forth,
I picked up my all, and I steered for the North;
Farewell to auld Reekie, policeman an' a',
May the devil be with them! says Erin-go-Bragh.

Now, all ye brave fellows that listen to my song,
I don't care a farthing to where you belong;
But I'm from Argyle, in the Highlands, so braw,
But I ne'er take it ill when called Erin-go-Bragh.

A SHILLING OR TWA.

WHILE cautious and canny we slip ourselves through
This wearisome warld just as other folks do,
May we aye frae our pockets be ready to draw,
Coming clink frae our pockets a shilling or twa.
 Oh! what a grand thing is a shilling or twa,
 Eh! what a grand thing is a shilling or twa;
 Through country or town, while we trudge up and down,
 It's a round ready passport, a shilling or twa.

If lads wi' young lasses in favour would be,
They maun aye hae some present ready to gie;
Such as raisins or sweeties, or something that's braw,
Although it should cost them a shilling or twa.
 Oh! what a grand thing is a shilling or twa,
 Eh! what a grand thing is a shilling or twa;
 The lads frae their lasses get cuddles and kisses,
 And, oh! how sweet this is for a shilling or twa!

Oh, a penniless pocket's a pitiful case,
For it soon gars an old friend put on a new face;
But sour looks and strange faces will a' wear awa
If we can but show them a shilling or twa.
 Oh! what a grand thing is a shilling or twa,
 Eh! what a grand thing is a shilling or twa;
 Friendship in need is friendship indeed,
 But the best friend ava is a shilling or twa.

When the big man o' business, by fortune unblest,
Is forced as a bankrupt to appear in the list,
He can clear aff his debts an' get rid of the law
By paying each pound wi' a shilling or twa.
 Oh! what a grand thing is a shilling or twa,
 Eh! what a grand thing is a shilling or twa;
 Great sums can be paid and fortunes re-made
 By sleight-of-hand trade by a shilling or twa.

But a poor man in debt is harassed every day,
He is lawed and decreed wi' expenses to pay,
His wages arrested, his gear ta'en awa—
Nae credit, nae comfort, nae shilling or twa.

Oh! what a grand thing is a shilling or twa,
Eh! what a grand thing is a shilling or twa;
May the poor of our land ne'er want in their hand
The ready command of a shilling or twa.

Now, the great cause of debt and old Scotland's scaith too,
Is the devil's ain dram, whisky's blazes of blue,
For baith men and women sneer at teetotal law,
And spend in blue ruin a shilling or twa.

Oh! what a grand thing is a shilling or twa,
Eh! what a grand thing is a shilling or twa;
This nane can gainsay when spent the right way,
But woe when we stray wi' a shilling or twa.

A few years ago I appealed to the readers of a weekly newspaper for this
old song, but was only successful in recovering a couple of verses of it from
an old lady in Kilmarnock.   This lady informed me that she was over eighty
years of age, and that the song was a great favourite in her girlhood days.
I subsequently got the complete song, as here printed, in an old " broadside "
published in Glasgow many years ago.

Underneath I give another and more modern version of the song which I
culled from a weekly newspaper about 35 years ago.
The author was given as one William Fleming.

A SHILLIN' OR TWA.
(ANOTHER VERSION.)

Awa, wi' your dearies and juice o' the vine,
I sing nae the praises o' women or wine;
Some vain rhyming bardies wha coo like the dove,
And dream o' the wild, witching glamour o' love,
Frae sly glancin' een inspiration may draw,
But gie me the glint o' a shillin' or twa,
    Shillin' or twa, shillin' or twa,
A bonnie, bright, siller white shillin' or twa!

I carena for honour, I carena for fame,
An' naething to me is the boast o' a name;
Let proud gifted statesmen and heroes o' war
Rejoice in their ribbon, their clasp, or their star,
But the bonniest medals that ever I saw
Could ne'er be compared to a shillin' or twa,
    Shillin' or twa, shillin' or twa,
A bonnie, bright, siller white shillin' or twa!

Amid a' the trouble, vexation, and strife
We meet in this warl' as we journey through life,
The crosses and cares, by whatever decree,
That somehow or ither we a' hae to dree,
'Tis pleasin' to ken ye're at naebody's ca',
And on unco guid terms wi' a shillin' or twa,
  Shillin' or twa, shillin' or twa,
A bonnie, bright, siller white shillin' or twa!

When fortune is smilin' and blessing's flow free
Fu' mony blythe frien's roon' your board ye will see;
But thankless as grumphies they'll bid ye guid-day,
If ever you happen to slip down the brae.
When cauld bitter blasts of adversity blaw,
There's nae frien' on earth like a shillin' or twa,
  Shillin' or twa, shillin' or twa,
A bonnie, bright, siller white shillin' or twa!

MISS GORDON O' GIGHT.

O, WHARE are ye gaun, bonnie Miss Gordon,
  O, whare are ye gaun sae bonnie and braw?
Ye're gaun wi' Johnny Byron
  To squander the lands o' Gight awa.

Your Johnny's a man frae England jist come,
  The Scots dinna like his extraction ava,
But tak' ye gude tent, for he'll spen' a' your rent,
  And fast draw the lands o' Gight awa.

The shootin' o' guns and the rattlin' o' drums,
  The bugle in the woods and the pipes in the ha',
The beagles a-howling, the hounds a-growling,
  These sounds will soon gar a Gight gang awa.

The castle and the estate of Gight in the parish of Fyvie, Aberdeenshire, came about the year 1479 into the possession of William Gordon, third son of the second Earl of Huntly. He was killed at the battle of Flodden in 1513. There is an old prophecy to the effect that:—

When the heron leaves the tree,
The laird o' Gight will landless be.

On 12th May, 1785, Catherine Gordon, heiress of Gight, married the honourable John Byron, son of Admiral Byron, a wild young fellow. She became the mother of the poet, Lord Byron. Soon after the marriage the estate was sold, and the herons which had built their nests for many years in a fine tree near the castle took up their abode in the woods of Haddo House. The fear of the people on the estate, on hearing that Miss Gordon was about to marry Byron, found expression in the foregoing song.

THE WARK O' THE WEAVERS.

WELL we're a' met thegither here tae sit an' tae crack,
Wi' glesses in oor hands and oor wark upon oor back;
But there's no a trade among us a' can either mend or mak'
    But what wears the wark o' the weavers.
      If it warna for the weaver what wad we do?
      We wadna get claith made o' oor woo',
      We wadna get a coat, neither black nor blue,
        Gin't warna for the wark o' the weavers.

There's the hiremen, they mock us, and crack aye aboot's,
They say we're thin-faced and bleached-lookin' cloots;
But yet for a' their mockery they canna dae wi'oot's,
    Na! they canna want the wark o' the weavers.
    Chorus.

There's oor wrichts, an' oor sclaters, an' glaziers an' a',
Oor doctors, an' ministers, an' them that live by law,
And oor freends in Sooth Ameriky—though them we never saw,
    Yet we ken they wear the wark o' the weavers.
    Chorus.

There's our sailors an' sodgers, we ken they're very bauld,
But if they hadna claes, faith they couldna fecht for cauld;
The high an' low, the rich and puir, a'body young and auld
    Mair or less need the wark o' the weavers.
    Chorus.

Some folks are independent o' ither tradesmen's wark,
For women need nae barber, an' dykers need nae clerk;
But yet they cannot dae wi'oot a coat or a sark,
    Na! they canna want the wark o' the weavers.
    Chorus.

So the weaving a trade is that never can fail,
As lang's we need ae cloot to keep anither hale;
So lat us aye be merry owre a bicker o' guid ale.
    An' here's health an' lang life tae the weavers.
    Chorus.

Towards the middle of last century, this spirited song was very popular
in Forfarshire and other centres of the handloom weaving industry. Its
author was a Forfar weaver, David Shaw. who publi hed two small collections
of his poems, the best of which are " The Forfar Pensioner " and " Tammie
Treddlefeet." He died in Forfar in 1856, in his seventieth year.

THE KNIGHTS OF MALTA.

COME all ye knights, ye knights of Malta,
  In your glittering armour shine,
Assist your good and worthy Prince
  To protect the ark divine;
    For we are the true-born sons of Levi,
      Few on earth with us compare;
    We are the root and branch of David,
      That bright and glorious morning star.

With trembling steps I slow advanced,
  Sometimes I knocked both loud and shrill,
Until a knight in armour bright
  Demanded me what was my will.
    For we are the free-born sons of Levi,
      Few on earth with us compare;
    We wear the black and scarlet garter,
      And on our left breast a blazing star.

After some questions being asked,
  To which I answered with some fear,
They told me neither Turk nor heathen
  Could by any means enter here.
    For we are the true-born sons of Levi, etc.

With a cross and star placed on my breast,
  And Justice girded my loins all around,
Always remember the twelve stones
  On Jordon's banks are to be found.
    For we are the free-born sons of Levi, etc.

Noah planted the first garden;
  Moses planted the first rod;
He smote the waters for the Egyptians,
  And turned the Jordon into blood.
    For we are the true-born sons of Levi, etc.

As Joshua and I passed over Jordan,
  These twelve stones we bore along;
It was the twelve priests and our grand master
  Who carried the Ark of God along.
    For we are the free-born sons of Levi, etc.

There were seven trumpets of rams' horns
    Sounded loud before the Ark;
Gilgal was our resting-place,
    And there we left our holy mark.
        For we are the true-born sons of Levi, etc.

Come, all you brethren and join with me,
    And bear the cross as I have done;
Come, enter into this blessed temple
    Fitted near Jerusalem.
        For we are the free-born sons of Levi, etc.

Broad is the way that leadeth to destruction,
    Many there be that'll go therein;
Come ye to me and to my habitation,
    For Solomon's temple's free from sin.
        For we are the true-born sons of Levi,
            Few on earth with us compare;
        For we are the root and branch of David,
            That bright and glorious morning star.

THE LION'S DEN.

THERE were two brothers, both noted warriors,
    Who fell in love with a lady gay;
And for to win her was their endeavour—
    They tried to gain her both night and day.
The one of them he was a captain,
    Commanded by brave Colonel Carr;
While the other he was a brisk lieutenant
    On board the *Tiger*, a man-of-war.

The lady made a bold resolution
    That she would wed no man but he
Who would prove himself to be a man of valour,
    Either on the land or on the sea.
She called her coach to be made ready
    In early morning by the break of day,
And with her two gallants rode o'er the mountains
    Until they came where the cannons lay.

And when they came into the tower
    She threw her fan in the lions' den,
Saying—" Either of you that would gain a lady
    Must bring me back my fan again."

Then out did speak the faint - hearted captain,
  For he was sore distressed in mind—
" In battle I was ne'er called a coward,
  And to fight my foes I am well inclined;

" But among these lions, bears, and tigers,
  I think my life would no ransom prove;
I will not venture my life in danger,
  Though I should never gain your love."
Then out did speak the bold lieutenant,
  With a voice like thunder, both loud and shrill,
" Oh, I will venture my life in danger,
  All for to gain my love's goodwill."

So while they went into the tower
  The lions all looked fierce and grim,
But well behav'd the bold lieutenant,
  His looks were ten times as fierce as them.
Then from his side he drew a rapier,
  Two of the lions and he did kill;
When the others saw his manly courage
  Down at their conquerer's feet they fell.

He stepped down the fan to lift up,
  This courteous warrior made no delay:
While the lady in her coach sat trembling,
  Lest he'd become the lions' prey.
But when she saw the bold hero coming,
  And that to him no harm was done,
With open arms she did embrace him,
  Says—" Take the prize, love, ye now have won."

It was not long till the King got notice
  That two of his lions had been slain;
Yet he was not at all displeased,
  But gave him honour for the same.
He advanced him from being a first lieutenant,
  And made him Admiral of the blue,
And soon the lady and he were married;
  This lets us see what love can do.

This ballad has long been a favourite amongst country people, but so far
as I can ascertain it has only once appeared in print before, namely—in
Christie's Traditional Ballad Airs of the North. Christie states that Leigh
Hunt composed his poem. " The Glove and the Lion." from this ballad.

THE BANKS O' SKENE.

WHEN I was just a rantin' girl,
　About the age of sixteen,
I fell in love wi' a heckler lad
　Upon the banks o' Skene.
　　I fell in love, etc.

And I cut a' my hair afore,
　Sae did I it ahin',
And I put on a suit o' claes,
　A boy as gin I'd been.
　　And I put on, etc.

Syne I gaed to the heckler lad,
　Upon the banks o' Skene,
An' said, " If ye want for apprentice boys,
　It's here I'm I for ane."
　　And said, etc.

Said he, " Ye are a bonnie boy,
　And ye're baith neat and clean,
But I'll mak' you the heckler's wife,
　Upon the banks o' Skene."
　　But I'll, etc.

I WISH MY GRANNY SAW YE.

I AM Johnny Raw, a civil chiel,
I was reared up in the country,
Nae doubt ye winna ken me weel,
I'm a' the way frae Fintry;
Although I'm boosey yet I'm fly,
Among the lasses I'm a pry,
And after me they a' do cry,
　" I wish my Granny saw ye.

　　　" Tut's gae awa, ye mean tae blaw,
　　　I ken ye're up tae a thing or twa,
　　　As sure as death, man, Johnny Raw,
　　　　I wish my Granny saw ye."

I woo'd a lass a gey lang time,
She was a carter's dochter;
At length I thought I'd mak' her mine,
The wedding dress I bought her;
Says I, " My lass, noo be sincere,
So name the day and be my dear."
She laughed, and whispered in my ear,
  " I wish my Granny saw ye."

Yestreen I strolled in Argyle Street,
When a lady said—" Do please, sir,
Will you hold my little baby sweet,
I'm feared the crowd will squeeze her?"
I took the bairn, and said I would,
I like to do the ladies good;
She said, as we pushed through the crowd,
  " I wish my Granny saw ye."

As we were pushing through the crowd,
Somehow I missed the lady;
Quite wonder-strucken there I stood,
She had left me with the baby.
But where she went I could not learn,
As in my arms I held the bairn;
The folks cry'd—" John, ye've got your fairin',
  I wish my Granny saw ye."

The folks a' gathered round about
And laughed at my condition;
Till up came twa policemen stout
And took me to the station;
To laugh at me they a' began,
And said I was a lucky man
To get a wean brought to my han',
  " I wish my Granny saw ye."

Before the Bailies the next day
I made my simple statement,
How the lady run away
And left me with the infant.
At length the Bailie he did say—
" You and the child may go away,
So find a nurse and for it pay,
  I wish my Granny saw ye."

THE SPORTS O' GLASGOW GREEN.

Air.—"Fye, Let us a' to the Bridal."

AE morn in the sweet month o' July,
  When calm and serene was the air,
Young Jockey had trysted wi' Jenny
  To gang wi' him in to the fair.

His sark was clean on frae the washing,
  His blue bonnet covered his brow,
His braw worsted hose, eh! how dashing!
  Says, " Jenny, what think ye o' me now?"

Jenny put on her bab and her tucker,
  And cuist her bit shawl on her back;
Syne rowed up her shoon and her stockings,
  They set to the road in a crack.

Says Jocky, " Will ye tak' a snuff here?"
  Says she, " Ye are gayan weel doon."
" There's surely as muckle as prime you,
  I'll fill it when we win to the town."

Wi' pechin' an' sweatin' an' trampin',
  They soon came in sight o' the town—
" Hoy, Jenny, come into the slap here
  And put on your stockings and shoon."

And when they came into the town then,
  The like o't they never had seen;
Young and auld, baith married and single,
  Were daun'ering down to the Green.

When they cam' to the foot o' auld Sautie,
  The shows a' appeared in their view;
Ilka chiel was oxtering his dawtie,
  And some o' the bodies were fou.

There were spinners, and clippers, and darners.
  Some rogues, and some dacent folk;
The chiels were a' merrily playing
  At prick the loop, dice, and black Jock.

Wi' pushin' and squeezin' and chirtin'
  They got in the midst o' the crowd,
And, oh! what a fifing and drumming,
  And showmen were crying aloud—

"Come, walk up now, ladies and gemmen,
  Ye ne'er saw the like in your life;
Here's the two smallest dwarfs in the world,
  And a giant frae the Kingdom of Fife."

When they got to the front o' the shows then,
  There was likely to hae been some strife—
A man and a woman were fighting,
  And wha was't but Punch and his wife.

And there was a fleesome-like body,
  And, oh! for to jump he was dreich;
He leugh aye, and shruggit up his shouthers,
  And girn'd at the folk wi' his teeth.

Quo' Jockey, "I'm wearit wi' looking,
  Hoot, Jenny, my lass, come awa',
We'se hae a bit peep at the wild beasts,
  They say they're the best o' them a'."

There was ae beast wi' lang legs and short anes,
  Twa young anes keeked oot i' its wame;
There were monkeys, and peacocks, and parrots,
  And beasts that they kentna their name.

Quo' Jockey, "I've read in a beukie
  O' an elephant that ainst had got drunk,
It put its lang pipe in a bunghole,
  And what was this pipe but a trunk!

That ugly beast there's the same o't,
  It's said it cam' oot frae its head."
Quo' Jenny, "That's only the nose o't,
  Eh! eh! that's a trunkin' indeed."

"That a trunk! you puir stupid haveral!
  I ne'er heard the like a' my days!
Isna a trunk a box covered wi' calf skin
  For hauding folks' shoon and their claes?

"And common sense tae might hae telt ye
The truth; for instance, suppose—
Could a trunk e'er win in at a bunghole,
  Or a beast carry ane at its nose?"

Quo' Jocky, "It's lang since the morning,
  And, faith, now I'm turning right yaup."
On purpose for to get a corning,
  The twa then began for to stap.

They daun'ert awa down by Clyde Street,
  For a house that their fancy might please,
And at the wast end o' the Briggate
  They landed in Lucky M'Nee's.

Ye ken she was a braw canty housewife,
  And kept a gude mouthfu' o' dram,
Chiels that faun the ground o' their stomachs,
  Their bellies she brawly could cram.

Quo' Jockey, " We've been at the shows, lass,
  And we've seen some excellent fun;
Come, gie us a gill o' your whisky,
  Twa bowls o' your kail, and a bun."

Says Jenny, " There's nae use in a' that, na,
  For eneuch is as guid as a feast;
Whisky aye gies me a sair head, man,
  And mak's yoursel', Jock, like a beast."

" But, callans, since this is the fair day,
  And your bawbees you're sawing awa,
Come, leave aff your fuddlin' and drinkin'
  And tak' a gude reel in the ha'."

As the carle was gathering the pennies,
  To strike up wi' vigour and glee,
A chiel tipp'd Jock's lass on the shouther,
  And says, " Lassie, will ye dance wi' me?"

But Jock was as gleg as a razor,
  And he cries out, " Freen', that's no fair."
Says the fellow, " If ye want for to quarrel,
  I'll tip you the rigs o' the fair."

Forfauchen wi' drinking and dancing,
  The twa they cam' toddling hame;
Wi' rugging and riving and drawing
  They baith were wearied and lame.

Now, whan they got hame in the morning,
  Daylight was beginning to peep;
Jock hirselt awa to the blankets
  And healed his sair head wi' a sleep.

This is a description of Glasgow Fair by an unknown writer. So
far as I can ascertain, this song has only appeared but once in print before,
viz., in the *Scottish Songster*, long out of print.

ELLEN OF ABERDEEN.

My earthly pleasures now are fled,
  My joyful days are done,
Since Ellen in her grave was laid
  And her sands of life are run.

No friends on earth young Ellen had
  To shed a silent tear,
Of parents both she was bereft
  In her eleventh year.

The trouble that my Ellen had
  Defied the doctor's skill;
She closed her eyes, and bade farewell
  At her Redeemer's will.

Her days were numbered on this earth,
  Her age scarce seventeen;
She was an honour to the female sex,
  And the pride o' Aberdeen.

There was one request she asked of me,
  Since nothing could her save,
That I would see her last remains
  Laid decent in the grave.

The tender words did pierce my heart
  As I sat by her side;
That night young Ellen breathed her last,
  She would have been my bride.

In memory still I mourn the day
  Death tore her from my arms;
A fairer flower ne'er decked the field
  Than Ellen in her charms.

She was all that my fond heart desired,
  Her death makes me repine,
To see a maid so young in years
  Ta'en from the stage of time.

No more I'll view that virgin pure,
  Whom many did admire;
She was like a flower just newly sprung
  In all its rich attire.

We'll meet nae mair at the Auldton kirk,
  Nor at the Bridge o' Don;
We'll meet nae mair at the auld fir well,
  Our pleasures are all gone.

Oft in the churchyard have I strayed
  To view her green turf bed;
Methinks her dust yet heaves a sigh
  Though mingled with the dead.

A pilgrim here I'm left to steer
  Till I reach yon happy shore;
Then I'll be with my Ellen dear
  When we meet to part no more.

The words of the ballad was sent to me by Mr. Robert Mellis, West Folds,
Huntly, and the characteristic old ballad air was sent to me by Mr. Gavin
Grieg, M.A., New Deer, who noted it down from the singing of a country
person. Mr. Grieg informed me that the same air with a second strain added
is to be found in Petries' *Ancient Irish Music.*

DANNY SIM'S SOW.

THERE was a drunken collier, they ca'd him Danny Sim,
And mony a curious anecdote I could relate o' him,
And this is ane amang the rest that may be tell't thro' town and
    clachan,
How he cheated the butcher o' his pork and set the parish a'
    a-lachin'.

  Whack, row de dow, row, fall all de doo a daddie,
  Whack, row de dow, row, fall all de doo a dee.

To buy the sow a peck of draff Danny set out wi' glee,
And he met in wi' Sailor Sandy down by Ramsay's brewery;
Sic frien'ship was between the twa they ne'er could part without
    a drappie,
And though their fortune was but sma' they passed the nicht
    thegither happy.
                Whack, row, etc.

Then Danny in his majesty cam' hame jist rowin' fou',
But lang afore daylight cam' in he heard the hungry sow
Roarin' like the Bars o' Ayr, and tearin' doun baith stobs and
    biggin';
O, Gissey, lass, I've drunk the draff, so ye must starve or eat the
    riggin'.
                Whack, row, etc.

Then Danny's wife began to flyte and curse his drunken bags,
"Nae won'er that your wife and bairns they do rin in rags;
You to gang and drink the draff and leave the sow without her
    supper—
And nae to beat about the bush, sure, Sailor Sandy's little
    better."
                Whack, row, etc.

Then Danny's blood began to boil, and he's gane to the laft,
And gazing all around him he spied an auld pick shaft
That aften served in time of need, it never failed in any riot,
Likewise, it was the very thing to mak' a scolding wife be quiet.
                Whack, row, etc.

Noo, Danny's wife she spied the shaft and took the road wi'
    speed,
For she kent it was the only way to save a broken head;
But woe betide poor grumphy's hide, for she got such an awful
    rungin',
By every thump 'tween neck and rump, she swelled and fattened
    most uncommon.
                Whack, row, etc.

Noo, Danny kent a butcher-man that had a muckle purse,
And being acquaint wi' him for lang he gae him the offer first,
Saying, "Come and buy my muckle sow, she's ripe and ready
    for the gully,
And as we've been sae lang acquaint, I'll gi'e you the offer,
    Willie."
                Whack, row, etc.

Then Willie cam' and saw the sow, and bade him three pound
    ten;
" Na, na," quo' Dan, " that winna dò, so ye maun bid again ";
" Noo, noo," quo' Will, " I'll tell you what, we'll no cast out
    about the maitter,
But since we've been sae lang acquaint, we'll jist exactly drink
    the differ."
                        Whack, row, etc.

Noo, Danny he held up his hands as she was gaun awa,
For he weel could act the hypocrite, and lat the tears downfa',
Saying, " Fare-ye-weel, my muckle sow—tak' her, Will, ye're
    welcome till her,
But, as sure as death we wadna part had it no' been for want o'
    siller."

    Whack row de dow, row, fal al de doo a-daddy,
    Whack row de dow, row, fall all de dow a-day.

PART V.

(b) Ballads.

THE DOUGLAS TRAGEDY.

"RISE up, rise up, now, Lord Douglas," she says,
 "And put on your armour bright;
Let it never be said that a daughter of thine
 Was married to a lord under night."

"Rise up, rise up, my seven sons so bold,
 And put on your armour so bright;
And take better care of your youngest sister,
 For your eldest's away the last night."

He's mounted her on a milk-white steed,
 And himself on a dapple grey,
With a buglet horn hung down by his side,
 And lightly they both rode away.

Lord William lookit o'er his left shoulder
 To see what he could see;
And there he spy'd her seven brothers bold
 Come riding over the lea.

" Light down, light down, Lady Marg'ret," he said,
  " And hold my steed in your hand,
Until that against your seven brothers bold
  And your father I make a stand."

She held his steed in her milk-white hand,
  And she never shed one tear,
Until that she saw her seven brothers fa'
  And her father (hard fighting) she loved dear.

" Oh, hold your hand, Lord William!" she said,
  " For your strokes they are wondrous sair;
Sweethearts I can get mony a ane,
  But a father I can never get mair."

Oh, she's ta'en out her handkerchief,
  It was o' the holland sae fine,
And aye she dighted her father's bloody wounds
  That were redder than the wine.

" Oh, chuse, oh, chuse, Lady Marg'ret," he said,
  " Oh, whether will ye gang or bide?"
" I'll gang, I'll gang, Lord William," she said,
  " For ye've left me no other guide."

He's lifted her on a milk-white steed,
  And himself on a dapple grey,
With a buglet horn hung down by his side,
  And slowly they baith rade away.

Oh, they rade on, and on they rade,
  And a' by the light of the moon,
Until that they came to yon wan water,
  And there they baith lighted doon.

They lighted doon to tak' a drink
  Of the spring that ran so clear;
And doon the stream ran the gude heart's blood,
  And sair she began for to fear.

" Hold up, hold up, Lord William," she said,
  " For I fear that ye hae been slain!"
" 'Tis naething but the shadow of my scarlet cloak
  That shines in the water sae plain."

Oh, they rade on, and on they rade,
  And a' by the light of the moon,
Until they came to his mother's ha' door
  And there they baith lighted doon.

"Get up, get up, Lady Mother," he said,
  "Get up and let me in!
Get up, get up, Lady Mother," he said,
  "For this night my fair lady I've win.

"Oh, mak' my bed, Lady Mother," he said,
  "Oh, mak' it braid and deep!
And lay Lady Marg'ret close at my back,
  And the sounder I will sleep."

Lord William was dead lang ere midnight,
  Lady Marg'ret lang ere day;
And all true lovers that go thegither
  May they have mair luck than they!

Lord William was buried in St. Marie's Kirk,
  Lady Marg'ret in Marie's quire;
Out o' the lady's grave grew a bonnie red rose,
  And out o' the knight's a brier.

And they twa met, and they twa plat,
  And fain they would be near;
And a' the warld might ken right weel
  They were twa lovers dear.

But by and rade the Black Douglas,
  And wow but he was rough,
For he pulled up the bonnie brier bush
  And flang't in St. Marie's Loch.

I learned this old ballad, both words and tune, from the singing of a
servant girl at a gathering at the Home Farm of Forglen (the seat of
Sir Robert Abercromby, Bart.), in the summer of 1878. and Mr. Allan,
A.L.C.M., Glasgow, kindly arranged the music.

THE BANKS OF SWEET DUNDEE.

It's of a farmer's daughter, so beautiful, I'm told,
Her parents died and left her five hundred pounds in gold;
She lived with her uncle, the cause of all her woe;
You soon shall hear this maiden fair did prove his overthrow.

Her uncle had a ploughboy young Mary loved full well,
And in her uncle's garden sweet tales of love would tell;
There was a wealthy squire who oft came her to see,
But still she loved the ploughboy on the banks of sweet Dundee.

It was on a summer's morning, her uncle went straightway,
He knocked at Mary's bedroom door, and unto her did say—
" Come, rise, my pretty maiden, a lady you may be;
The squire is waiting for you on the banks of sweet Dundee."

" A fig for all your squires, your lords, and dukes likewise.
My William he appears to me like diamonds in my eyes."
" Begone, unruly female, you ne'er shall happy be,
I mean to banish William from the banks of sweet Dundee."

Her uncle and the squire rode out one summer's day,
" Young William is in favour," her uncle he did say;
" Indeed, 'tis my intention to tie him to a tree,
Or else to bribe the pressgang on the banks of sweet Dundee."

The pressgang came to William when he was all alone,
He boldly fought for liberty, but they were six to one.
The blood did flow in torrents. " Pray, kill me now," said he,
" I would rather die for Mary on the banks of sweet Dundee."

This maid one day was walking, lamenting for her love;
She met the wealthy squire down in her uncle's grove.
He put his arms around her. " Stand off, base man," said she,
" For you've banished the only man I love from the banks of
    sweet Dundee."

He clasped his arms around her and tried to throw her down,
Two pistols and a sword she spied beneath his morning gown.
Young Mary took the pistols, his sword he used so free,
Then she did fire and shot the squire on the banks of sweet
    Dundee.

Her uncle overheard the noise, and hastened to the ground.
" O, since you've shot the squire, I'll give you your death-
    wound."
" Stand off, then," cried young Mary, " undaunted I will be—"
She the trigger drew and her uncle slew on the banks of sweet
    Dundee.

A doctor soon was sent for, a man of noted skill,
Likewise there came a lawyer to sign her uncle's will;
He willed his gold to Mary, who fought so manfully,
Then closed his eyes, no more to rise, on the banks of sweet
    Dundee.

Young William he was sent for, and quickly did return;
As soon as he came back again young Mary ceased to mourn.
The day it was appointed, they joined their hands so free,
And now they live in splendour on the banks of sweet Dundee.

GIGHT'S LADYE.

Music by Mr. Jas. B. Allan, A.L.C.M., Glasgow.

WILL ye gang to the Hielands, my bonnie love?
  Will ye gang to the Hielands, Geordie?
I'll tak' the high road gin ye tak' the low,
  And I'll be in the Hielands afore ye.

I'd rather for to stay on the bonnie banks o' Spey
  To see a' the fish boaties rowin',
Afore that I would gang to your high Hieland hill
  To hear a' the black kye lowin'.

He had not been in the high Hieland hills
  Months but barely twa, O,
When he was put in a prison strong
  For hunting the deer and the roe, O.

Where will I get a little wee boy
  That is both true and steady,
That will run on to the bonnie Bog o' Gight
  Wi' a letter to my ladye?

Oh, here am I, a bonnie wee boy
  That is baith true and steady,
And I'll run on to the bonnie Bog o' Gight
  Wi' a letter to your ladye.

When you come where the grass grows green
   You'll slacken your shoes and run, O;
And when you come where the bridge is broke
   You'll bend your bow an' swim, O.

And when you come to the bonnie Bog o' Gight
   You'll neither shout nor call, O,
But you'll bend your bow to your left breast
   Then leap in over the wall, O.

When he came where the grass grew green
   He slackened his shoes and ran, O,
And when he came where the bridge was broke
   He bent his bow and swam, O.

And when he came to the gates of Gight
   He did neither shout nor call, O,
But he bent his bow to his left breast
   And he leaped in over the wall, O.

When that the ladye the letter looked on,
   I wat little laugh got she, O;
Afore she had read it half-way down
   A saut tear blinded her e'e, O.

Gae saddle to me the grey horse, she cried,
   The broon never rode so smartly,
And I'll awa to Edinburgh town
   And borrow the life o' my Geordie.

When she came to the pier o' Leith
   The puir folk stood thick and mony.
She threw the red gowd right them among;
   Bade them pray for the life o' her Geordie.

When that she came to Edinburgh town
   The nobles there were mony,
Ilka ane wi' his hat on his head,
   But hat in hand stood Geordie.

O has he killed, or has he robbed,
   Or has he stolen ony?
Or what's the ill that my love has done
   That he's going to be hanged shortly?

He has not killed, he has not robbed,
　He has not stolen ony,
But he has hunted the King's young deer,
　So he's going to be hanged shortly.

Will the red gowd buy aff my love, she said,
　Will the red gowd buy aff Geordie?
Ten thousand crowns, if ye pay down,
　Ye'll get on your hat on your Geordie.

Then out it speaks Lord Montague
　(O woe be to his body),
This day we hanged young Charlie Hay,
　The morn we'll hang your Geordie.

She's taen the silk mantle frae her neck,
　And, O, but she spread it bonnie;
Wi' his hat in her hand she has begged all around,
　Till she's begged the life o' her Geordie.

Some gave crowns and some gave pounds,
　Some gave dollars mony;
The King himself gave five hundred crowns
　To get on her hat on her Geordie.

Then out it speaks Lord Montague
　(O wae be to his body),
I wish that Gight had lost his head,
　I might enjoyed his ladye.

But out it speaks the ladye herself,
　Ye need ne'er wish my body;
O ill befa' your wizened snout,
　Would ye compare wi' my Geordie?

Now since she s on her high horse set,
　And on behind her Geordie,
There was ne'er a bird so blythe in a bush
　As she was behind her Geordie.

First I was lady at bonnie Auchindoun,
　And next I was mistress at Kincraigie,
But now I'm guidwife at the bonnie Bog o' Gight,
　And I've ventured my life for my Geordie.

THE GYPSIE LADDIE.

THERE were three gipsies all in a row,
  And O but they sang bonnie, O;
They sang so sweet and so complete
  That they charmed the hearts of our ladies, O.

Lord Cassils' lady came downstairs
  With all her maids behind her, O;
With a bottle of red wine into her hand
  For to treat the gipsy laddies, O.

She's treated them all to a glass of red wine,
  Likewise a little ginger, O;
And one of them stepped her behind,
  Stole the gold ring from her finger, O:

Says, "Ye'll tak aff your bonnie silk dress,
  Put on a tartan plaidie, O,
And ye'll travel on a' the lee lang day
  And follow the gipsy laddie, O."

"I'll tak aff my bonnie silk dress,
  Put on a tartan plaidie, O,
And I'll travel on a' the lee lang day
  And follow my gipsy laddie, O."

"Surely you've got gold in store,
  And surely you've got treasures three,
And surely you've got all that you want,
  And three bonnie boys to amuse you wi'?"

"O yes, I have got gold in store,
 O yes, I have got treasures three,
O yes, I have got all that I want,
 And I've three bonnie boys to amuse me wi'.

"Last night I lay on a well-made bed,
 Wi' my guid lord beside me, O;
This night I'll lie in a tenant's barn
 Wi' a' the gipsies around me, O."

Lord Cassils he came home at night,
 A-calling for his lady O;
The ane denied, but the other replied,
 "She's awa wi' the gipsy laddies, O!"

"Gae saddle to me my bonnie black steed:
 Mak haste, mak haste, mak ready, O,
For I will neither eat nor drink
 Till I bring back my lady, O."

He rode east and he rode west,
 Till he came to yonder bogie, O,
And the bonniest lassie that ever he saw
 She was following the gipsy laddies, O.

There's sixteen o' ye, well-made men,
 Although ye are na bonnie, O,
And ye will a' high hangèd be
 For stealing Lord Cassils' lady, O.

Versions of this old ballad have appeared under the title of "Johnnie Faa,"
in several collections of Scottish song, but the above version, which is the one
most common in the North of Scotland, has not before been printed.

BONNIE JEAN O' BETHELINE.

Air.—"Glenlogie.

THERE were four-and-twenty ladies
 Dined in the Queen's ha',
Bonnie Jean o' Betheline
 Was the flower o' them a'.

There were four-and-twenty nobles
 Rode through Banchory fair,
And bonnie Glenlogie
 Was the flower o' them there.

Bonnie Jean at a window
　She chanced to sit nigh,
And on young Glenlogie
　She fixed her eye.

She called on her footman,
　And to him did say—
" O! what is that knight's name,
　And where does he stay?"

" He's o' the grand Gordons,
　Of great birth and fame;
He stays in Glenlogie,
　Lord George is his name."

Then she wrote a braid letter,
　And sealed it in haste,
To send to Glenlogie,
　For she thought it best.

And says—" O! brave Glenlogie,
　Unto me be kind,
I've laid my love on you,
　And told you my mind."

Then reading the letter,
　As he stood on the green,
Says—" I leave you to judge, sirs,
　What do women mean?"

Then he turned about sprightly,
　As the Gordons do a',
" Lay not your love on me,
　I'm promised awa."

When she heard his answer
　Her heart was like to break,
That she'd laid her love on him,
　And he so ungrate.

Then she called upon her maidens
　To put her to bed,
And take her fine jewels
　And lay them aside.

" My seals and my signets
　No more shall I crave;
But linen and trappin',
　A chest and a grave."

Her father stood by her
  Possessed by great fear,
To see his dear daughter
  Possessed with care.

Says—" Hold your tongue, Jeanie,
  Let a' your folly be;
I'll wed you to Dumfedline,
  He's better than he."

" O! hold your tongue, father,
  And let me alone;
If I get na Glenlogie
  I'll never hae ane.

" His bonnie jimp middle,
  His black rolling e'e;
If I get na Glenlogie
  I'm sure I shall dee."

But her father's old chaplain,
  A man of great skill,
Did write a braid letter,
  And penned it well:

Saying—" O! brave Glenlogie,
  Why must it be so?
A maid's love's laid on you,
  She'll die in her woe."

Then reading the letter
  His heart was like to break,
That such a leal maiden
  Should die for his sake.

Then he called on his footman,
  And also his groom,
Says—" Get my horse bridled
  And saddled full soon."

Before the horse was bridled
  And brought to the gate
Bonnie Glenlogie
  Was five miles on foot.

When he came to Betheline,
  He saw naething there
But weeping and wailing,
  Vexation and care.

Then out spake her father,
  With a tear in his e'e,
" You're welcome, Glenlogie,
  You're welcome to me."

" If ye make me welcome,
  As welcome's ye say,
Ye'll show me the chamber
  Where Jeanie does lay."

Before that she saw him
  She was pale and wan,
But when she did see him
  She grew ruddy again.

" O! turn, bonnie Jeanie,
  Turn ye on your side,
For I'll be the bridegroom,
  And ye'll be the bride."

When Jeanie was married,
  And her tocher was tauld,
Bonnie Jeanie Meldrum
  Was but sixteen years auld.

From an article in *The Huntly Express* of 24th January, 1881, by the late Dr. Shearer, headmaster, Gordon Schools, Huntly, I obtained the following information regarding this ballad:—" In the year 1562, Queen Mary was obliged to make a ' progress,' as it was then termed, through the North of Scotland, in order to put an end to the domestic troubles and broils which had arisen amongst the Northern nobility. The Queen lived for some weeks at the house of Fetternear, during which time she became acquainted with a young lady, Jean Meldrum, who soon became one of Mary's chief favourites. This by no means shy young lady having chanced to see Sir George Gordon of Glenlogie, as he rode through the villiage of Banchory, fell in love with him, but, unlike Shakespeare's maiden, ' who never told her love.' she despatched a letter to Sir George telling him that she must either have him for her husband or die. This rather unmaidenly proceeding had at first no effect on the knight, who only made light of it as a good joke. This soon threw the young lady into a violent fever, and then her father's chaplain undertook to explain the matter to Sir George, and succeeded so well that Glenlogie relented, and they were married. Several short versions of this ballad have been published in old collections of Scottish ballads under such titles as 'Glenlogie and ' The Wooing of Sir George Gordon,' but the above version, which is still sung by the country folks in Aberdeenshire and Kincardineshire, where Lady Jean wooed and won her husband, is the only correct and complete one."

THE LAIRD O' ROSLIN'S DAUGHTER,

OR, CAPTAIN WEDDERBURN'S COURTSHIP.

Andante.

THE Laird o' Roslin's daughter
　Walked through the woods her lane,
And by cam' Captain Wedderburn,
　A servant to the King.
He said unto his livery men,
　If it werna against the law,
He'd tak' her to his ain bed
　And lay her neist the wa'.

"I'm walking here alane," she says,
　"Amang my father's trees,
And you must let me walk alane,
　Kind sir, now, if you please;
The supper bell it will be rung,
　And I'll be missed awa;
Sae I winna lie in your bed
　At either stock or wa'."

He says, "My pretty lady,
　I pray give me your hand,
And ye'll hae drums and trumpets
　Always at your command;
And fifty men to guard you with
　That well their swords can draw;
Sae we'll baith lie in ae bed
　And ye'll lie neist the wa'."

"Haud awa frae me," she says,
  "And pray lat gae my hand,
The supper bell it will be rung,
  I can nae langer stand;
My father he will angry be
  Gin I be missed awa,
Sae I'll nae lie in your bed
  At either stock or wa'."

Then said the pretty lady,
  "I pray tell me your name?"
"My name is Captain Wedderburn,
  A servant to the King.
Though thy father and his men were here,
  O' them I'd have nae awe;
But would tak' you to my ain bed
  And lay you neist the wa'."

He lichtit aff his milk-white steed,
  And set this lady on;
And a' the way he walked on foot
  He held her by the hand;
He held her by the middle jimp
  For fear that she should fa',
To tak' her to his ain bed
  And lay her heist the wa'.

He took her to his lodging-house,
  His landlady looked ben:
Says, "Mony a pretty lady
  In Edinbruch I've seen,
But sic a lovely face as thine
  In it I never saw;
Gae mak' her doun a down-bed
  And lay her at the wa'."

"O, haud awa frae me," she says,
  "I pray you lat me be,
I winna gang to your bed
  Till ye dress me dishes three;
Dishes three ye maun dress me,
  Gin I should eat them a',
Afore I lie in your bed
  At either stock or wa'.

" It's ye maun get to my supper
  A cherry without a stane;
And ye maun get to my supper
  A chicken without a bane;
And ye maun get to my supper
  A bird without a ga';
Or I winna lie in your bed,
  At either stock or wa'."

" It's when a cherry is in the blume,
  I'm sure it has nae stane;
And when the chicken's in the shell,
  I wat it has nae bane.
An' sin' the flood o' Noah,
  The doo she has nae ga';
Sae we'll baith lie in ae bed,
  And ye'll lie neist the wa'."

" O, haud your tongue, young man," she says,
  " Nor that gate me perplex;
For ye maun tell me questions yet,
  And that is questions six.
Questions six ye'll answer me,
  And that is three times twa;
Afore I lie in your bed,
  At either stock or wa'.

" What's greener than the greenest grass?
  What's higher than the trees?
What's waur than an ill-woman's wish?
  What's deeper than the seas?
What bird sings first? and whereupon
  First doth the dew down fa'?
Ye'll tell afore that I lie down
  At either stock or wa'."

O, holly's greener than the grass;
  Heaven's higher than the trees;
The deil's waur nor a woman's wish;
  Hell's deeper than the seas;

The cock crows first; on cedar tap
  The dew does first down fa';
So we'll baith lie in ae bed,
  And ye'll lie neist the wa'."

"O, haud your tongue, young man," she says,
  "And gie your fleechin' ower;
Unless ye find me ferlies,
  And that is ferlies four.
Ferlies four ye maun find me,
  And that is twa and twa;
Or I'll never lie in your bed
  At either stock or wa'.

"It's ye maun get to me a plum
  That in December grew;
And ye maun get a silk mantel
  That waft was ne'er ca'd through;
A sparrow's horn; a priest unborn,
  This nicht to join us twa;
Or I'll nae lie in your bed
  At either stock or wa'."

"My father has some winter fruit
  That in December grew;
My mother has an Indian gown
  That waft was ne'er ca'd through;
A sparrow's horn is quickly found,
  There's ane on ilka claw,
And twa upon the neb o' him;
  And ye'll shall get them a'.

"There stands a priest outside the door
  Just ready to come in;
Nae man can say that he was born,
  Nae man, unless he sin;
A wild boar tore his mother's side,
  He out o' it did fa';
Sae we'll baith lie in ae bed,
  And ye'll lie neist the wa'."

Little kenned Grizzie Sinclair
  That morning when she rose,
That this would be the hindmost
  O' a' her maiden days.
But now there's no within the realm,
  I think, a blyther twa;
And they baith lie in ae bed,
  And she lies neist the wa'.

This humourous old song has always been a favourite amongst country folks. So far as I can ascertain, it appeared first in the *New British Songster*, published at Falkirk in 1783, and versions of it have appeared in collections and broadsheets at various times during the past century, but the music to which it is sung has not before been printed.

TO ROLL HER IN MY PLAIDIE.

THERE lives a lass by yonder burn,
  Wha jinks about the seggan,
And aft she gives her sheep a turn
  That feed amang the bracken.

    Could I believe she'd woo wi' me,
      In spite o' mam or daddie,
    I'd afttimes slip out owre yon lea
      And roll her in my plaidie.

Her breast to busk I'd violets pu'
  Frae yonder glen sae foggy;
And bluebells hingin' wat wi' dew
  Frae yonder den sae boggy.

    I maun awa, I canna stay,
      Should a' gan' tapsalteerie,
    Should boggles meet me in the way,
      This nicht I'll see my dearie.

I'll ben the spense an' dress a wee,
  Wi' knots and bots fu' gaudie;
For I canna rest until I see
  Gin she'll gang in my plaidie.

    Could I believe she'd woo wi' me,
      An' tak' me for her laddie,
    I'd afttimes slip out owre yon lea
      And roll her in my plaidie.

THE SHEFFIELD APPRENTICE.

Key D. {:m |f :- :m | r :- :r | l :- :- | s :- :d | m :- :r | d :- :d | d :- :- | - :- }

{:s | s :- :m | s :- :l | d' :- :- | t - :s | l :- :d' | m :- :f | s :- :- | - :- }

{:s | s :- :m | s :- :l | d' :- :- | t :- :s | l :- :d' | m :- :f | s :- :- | - :- }

{:m | f :- :m | r :- :r | l :- :- | s :- :d | m :- :r | d :- :d | d :- :- | - :- ||

I was brought up in Sheffield, but not of high degree,
My parents doted on me, they had no child but me;
I rolled in much pleasure, where'er my fancy led,
Till I was bound apprentice, then all my joys they fled.

I did not like my master, he did not use me well,
And took a resolution not long with him to dwell.
Unknown to my poor parents, from him I ran away,
And steered my course for London. Oh! cursed be that day!

A handsome lovely damsel, from Holland, she was there,
She offered me great wages to serve her for a year;
And after great persuasion with her I did agree
To go with her to Holland, which proved my destiny.

I had not been in Holland years but two or three,
Until my lovely mistress grew very fond of me;
She said her gold and silver, her houses, and her land,
If I'd consent to marry her, should be at my command.·

I said, " Dear honoured lady, I cannot wed you both,
And lately I have promised and made a solemn oath
To wed with none but Polly, your pretty chambermaid,
Excuse me, my dear mistress, for she has my heart betrayed."

Then in an angry passion away from me she's gone,
Swearing to be avenged on me before 'twas long;
For she was so perplexed she could not be my wife
That she soon laid a project to take away my life.

One day as I was walking all in the garden green,
The flowers they were springing delightful to be seen;
A gold ring from her finger, as she was passing by,
She slipped into my pocket, and for it I must die.

Now, in a few days after, in haste then I was call'd
Before a dreadful Justice to answer for the fault;
Though long I pleaded innocence, it was of no avail,
She swore so sore against me that I was sent to jail.

My mistress swore I robbed her, which ne'er was my intent,
Because I would not marry her, she did it from contempt;
From that place of confinement she brought me to the tree,
Oh! woe be to my mistress, for she has ruined me.

All you that stand around me, my wretched fate to see,
Don't glory in my downfall, but rather pity me!
Don't blame me, I am innocent; I bid the world adieu—
Farewell, my pretty Polly, I die for love of you!

This interesting old ballad was sent to me by Mr. James B. Allan,
A.L.C.M., music teacher, Glasgow, who noted down both words and music
from the singing of an old lady who picked them up in the North of
Scotland many years ago.

A version of the ballad appears in Dean Christie's *Traditional Ballad Airs*,
but the air that the words are set to in Christie's collection has two strains,
while Mr. Allan's air has but one. These old ballad airs have rarely more
than one strain, and consequently, Mr. Allan's one is, in all probability,
the original air to which the words were first set.

The ballad is apparently of English origin, and the plot or story is common
to both English and Irish folk-songs.

SIR JOHN GORDON.

MERRY was it in the green forest,
    Amang the leaves green,
When Sir John Gordon went out to hunt
    With bows and arrows keen.

He hunted east, he hunted west,
    He left his men so free,
Till, tired, he laid him down to rest
    Beneath the elfin tree.

And there he saw a vision sweet,
 He thought a dream dreamed he,
He opened his eyes, a lady sweet
 Bent o'er him on bended knee.

Her gown was o' the green, green silk,
 Her mantle o' velvet fine,
And from the mane of her milk-white steed
 Silver bells hung fifty-and-nine.

Sir John he started to his feet,
 Then down on bended knee
Cried, "Ave Marie! Queen of Heaven!
 For no mortal of earth I see."

"Oh, stop, I pray thee, Sir John," she cried,
 "That name belongs nae me,
I am the Queen of Fairyland,
 And have fa'en in love with thee.

"Now, if ye love me, kiss my lips,
 If that ye be na' fleyed;
But dinna press my lips, Sir John,
 If ye love any other maid."

"Betide me weal, betide me woe,
 Your rosy lips I'll kiss,
No weird shall ever daunton me,
 Or rob me of this bliss."

He kissed her once, he kissed her twice,
 He gave her kisses mony,
And aye he cried, "Your rosy lips
 Are sweeter than the honey."

She mounted on her milk-white steed,
 She's taken Sir John behind;
And aye where'er her bridle rung
 He flew swifter than the wind.

"My dear Sir John, my bonnie Sir John,
 Since ye hae kissed me,
Through weal or woe, as it may chance,
 Seven years my slave ye maun be."

"Seven years," he cried; "seven thousand years!
 Oh! what were that to me?
Only so that I may enjoy
 The charms of my fair lady."

Q

And on they rode and further on,
  And swifter than the wind,
Until they reached a wide desert,
  Left all living thing behind.

And on they rode, and further on,
  Through rivers above the knee;
Till they saw neither moon nor stars,
  And heard the roar of the sea.

And they rode on, and further on,
  And they waded through blood to the knee.
Alas! alas!" he said, " what's this?
  'Tis the blood shed in your false country."

And still she pricked her milk-white steed,
  And fleeter than the wind he flew;
And Sir John Gordon then began
  Dearly his folly for to rue.

And they rode on, and further on,
  Till it was mirk, mirk night,
And horrid vipers round them twined
  And hissed with all their might.

And on they rode, and further on,
  Through plains full of dead men's banes,
And horrid hags, with ravenous claws,
  Picked the banes of unchristened weans.

" What think ye, think ye, now, Sir John,
  O' the kiss ye gae to me?
Full well I see ye dearly rue
  The love that blin's the e'e."

Sir John was brave, and very brave,
  And very brave was he—
The sights and sounds he heard and saw
  Gar't him his folly dree.

" And now, Sir John, ye maun haud your tongue
  Whatever ye hear or see;
For if ye speak a word in Elfland,
  Ye'll ne'er see your ain countree."

And they cam' to that bonnie land,
  Seven years there he lived so free,
And never a word Sir John he spak'
  For all he did hear and see.

She has clothed him in a coat of crimson cloth,
And shoes of velvet green,
And seven long years of happiness
He has passed with the Elfin Queen.

" Fareweel, fareweel, my noble lord,
Your promise you've kept to me;
But mine ye maun be if ye tell on earth
What here ye did hear and see."

'Twas seven years, and seven lang years
Ere Sir John on earth was seen;
He came with a coat of the crimson cloth,
And shoes of the velvet green.

The late Dr. Shearer, headmaster, Gordon Schools, Huntly, about thirty years ago noted down a number of old ballads from the recitation or singing of old residents of that district. Nearly all of these ballads were variants of old specimens of the Scottish minstrelsy, and they appeared from time to time in the columns of *The Huntly Express*, the proprietor of which has kindly permitted me to bring before my readers the most remarkable ballad of the lot. In the first place this story in verse of Sir John Gordon is either a modern production evolved from " Thomas the Rhymer " in *The Border Minstrelsy*, or it is a genuine north-country version of that great ballad, which has been modernised by someone not long dead. For example, examine the structure of the sixth verse. Anything more strictly up-to-date than this verse it would be hard to find in the whole realm of poetry or doggerel. There are some other modern expressions which the reader will notice. but with all this decided modernity, there appears over the *tout ensemble,* the outline of a disfigured old ballad, perhaps the original of " Thomas the Rhymer." In that fine specimen of Border Minstelry there are some bits almost too fine to be the composition of an " auld makar." Take these instances, after the pair " had rode on and further on." The fairy showed true Thomas the three roads leading to Heaven, hell, and fairyland:—

" Oh, see ye not yon narrow road,
So thick beset with thorns and briers—
That is the path of righteousness,
Tho' after it but few inquires.

" And see ye not that braid, braid road.
That lies across that lily leven—
That is the path of wickedness,
Tho' some call it the road to Heaven.

" And see ye not that bonnie road,
That winds about the fernie brae—
That is the road to fair Elfland,
Where thou and I this night maun gae."

My own impression is that " Sir John Gordon " is an old ballad which has been much injured by some modern " improver," and that " Thomas the Rhymer " was greatly benefited by the poetic skill of Sir Walter Scott, who may even have made interpolations of his own.

It is worthy of note that the late Dr. Shearer, a much-respected gentleman, printed the ballad of " Sir John Gordon " without comment of any kind, as if he did not know of its great similarity to ""Thomas the Rhymer."

THE DOWIE DENS O' YARROW.

THERE lived a lady in the south,
  You could scarce have found her marrow;
She was courted by nine gentlemen,
  And the ploughman laddie o' Yarrow.

As he came ower yon high, high hill,
  And down yon glen so narrow,
There he spied nine gentlemen
  Come to fight with him on Yarrow.

If I see all, there's nine to ane,
  And that's an unequal marrow;
But I will take you three by three,
  And I'll slay you all on Yarrow.

Then three he slew, and three withdrew,
  And three lay deadly wounded,
Till her brother John stepped in behind
  And pierced his body through.

Go home, go home, ye false young man,
  And tell your sister sorrow,
That her true love John lies dead and gone
  In the dowie dens o' Yarrow.

As she came ower yon high, high hill,
  And down yon glen so narrow,
It's there she spied her brother John
  Returning home from Yarrow.

O, brother, dear, I've dreamt a dream,
  And I fear it will prove sorrow,
For I dreamt that you were spilling blood
  In the dowie dens o' Yarrow.

O, sister, dear, I'll read your dream,
　And I'm sure it will prove sorrow,
Your true love John lies dead and gone,
　A bloody corpse in Yarrow.

She wrung her hands and tore her hair
　Wi' muckle grief and sorrow,
For she dearly loved her true love John,
　The ploughman laddie o' Yarrow.

This lady's hair being three-quarters long,
　And the colour of it was yellow,
She's tied it round her middle jimp,
　And she carried him home from Yarrow.

O, daughter, dear, dry up your tears,
　And dwell no more in sorrow,
And I'll wed you to one of a higher degree
　Than the ploughman laddie o' Yarrow.

O, father, ye hae seven sons,
　Ye can wed them a' to-morrow,
But a fairer flower than my true love John
　There never bloomed in Yarrow.

Now this lady, she being in distress
　For her love who died on Yarrow,
She flung herself in her father's arms,
　And died through grief and sorrow.

HARRY LUMSDALE'S COURTSHIP.

First when Harry cam' to Clatt,
　Wi' saddled horse and bridle keen,
He bantered a' the Gerrie lairds
　Ere he got hame his bonnie Jean.

" O bonnie Jean, wilt thou go
　Up to Auchindoir wi' me?
I'll row thee in my Highland plaid,
　As wi' thee I wad live and dee.

" I'm nae born heir to much free land,
　But I hae interests comin' in;
I'll mak' ye live as lady-like
　As ony ane o' a' your kin."

"Though I'm nae maister o' mysel',
　　Yet I'm willin' to tak' advice;
Maidens that ower soon consent,
　　People count they are not wise.

"Ye may at my mither speir,
　　Gin she the bargain will fulfil;
And afterwards ye may come back
　　And kiss and clap me at your will.

"I think by this we're baith agreed,
　　What needs there ony mair delay?
Her consent, and our contract—
　　And after comes our wedding day."

Then procurators they did employ,
　　Thinking her mither's heart to win;
But aye they cam' quite out o' tune,
　　She bade them bide and coup the swine.

"My dochter Jean, she's nae sae auld,
　　But she may wait these twa-three year,
And then a fairer flower may spring
　　Than ever ye hae seen, I'm seer."

"His countenance it is sae bright
　　His person it may well be seen,
A fairer flower, mither, I fear,
　　Will never pace upon your green.

"Wi' his fine coat and tartan kilt,
　　And his braw lovely shoulder belt,
And his gay plaiding to his knee,
　　That's the lad that pleases me.

"I've had wooers nine or ten,
　　Far below my ain degree,
But it's ne'er be Rhynie's second son
　　Shall ever be a match for me."

Then out it spak' bold Towie o' Clatt,
　　And Newton Gordon, he spak' then:
"Tho' I had daughters nine or ten,
　　I'd waur them a' on sic a man."

Then Harry he spak' out at last,
　　His passion then began to swell:
"O, since it's sae, I maun be gane,
　　The girl is nae for me at all.

" Then, fare ye weel, my Jeanie fair,
　　Since to my suit you'll nae comply,
Now for your sake I'll never come
　　To court a wife sae far away.

" I'll gae hame as I cam' forth,
　　And spy some fauts about my town;
And afterwards I will gae pay
　　My best respects to Betty Brown.

" Jeanie's gude, and gude enough,
　　I lov'd her ance as I do swear;
There's nae a lass in Gerrie roun'
　　That could wi' Betty ance compear.

" For wisdom, wit, and beauty bright,
　　The ladies a' she does outshine;
I might hae pou'd as fair a flower,
　　And stayed at hame amang my kin.

" It was my custom ear' and late
　　For to view the Mill o' Clatt,
And spend my time and money too,
　　Bonnie Jeanie, courtin' you.

" So, fare ye weel, ye saucy dame,
　　I wish your face I ne'er had seen;
Since ye will nae consent to me
　　I'll wyle a girl as gude as thee."

Then Harry's on the Moray road,
　　And Jeanie's to Knockespock gane,
Wi' mony a heavy sigh and sob
　　For Harry Lumsdale back again.
　　　　O for him back again!
　　　　O for him back again!
　　　　I wad gae a' Knockespock's land
　　　　For ae shak' o' my Harry's hand.

Harry gaed in by yon stane park,
　　Sometimes light, and sometimes dark;
O a' the lads that I do see,
　　My Harry is the lad for me.

Burns took this old ballad as a model for his song " My Harry was a
Gallant Gay."

THE BONNIE MILL-DAMS O' BINNORIE.

THERE were twa sisters lived in a bower,
    Binnorie, O Binnorie,
There cam' a knight to be their wooer,
    By the bonnie mill-dams o' Binnorie.

He courted the eldest wi' glove and wi' ring,
    Binnorie, O Binnorie,
But he lo'ed the youngest aboon a' thing,
    By the bonnie mill-dams o' Binnorie.

The eldest she was vexed sair,
    Binnorie, O Binnorie,
And sairly envied her sister fair,
    By the bonnie mill-dams o' Binnorie.

Upon a morning fair and clear,
    Binnorie, O Binnorie,
She cried upon her sister dear,
    By the bonnie mill-dams o' Binnorie.

"O sister, sister, tak' my hand,
    Binnorie, O Binnorie,
And let's go down to the river strand
    By the bonnie mill-dams o' Binnorie.

She's taen her by the lily hand,
    Binnorie, O Binnorie,
And down they went to the river strand
    By the bonnie mill-dams o' Binnorie.

The youngest stood upon a stane,
    Binnorie, O Binnorie,
The eldest cam' and pushed her in,
    By the bonnie mill-dams o' Binnorie.

" Sister, sister, reach your hand,
    Binnorie, O Binnorie,
And ye sall be heir o' half my land
    By the bonnie mill-dams o' Binnorie.

" O sister, sister, reach but your glove,
    Binnorie, O Binnorie,
And sweet William sall be your love,
    By the bonnie mill-dams o' Binnorie."

Sometimes she sank and sometimes she swam,
    Binnorie, O Binnorie,
Till she cam' to the mouth o' yon mill-dam,
    The bonnie mill-dams o' Binnorie.

Out then cam' the miller's son,
    Binnorie, O Binnorie,
And he saw the fair maid soomin' in
    To the bonnie mill-dams o' Binnorie.

" O father, father, draw your dam,
    Binnorie, O Binnorie,
There's either a mermaid or a swan
    In the bonnie mill-dams o' Binnorie."

The miller quickly drew the dam,
    Binnorie, O Binnorie,
And there he found a drowned woman
    In the bonnie mill-dams o' Binnorie.

Round about her middle sma',
    Binnorie, O Binnorie,
There was a gowden girdle braw,
    By the bonnie mill-dams o' Binnorie.

All amang her yellow hair,
    Binnorie, O Binnorie,
A string o' pearls was twisted rare,
    By the bonnie mill-dams o' Binnorie.

On her fingers lily-white,
    Binnorie, O Binnorie,
The jewel-rings were shining bright,
    By the bonnie mill-dams o' Binnorie.

By there cam' a harper fine,
    Binnorie, O Binnorie,
Who harped to nobles when they dine,
    By the bonnie mill-dams o' Binnorie.

And when he looked that lady on,
    Binnorie, O Binnorie,
He sighed and made a heavy moan,
    By the bonnie mill-dams o' Binnorie.

He's ta'en three locks o' her yellow hair,
    Binnorie, O Binnorie,
And wi' them strung his harp so rare,
    By the bonnie mill-dams o' Binnorie.

He went into her father's hall,
    Binnorie, O Binnorie,
And played his harp before them all,
    By the bonnie mill-dams o' Binnorie.

And sune the harp sang loud and clear,
    Binnorie, O Binnorie,
" Fareweel, my father and mither dear,
    By the bonnie mill-dams o' Binnorie."

And neist when the harp began to sing,
    Binnorie, O Binnorie,
'Twas, " fareweel, sweetheart!" said the string,
    By the bonnie mill-dams o' Binnorie.

And then as plain as plain could be,
    Binnorie, O Binnorie,
" There sits my sister wha drowned me,
    By the bonnie mill-dams o' Binnorie."

MY LOVELY NANCY.

Down in yon wild and lonely glen,
　Beset by many a lofty mountain,
Far frae the busy haunts o' men,
　Ae day as I gaed out a-huntin'—

To me it was a happy day—
　That day I fixed my roving fancy,
'Twas herding sheep on yon hillside
　I first spied my lovely Nancy.

Her coat was white, her gown was green,
　Her middle was baith neat and slender,
And her coal-black eyes and downcast sighs
　They caused my heart no more to wander.

Says I—" My lass, if ye wad gang
　To sleep wi' me on bed o' feather,
In silk an' scarlet I'll mak' you shine
　If you'll leave the muirs amang the heather."

" Young man," she said, " your offer's good,
　But I fear you only jest in laughter;
For you're perhaps some rich squire's son,
　While I am only a shepherd's daughter."

I've been at balls and masquerades,
　I've been in London and Balquhidder,
But the bonniest lass that e'er I saw
　Was herdin' sheep amang the heather.

Fareweel to balls and masquerades,
　Fareweel to London and Balquidder,
For the bonniest lass that e'er I saw
　Nae langer herds amang the heather.

Noo, since I've got her to mysel',
　Wi' her I mean to live contented,
For she's bonnier far than the heather bell;
　Fareweel, fareweel, my cares are ended.

THE MAIDEN OF DRUMDURNO.

Busy baking for her bridal
　Durno's maiden lilts wi' glee,
When a roader, handsome, idle,
　Saunters in, and thus says he—
" Baking sets you well indeed
If you make but greater speed."

Gaily she retorts his banter—
　" Little care I how I bake,
But though I dislike a vaunter
　Few could blame the speed I make."
Scornfully she tossed her head,
And another bannock spread.

" Quick or slowly—fair and saucy—
　Ere your firlot's end you see,
I engage to lay a causey
　Up the craigs of Bennochie;
If should I the contest gain,
I your hand and heart obtain."

She on such a foolish wager
　Lightly granted what he asked;
He, like an undaunted stager,
　Dared what a legion tasked.
Stone to stone ascends the slope,
Quick is labour cheered by hope!

Now her work of love is closing,
　And the lav'rock's song is still;
Day, her dewy wings composing,
　Leaves the gloaming on the hill.
Mary, with a fieldward glance,
Chides her Jamie's slow advance.

What arrests her eye so glassy
　Makes her glowing cheek turn pale?
Can that be a well-laid causey
　Stretching upwards from the vale?
Must a lightly-spoken jest
Tear her from her Jamie's breast?

Near the roader's step is stealing,
  Noiseless as the baukie's wing;
Now she sees the road revealing
  He who flatters but to sting.
Fast she flies, as fast pursued,
·Straining for Pittodrie wood.

" Jamie!" shrieks the frantic maiden
  As she wildly scans the hill,
But a heavy hand is laid on
  Mary's arm; her heart is still.
Traitor, now the maiden clasp!
Now the lifeless granite grasp.

Lone and last of all the Clachan,
  With her bake-brod and her spade;
Ay, she bids the maids of Buchan
  Guard the vows that love has made.
Love is holy, love is solemn,
Think of this mysterious column.

The maiden stone of Bennochie stands in the parish of Chapel of Garioch,
in Aberdeenshire, about equal distance from Pitcaple and Oyne Railway
Stations. Its height is ten feet six inches. It is of red granite. It was old
in the time of Wallace and Bruce. Information can be had regarding it in
Stuart's *Sculptured Stones of Scotland* and in May's *Memoirs of the Family
of Leslie*.

While on a holiday in Strathbogie lately, I was, through the courtesy of
the proprietors of *The Huntly Express*, able to gather the following
particulars regarding the foregoing ballad, which is well-known to the
inhabitants of the Strath. The maiden of Drumdurno, whose home was a
a farm house of that name at the foot of Bennochie, was busily engaged
baking her bridal cakes when a stranger sauntered into the kitchen, and
after observing her movements for some time he remarked that her employment set her well if she only came more speed. " I do not know whether
it sets me well or not," she replied, " but I think few could grudge the
speed." After a great deal of bantering on this subject, the stranger laid
a bet that before she baked ·her firlot of meal he would causeway a road
to the top of Bennochie, but he made it a condition that if he should win
she must become his bride. To this apparent absurd proposal the thought-
less girl gave her consent at once. When she was at her last bannock, and
evening was setting down upon the hill, she went to the door to see whether
Jamie, her betrothed, was yet in sight, as she expected him that evening.
But what was her consternation to find, on looking towards the hill that
a road to the top had been completed, and that the stranger, whom she
now recognised as the enemy of mankind, from the work he had finished,
was approaching to claim his reward. She at once left the house and fled
towards the woods of Pittodrie, hoping to meet her Jamie, who she knew
would protect her. The prayer for deliverance from her persecutor was
answered, however, in a different way from what she expected. The
foul thief pursued her in flight, but just as he was about to clasp her in
his arms she was turned into the Maiden Stone, and only the piece broken
from her shoulder remained in his grasp. The marks on the stone were
believed by our ancestors to be the bake brod and bread spade, the marks
of which were on her apron when she fled from her home.

CAIRN-O'-MOUNT.

As I rode down by the Brig o' Dye,
   And past yon hill o' broom,
A maiden sang right merrily,
   Just as the sun gaed down.

"It's Cairn-o'-Mount is bleak and bare,
   And cauld is Clochnaben,
And you will see the snaw lie there
   Alang the summer's end."

I lighted off my dapple grey
   And walked by her side,
Saying, "Lassie, I have lost my way
   Upon your moors so wide.

"Oh, war me o' your face so fair,
   Your een so bonnie blue,
The longest day I'd blythely share
   To kiss your cherry mou'.

"Oh, lassie, will you gang wi' me,
   And leave your cauldrich glen?
Wi' a' my kin ye'll bear the gree,
   There's wealth baith but and ben.

"Wi' silks and satins buskit braw,
   And ribbons for your hair,
And maids to answer when you ca',
   So, can you wish for mair?

"O lassie, ye maun think a wee,
   My lands are far and wide,
I've gold in banks, and ships at sea,
   So come and be my bride.

"My father left me lairdships twa,
   A coach at my command,
I'll make you lady o'er them a',
   If you'll give me your hand."

" Though Cairn-o'-Mount is bleak and **bare,**
  You're no a match for me;
My Donald he is a' my care,
  Ride on and let me be.

" He meets me on yon hill so green,
  His heart is leal and true,
If Donald heard my angry scream
  He soon would make you rue."

" O lassie, think, your Donald's poor,
  Has neither horse nor coo;
A shepherd straggling o'er the moor
  Is not a match for you."

" Cairn-o'-Mount is bleak and bare,
  And cauld is Clochnaben;
I'd rather meet my Donald here
  Than be fair Scotland's queen."

" O lassie, I am loath to tell,
  You throw your love awa;
Your Donald brawly kens himsel'
  Last gloamin' what I saw.

" As I rode by his shielin' door
  I spied a Highland maid,
Your Donald kissed her o'er and o'er,
  And rolled her in his plaid."

" Though you would swear wi' solemn oath
  What you have told to me,
I would not dread my Donald's faith
  But say, " Base loon, ye lee."

It's he's thrown off his lowland dress,
  Combed down his yellow hair,
Saying, " Lassie, ye've been true to me,
  And now we'll part nae mair.

" Nae mair I'm shepherd o' the **glen,**
  But laird ayont the Dee;
And since ye have been true to me,
  I'll aye prove true to thee."

The author of this ballad was Alexander Balfour, who was born in the parish of Monikie, Forfarshire, in 1767, and died in Edinburgh in 1829.

THE LASS O' BENNOCHIE.
(FIRST VERSION.)

'Twas at the back o' Bennochie,
  Where swiftly flies the swallow,
That there a bonnie lassie lived,
  I longed to make my marrow.

When first I tried her love to win,
  She did not seem to know me,
But looked shy and disdainfully,
  And would say nothing to me.

But now she kindly smiles on me,
  And likes to see me comin';
I am the proudest of lovers all,
  For my love's a gentle woman.

My love is like the lily fair,
  Down by yon bush of roses,
The more I look, the more I love,
  And the more my heart rejoices.

O, do not grieve to break your heart,
  Nor spoil your eyes with weepin',
Though distance does our bodies part,
  Our hearts together are keepin'.

Though you and I, love, now must part,
  Though we are now kept under,
Think on the time that will soon draw near
  When we'll meet no more to sunder.

THE LASS O' BENNOCHIE.
(SECOND VERSION.)

'Twas at the back o' Bennochie,
  Where swiftly flies the swallow,
'Twas at the back o' Bennochie,
  Where first I chose my marrow.

There I fell in love wi' a bonnie lass,
  At the feeding o' the cattle;
But her father soon beguiled me,
  And sent me off to battle.

Out over hills, out over dales,
  Through groves and lonely valleys,
I was sent from Bennochie,
  'Twas done for spite and malice.

But peace did come and I cam' home,
  And enquired for my dearie;
They told me no such one was there,
  Which filled my mind with fury.

But my love she heard and she knew my voice,
  And she looked from a window,
And said, " I'm here but I daurna' come,
  For double deals us sunder."

I walked away to calm myself,
  Being in an angry passion,
But my passion grew and my sword I drew,
  And so boldly I gaed to her.

I made open doors o' double deals,
  I gar'd locks and bars to flee me;
I made open doors o' double deals,
  And I took my dearie wi' me.

Her uncle and her uncle's men,
  So quickly they did follow,
But I bade them a' turn back again,
  If they their lives did value.

I've been in wars where cannons roar,
  Where drums and bullets rattle,
He that cannot fight for his heart's delight,
  How could he fight in battle?

It's nae for gold or warld's gear
  That we lo'e ane anither;
Now we'll join hands in wedlock bands,
  And we'll live and die together.

There are three versions of " The Lass o' Bennochie," and the stories told in each are somewhat different. The following particulars regarding the ballad appeared in *The Huntly Express* of 27th December, 1879:—

" Miss Erskine, daughter of the Laird of Pittodrie, who had accompanied her uncle, Lord Forbes, to Fort Augustus, of which he was governor, about the year 1765, met with an officer, a Lieutenant Knight, with whom she fell in love. As she was an only child and an heiress, her parents were much opposed to her marrying one whom they considered much beneath her in rank. Perseverance was, however, rewarded in this case, and they were married in 1770. Their descendents are known as the Knight-Erskines of Pittodrie."

The estate of Pittodrie is at the foot of the Hill of Bennochie.

THE LASS O' BENNOCHIE.

(THIRD VERSION.)

I ONCE did love a lady fair,
She was a beauty all did declare,
For the fairest flower in the north countrie,
Was the bonnie lass o' Bennochie.
She was heir to baith house and lan',
While I was but a poor man's son;
It was her birth and high degree
That parted my sweet love and me.

For her father came to know
That I did love his daughter so,
He Judasly betrayed me
For lighting in her company.
'Twas at Old Rayne that I was taen
A prisoner for Lady Jean;
In fetters strong then I was bound
And carried into Aberdeen.

I was embarked from the shore
To see my native land no more,
In Germany a soldier to be,
All for the lass o' Bennochie.
Her father said, " Your tears refrain,
To weep for him is all in vain,
I have a better match for thee,
To enjoy the lands o' Bennochie."

" He was the lover of my youth,
In pledge he was my faith and troth,
I've made a vow that I'll wed with none,
If my true love be dead and gone."
On every finger she put a ring,
On her third finger she put three;
And she is on to High Germanie,
In hopes her lover there to see.

And she put on the robes o' green
That were most lovely to be seen,
And had he been a crowned king,
This fair lady might have been his queen.

And when she came to Germanie,
It was her fortune there to see
Her lover on a rampart hie,
As he was standing senterie.

" Ye're welcome here, my dearest dear,
You are thrice welcome unto me,
There's not a face so full of grace
In all the land of Germanie."
With much delight these lovers met,
Full joyfully as it is told,
And she changed her dress from the worst of lace
To crimson and scarlet, well trimmed with gold.

So when her father came to know
That his daughter abroad had gone,
He sent a letter by express,
To call these lovers quickly home.
Then Willie Knight got a free discharge,
All for his love for Lady Jean,
And now he is a wealthy laird
Into the shire of Aberdeen.

THE GALLANT GRAHAMS.

As I was crossing ower Boyne Water,
  My frien's an' acquaintances to see;
For the killing o' an English lord
  My gude braid sword they've ta'en frae me.
As I looked over my left shoulder,
  It was to see what I could see,
An' there I spied a bonnie boy
  Wi' heavy irons to lay on me.

    O! the Grahams, the gallant Grahams,
      Had the gallant Grahams but stood by me,
    The dogs might dook in English blood
      Ere ae foot's breadth I'd flinch or flee.

They led me up through Carrickfergus,
  Wi' a strong guard they had on me;
An' they led me down to a dungeon deep,
  Ae peep o' licht I could never see.

But if I had back my gude red coat
  An' my braid sword they took frae me,
I would throw the dogs into yonder bogs,
  Frae the smell o' powder I would never flce.
    O! the Grahams, etc.

There lives a irlie in Coleraine,
  An' she lives down by yonder quay,
An' if she knew my state o' mind
  What a sorrowful girlie she would be.
I asked a sicht o' the double darbies[1],
  A sicht o' them was granted me;
An' wi' them I knocked the gaoler down,
  An' I've set bold Johnstone at liberty.
    O! the Grahams, etc.

As I walked out in the evening clear,
  To view the fields and take the air,
'Twas there I spied my aged father,
  He was tearing out his auld grey hair.
O! hold your hands, now, my aged father,
  Let a' your cares and troubles be,
For I hae knocked the goaler down,
  An' I've set bold Johnstone at liberty.
    O! the Grahams, etc.

So, fare ye well, ye Carrickfergus,
  An' fare ye well, ye gallows tree;
An' fare ye well, my gaoler laddie,
  Till I come back to pay your fee.
O! the Grahams, the gallant Grahams,
  The Grahams were a' gude frien's to me;
An' if the Grahams had been here the nicht
  Ae foot o' ground I would never flee.
    O! the Grahams, etc.

[1] Handcuffs.

This genuine old Scoto-Irish ballad was sent to me by Mr. Robert Mellis,
West Folds, Huntly. The scene is laid in the North of Ireland, but the
hero and the "Gallant Grahams," whom he so often refers to, are distinctly
Scottish, and evidently from the Borders. The Grahams or Graemes (as
the name was more commonly spelt), were ardent supporters of the Stuart
cause, and it is a matter of history that a large number of them settled in
Ireland after the Revolution in 1688.

M'PHERSON'S FAREWELL.

FAREWELL, ye dungeons dark and strong,
  The wretch's destinie!
Macpherson's time will not be long
  On yonder gallows-tree.
    Sae rantingly, sae wantonly,
      Sae dauntingly gaed he;
    He played a tune and danc'd it roun',
      Below the gallows-tree.

Oh, what is death but parting breath?
  On many a bloody plain
I've dar'd his face, and in this place
  I scorn him yet again!
    Sae rantingly, sae wantonly, etc.

Untie these bands from off my hands,
  And bring to me my sword;
And there's no a man in all Scotland
  But I'll brave him at a word.
    Sae rantingly, sae wantonly, etc.

I've lived a life of strut and strife;
  I die by treacherie;
It burns my heart I must depart
  And not avenged be.
    Sae rantingly, sae wantonly, etc.

Now, farewell light—thou sunshine bright,
  And all beneath the sky!
May coward shame disdain his name
  The wretch that dares not die.
    Sae rantingly, sae wantonly,
      Sae dauntingly gaed he;
    He played a tune and danc'd it roun',
      Below the gallows-tree.

The above song, which was written by our national poet, is modelled upon an older ballad known as " Macpherson's Rant " which, tradition tells us, was composed by Macpherson himself. There are several variants of the ballad, but the one here printed was the favourite in the farm-kitchens of the counties of Aberdeenshire, Banff, and Moray, in my boyhood days.

MACPHERSON'S RANT.

I've spent my time in rioting,
   Debauch'd my health and strength,
I've pillag'd, plunder'd, murdered,
   But now, alas! at length
I'm brought to punishment direct,
   Pale death draws near to me;
This end I never did project,
   To hang upon a tree.

To hang upon a tree! a tree!
   That cursed, unhappy death!
Like to a wolf to worried be
   And choaked in the breath.
My very heart would surely break,
   When this I think upon,
Did not my courage singular
   Bid pensive thoughts begone?

No man on earth that draweth breath
   More courage had than I;
I dar'd my foes unto their face,
   And would not from them fly;
This grandeur stout, I did keep out,
   Like Hector manfullie,
Then wonder one like me so stout
   Should hang upon a tree.

Th' Egyptian band I did command
   With courage more by far
Than ever did a general
   His soldiers in the war.
Being fear'd by all, both great and small,
   I liv'd most joyfullie;
O, curse upon this fate of mine,
   To hang upon a tree!

As for my life, I do not care,
   If justice would take place,
And bring my fellow plunderers
   Unto this same disgrace.

For Peter Brown, that notour loon,
  Escaped and was made free;
O, curse upon this fate of mine
  To hang upon a tree!

Both law and justice buried are,
  And fraud and guile succeed,
The guilty pass unpunished,
  If money intercede.
The Laird of Grant, that Highland saunt,
  His mighty majesty,
He pleads the cause of Peter Brown
  And lets Macpherson dee.

The dest'ny of my life contriv'd
  By those whom I oblig'd,
Rewarded me much ill for good
  And left me no refuge.
For Braco Duff, in rage enough,
  He first laid hands on me;
And, if that death would not prevent,
  Avengèd wou'd I be.

As for my life it is but short,
  When I shall be no more;
To part with life I am content,
  As any heretofore.
Therefore, good people all, take heed,
  This warning take by me,
According to the lives you lead
  Rewarded you shall be.

A great many improbable things, and much sentimental rubbish, has been
written from time to time regarding the life, arrest, trial and execution
of James Macpherson, consequently, the following facts, collected from
many different sources, may be of interest to my readers: —

He was born of a beautiful gipsy woman who, at a great wedding,
attracted the notice of a half intoxicated Highland gentleman. He
acknowledged the child and had him reared in his house until he lost his
life in bravely pursuing a hostile clan to recover a spreach of cattle taken
from Badenoch. The gipsy woman, hearing of this disaster in her rambles
the following summer, came and took her boy; but she often returned with
him, to wait upon his relations and clansmen, who never failed to clothe
him well, besides giving money to his mother. He grew up to beauty,
strength, and stature rarely equalled. We are informed that his sword,
which was up to recent times preserved in Duff House, Banff, was so
heavy that few men could carry it, far less wield it, as a weapon of war.

THE LOCH O' THE AUDS.

AE nicht i' my fun, when late I wis rovin',
　The road by Craigherbs as I chancèd to stray,
It wisna jist midnicht, but dusk i' the gloamin',
　When nature did smile i' the month o' sweet May.

The sun he gaed doon ower the back o' Langforty,
　And bidden gude-nicht to the vale o' the Boyne;
The marraless youngsters were langin' for sportin',
　And toddlin' aboot wi' their sweethearts to join.

The woods wi' the yells o' the owlets were ringin',
　The poddocks were croupin' frae the loch o' the Auds,
The lapwing did screech, while the mavis was singin',
　And toddlin' aboot were the rabbits and bauds.

While flutterin' his wings, the beautiful pheasant,
　His clarion resounded while mountin' the trees;
The odour a' roun' was delightful and pleasant,
　The sweet-scented birks felt the dew frae the breeze.

Amused wi' the scene, for a wee contemplation
　I jist sat me doon to consider their joy,
When up cam' a gimmer o' first-rate temptation—
　I kent by her gab she belanged to Portsoy.

Her visage was fair and her looks were bewitchin',
　I thought that the jade had a sly, rollin' e'e;
A rambler by chance thought the charmer enrichin',
　And fraught wi' delusion, enamoured wis he.

Through a bush o' green arns I saw how he kissed her,
　And swore for her sake he was wretched in love;
How fondly he hugg'd her, embrac'd and caress'd her,
　And vow'd that he never unconstant would prove.

I couldna' but lauch at the flatterin' orations—
　When passion is strong the affection is true;
I thought that young women, by dissimulation,
　Are often ensnared by the tune o' ba-loo.

Then up a gay sweetheart cam' toddlin' to meet her,
　Lang dabbled wi' love, that he thought her his ain,
But faith! I was sorry to see him, puir creatur',
　Fan aff flew the jade frae his grasp wi' disdain.

Nae doubt but the lad was a sma' thing affrontit,
  And nae muckle winner, wi' comin' sae far;
On the pow o' his rival he yet may resent it:
  Appearances hae the foreboddin' o' war.

Yet I wondered to see him how canny he stood it,
  Embarrased ae moment, sin lached at the fun;
By the shake o' a troy, wi' this he concluded,
  He wouldna encounter his Ellen to win.

Guid help us! puir bodies get awfu' disasters
  While waddlin' through time, amid sorrow and cares;
While love's awfu' delusion our wisdom it masters,
  And reason is marr'd when beauty ensnares.

But doited and daft, coupit heels ower body,
  Some thousands by powder's been hobbled awa;
But curse their existence that swang in the wuddie,
  For women have had the occasion o' a'.

But still it's but nat'ral to ha'e a bit dearie,
  A lovely bit lassie yer ain for to ca';
It keeps the affections sae couthie and cheerie,
  If they cu'd but only be trusted ava.

Tak' warnin', ye youngsters, ere thus ye be slighted,
  And bridle your passions ere women ye trust:
The scene has grown dreary—lest I be benighted,
  I'll bid ye gude-nicht, an' be toddlin' I must.

The hireman is aff for a sharp to his couter,
  An' maybe a crack i' the smiddy forbye,
Or either for tackets he's gaen to the souter,
  An' the maidens were singin' and milkin' the kye.

While auld, cankert daddy was lichtin' his cutty,
  An' loosin' his buttons and hobblin' to bed;
The housewife was darnin' or cleanin' a mutty,
  An' booin' the hens frae the tod an' the gleg.

A version of this song, consisting of about a dozen verses, was common in the farm-kitchens and bothies of Banffshire and part of Aberdeenshire between 60 and 70 years ago. From a small book entitled *Tales of the North.* printed at the *Banffshire Journal* Office, Banff, in 1896, it appears that the author was a Mr. A. Cumming, farmer at Auds, Boyndie, Banff-shire. Mr. Cumming was born at Keith in 1803, and died at Auds on 12th February, 1848.
  I am indebted to the above book for the additional five verses here printed. The song was sung to a variant of the air known as " The Lass of Glenshee."

JOCK SCOTT.

Come all my friends, both far and near,
  And listen to my sang;
I've penned it with a troubled mind,
  To hold me on, though lang.

The girl I left behind me,
  That grieves me more than a';
And her I will remember,
  Though I be far awa.

First time I saw my Mary,
  'Twas in the month of May,
Down by her father's dwelling
  I carelessly did stray.

Upon her I did cast an eye,
  But she ne'er looked behind;
Her cheeks were blooming like a rose,
  I wished that she'd been mine.

Her father did a servant want,
  With him I did agree;
Six months with him then I was bound
  His servant for to be.

We spent the time wi' mirth and glee,
  While Mary was me near;
'Twas in the pleasant summer months
  When little birds sang clear.

I soon my lassie's heart did win,
  All with her own consent;
Her parents thought to stop our love,
  With me was not content.

Then I went from her father's place,
  Just to a neighbouring toon;
And, in spite of all, I went to her
  Oft as the sun gaed down.

Between us twa we set the time
  We meant to take our flight;
And arm-in-arm we did march on
  All in the gloom of night.

It was a distance of six miles
　We cheerily marched along;
Tho' dark and dreary was the night,
　On it we thought not on.

First into a licensed house,
　Refreshments we got there;
And then into my father's house,
　All in the morning ear'.

But then our sorrows did begin,
　Her father did pursue's,
And grieved was I to see his face,
　For he did her abuse.

He has set her on a horse,
　She's torn awa from me;
She stretched out her little hand,
　For tears she could not see.

She was forced back again,
　And sore it grieved me;
But she sent word just that same night
　That she would constant be.

It was twelve months after this
　Or I my love did see;
'Twas on a holiday we met,
　Right happy then was she.

Between us twa we set the time
　We meant to go away;
Eight miles she met me on the road
　On the appointed day.

To Aberdeen we cheerily went;
　We soon got joined there;
And home again we did return
　And to them did declare.

Nine months we lived together,
　Love smiled between us twa,
And we both inclined to go away
　To North America.

But now the hopes of this is past;
    For forgery I've been ta'en,
And here I lie to wait my trial
    In the jail o' Aberdeen.

Her father he has put me here,
    I'm sure it is a shame;
The county fiscal he has told
    That I did forge his name.

But innocent I'll plead of it,
    And ever will deny;
And if that I do justice get
    I will them all defy.

THE LOWLANDS LOW.

OUR ship she was built o' the bay oak tree,
    Eckie, diddle O, in the Lowlands low,
And her name it was called the *Sweet Kumadee*,
    As she sailed in the Lowlands low.

We hadna sailed a league but only three,
    Eckie, diddle O, in the Lowlands low,
Until that we spied a French galleon,
    She was sailing for the Lowlands low.

Out spak' our cabin-boy, out spak' he,
    Eckie, diddle O, in the Lowlands low,
Says, "Captain, oh captain, oh what will ye gie me
    If I sink yon French galleon, O?"

"I'll gie ye gold, and I'll gie ye fee,
    Eckie, diddle O, in the Lowlands low,
And my eldest daughter your wedded wife to be,
    If ye sink yon French galleon, O."

"Then roll me up in a black bull's hide,
    Eckie, diddle O, in the Lowlands low,
And throw me overboard for to sink or to swim,
    And I'll sink yon French galleon, O."

They've rolled him up in a black ball's hide,
  Eckie, diddle O, in the Lowlands low,
And they've thrown him overboard for to sink or to swim,
  For to sink yon French galleon, O.

The boy bent his breast, and away swam he,
  Eckie, diddle O, in the Lowlands low,
Until that he came to the French galleon
  A-sailing for the Lowlands low.

He had a lot of fine instruments,
  Eckie, diddle O, in the Lowlands low,
And four-and-twenty holes he has pierced in her sides,
  While she sailed for the Lowlands low.

Then the boy bent his breast and away swam he,
  Eckie, diddle O, in the Lowlands low,
Until he came to the *Sweet Kumadee*,
  As she sailed for the Lowlands low.

" Come, throw me a rope and pull me on board,
  Eckie, diddle O, in the Lowlands low,
And prove unto me as good as your word,
  For sinking yon French galleon, O."

" I winna throw you a rope and pull you aboard,
  Eckie, diddle O, in the Lowlands low,
But I'll let you swim till you sink in the sea,
  As sank yon French galleon, O."

" If you dinna throw me a rope, nor pull me on board,
  Eckie, diddle O, in the Lowlands low,
I'll sink you as true as my word
  As I sank yon French galleon, O."

They've thrown him a rope, and they've pulled him on board,
  Eckie, diddle O, in the Lowlands low,
And the captain has proved just as true as his word
  For sinking yon French galleon, O.

He's gien him gold and he's gien him fee,
  Eckie, diddle O, in the Lowlands low,
And his eldest daughter his wedded wife to be,
  For sinking yon French galleon, O.

CHARLIE MACKIE.

THERE lived a farmer on Islaside,
    Possessions he had mony;
He had an only daughter fair,
    Her name was callèd Annie.

Her father he had servants there,
    And wi' them she was richt happy,
She could hae spent a lang simmer's day
    In the plaid wi' Charlie Mackie.

When her father came to know,
    It made him richt unhappy.
Says, "Annie, dear, ye'll hae nae share
    Gin ye follow Charlie Mackie."

"Oh, father dear, keep a' your gear,
    It will never mak' me happy;
Though shoes and stockings I had nane,
    I wad follow Charlie Mackie."

He's taen his staff into his hand,
    And through the fields he wandered,
And when he cam' where the shepherd was,
    He was richt broken-hearted.

"How does your sheep thrive, shepherd?" he said,
    "Does your lammies a' thrive bonnie?
And what is this that I do hear
    Concerning you and Annie?"

"Oh, farmer dear, I'll be plain and tell,
    May it ne'er be your displeasure,
If we carry on as we hae begun,
    You will infeft the treasure."

Charlie he cam' hame at nicht,
    And supper scarce was ended,
When Annie she cam' doon the stair,
    And wi' tears her e'en were blinded.

She lookit east and she lookit west,
   And she lookit richt unhappy,
And for ae look she gae to the lave,
   She gae twa to Charlie Mackie.

Her father he cam' ben himsel',
   Wi' a canny step and steady;
Wi' an angry look and unruly voice,
   Says, " I want you, Charlie Mackie."

Charlie followed him to the door,
   Where he paid him doon his wages;
Says, " Ye'll tak' your staff and your collie dog,
   And get ye gone richt early."

" Oh, weel may a' your yowies thrive,
   And sae may every lammie,
And may never frost your corn blast,
   Nor a lover gain your Annie."

When Charlie reached his father's door
   He was welcomed there by many—
" For seven years I will retire,
   And then return for Annie."

When seven lang years were come and gane,
   Her rosy cheeks were fading;
The doctors a' did her advise
   Take a summer o' sea-bathing.

As she gaed doon by bonnie Aberdeen,
   And a little below her lodgin',
And before she scarce kent where she was
   She was accosted by a sodger.

Says, " Will ye gang wi' me, my love,
   Will ye sail the saut seas wi' me?
And the hinmost saxpence that I hae
   I'll share that saxpence wi' ye."

" I wadna follow a man," she says,
   " Far less wad I a sodger;
So lay your love on some other one
   To share that saxpence wi' ye."

" What aileth thee, my dearest dear?
　　What mak's you so unhappy?"
" Oh, nothing at all, kind sir," she said,
　　" But a word from Charlie Mackie."

" Dry up your tears, let your weeping cease,
　　If that mak's you unhappy;
Instead o' ane ye'll get thousands ten—
　　I'm your faithful Charlie Mackie.

" The first time that I saw you, love,
　　We were on the links parading;
And the drummer to the fifer said,
　　" Isna that a bonnie lady?

" The next time that I saw you, love,
　　Was at the castle bonnie;
And weel did I ken by your weel-faur'd face
　　Ye were Milton's bonnie Annie."

I noted down this song from the singing of Robert Mellis, West Folds,
Huntly, at a social gathering at the Farm of Wellheads, near Huntly, in
August, 1908.

WILLIE'S DROWNED AT GAMERIE.

" O WILLIE's fair, and Willie's rare,
　　And Willie's wondrous bonnie;
And Willie says he'll marry me,
　　Gin e'er he marry ony."
" O ye'll get Jamie, or ye'll get George,
　　Or ye'll get bonnie Johnny;
Ye'll get the flower o' a' my sons,
　　Gin ye'll forsake my Willie."

" O Willie's fair, and Willie's rare,
　　And Willie's wondrous bonnie;
There's nane wi' him that can compare,
　　I lo'e him best o' ony."
On Wednesday, that fatal day,
　　The people were convenin';
And there were mair than three score and ten
　　To gang to the bridesteel wi' him.

"Ride on, ride on, my merry men a',
   I've left something behind me;
I've forgot to get my mother's blessing,
   To gae to the bridesteel wi' me."
"Your Peggy she's but bare fifteen,
   And ye are scarcely twenty;
The water at Gamerie is wide and deep.
   My heavy curse gang wi' ye!"

Then they rode on, and further on,
   Till they came on to Gamerie;
The wind was loud, the waves were proud,
   And wi' the stream gaed Willie.
Then they rode on, and further on,
   Till they came to the kirk o' Gamerie;
And every one on high horse sat,
   But Willie's horse rode toomly.

When they arrived at that place,
   The people fell a-mourning;
And a council held among tham a',
   And sairly wept Kinmundy.
Then out it speaks the bride hersel',
   Says, "What means a' this mourning?
Where is the man among you a'
   That shou'd gie me fair wedding?"

Then out it speaks his brother John,
   Says, "Meg, I'll tell you plainly,
The stream was strong, the clerk rode wrong,
   And Willie's drowned at Gamerie!"
She put her hand up to her head,
   Where she had ribbons mony,
And tore them a', and let them down fa',
   And syne she ran to Gamerie.

She sought him up, she sought him down,
   Till she was wet and weary;
And in the middle part of it,
   'Twas there she got her dearie.
She straiked back his yellow hair,
   And kiss'd his mou' sae comely:
"Your mither's he'rt be as wae as thine,
   And we'll baith sleep at Gamerie."

R

MY GEORDIE O, MY GEORDIE O.

THERE was a battle in the north,
And rebels there were mony,
And mony ane got broken heads,
  And taken was my Geordie.

> My Geordie O, my Geordie O,
> O, the love I bear to Geordie;
> For the very ground I walk upon
> Bears witness I love Geordie.

As she gaed up the Tollbooth stair,
  The cripples there stood mony,
And she dealt the red gowd them amang,
  To pray for her love Geordie.
> My Geordie, etc.

And when she came into the hall
  The nobles there stood mony;
And ilka ane stood hat on head,
  But hat in hand stood Geordie.
> My Geordie, etc.

Up he spak' a norlan' lord,
  I wat he spak' na bonnie:
" If ye stay here a little while
  Ye'll see Geordie hangit shortly."
> My Geordie, etc.

Then up bespak' a baron bold,
  And o' but he spak' bonnie:
" If ye'll pay down five hundred crowns
  Ye'll get your true-love Geordie."
> My Geordie, etc.

Some gave crowns, and some gave pounds,
  Some lent her guineas mony,
And she's paid down five hundred crowns,
  And she's gotten her true-love Geordie.
> My Geordie, etc.

When she was mounted on her steed,
   And on behind her Geordie,
Nae bird on brier e'er sang sae sweet
   As the young knight and his ladie.
     My Geordie O, my Geordie O,
     O, the love I bear to Geordie;
     The very stars in the firmament
     Bear token I love Geordie.

The hero of this ballad was George, fourth Earl of Huntly, who was afterwards slain at the battle of Corrichrie on 28th October, 1562.

THE QUEEN'S MARIES.

LAST nicht the Queen had four Maries,
   This nicht she'll hae but three,
She'd Mary Beaton, an' Mary Seaton,
   An' Mary Carmichael an' me.

O, little did my mammie think
   The day she cradled me,
That I wad dee sae far frae hame,
   Or hang on a gallows tree.

O, tie a napkin roun' my e'en,
   An' no lat me see to dee;
An' never send word to my father or mither,
   They're far awa owre the sea.

I wish I cou'd lie in our ain kirkyard,
   Aneath yon auld oak tree,
Where we pu'd the rowans and strung the gowans,
   My brithers an' sisters an' me.

But what care I for a nameless grave,
   When I've hopes for eternitie;
I'll pray that the faith of the dying thief
   Should be granted through grace to me.

Last nicht the Queen had four Maries,
   This nicht and she'll hae but three,
She'd Mary Beaton, an' Mary Seaton,
   An' Mary Carmichael an' me.

This song is founded on an incident related in the old ballad of " Mary Hamilton," who was accused of child murder, in the reign of Mary Queen of Scots.

LORD RANDAL.

WHERE have ye been a-hunting, Lord Randal, my son?
Where have ye been a-hunting, my handsome young man?
Down in yon meadow, mother; make my bed soon,
For I'm weary, weary wandering, and fain wad lie down.

Have you had any supper, Lord Randal, my son?
Have you had any supper, my handsome young man?
Oh yes, I've got supper, mother; make my bed soon,
For I'm weary, weary wandering, and fain wad lie down.

What got you for your supper, Lord Randal, my son?
What got you for your supper, my handsome young man?
A dish of small fishes, mother; make my bed soon,
For I'm weary, weary wandering, and fain wad lie down.

What like were those fishes, Lord Randal, my son?
What like were those fishes, my handsome young man?
Yellow backs wi' speckled bellies, mother; make my bed soon,
For I'm weary, weary wandering, and fain wad lie down.

Oh, who did you sup with, Lord Randal, my son?
Oh, who did you sup with, my handsome young man?
I supped with my sweetheart, mother; make my bed soon,
For I'm weary, weary wandering, and fain wad lie down.

I fear you are poisoned, Lord Randal, my son,
I fear you are poisoned, my handsome young man.
Oh yes, I am poisoned, mother; make my bed soon,
For I'm weary, weary wandering, and fain wad lie down.

What will you leave to your father, Lord Randal, my son?
What will you leave to your father, my handsome young man?
My houses and land, mother; make my bed soon,
For I'm weary, weary wandering, and fain wad lie down.

What will you leave to your mother, Lord Randal, my son?
What will you leave to your mother, my handsome young man?
My purse and my money, mother; make my bed soon,
For I'm weary, weary wandering, and fain wad lie down.

What will you leave to your brother, Lord Randal, my son?
What will you leave to your brother, my handsome young man?
My horses and hounds, mother; make my bed soon,
For I'm weary, weary wandering, and fain wad lie down.

What will you leave to your sister, Lord Randal, my son?
What will you leave to your sister, my handsome young man?
My watch and my jewels, mother; make my bed soon,
For I'm weary, weary wandering, and fain wad lie down.

What will you leave to your sweetheart, Lord Randal, my son?
What will you leave to your sweetheart, my handsome young
    man?
Yon tow and yon halter that hangs on yon tree,
And that's what she'll get for the poisoning of me.

HEY WI' THE ROSE AND THE LINDSAY, O.

A MINISTER's daughter in New York,
  Hey wi' the Rose and the Lindsay, O;
She's fa'en in love wi' her father's clerk,
  Down by yon green wood sidey, O.

She's courted wi' him seven years and a day,
  Hey wi' the Rose and the Lindsay, O;
Till this young man did her betray
  Down by yon green wood sidey, O.

She lean'd her back against a tree,
  Hey wi' the Rose and the Lindsay, O;
And there she bore him babies three
  Down by yon green wood sidey, O.

She'd ta'en out a little pen-knife,
  Hey wi' the Rose and the Lindsay, O;
And she has ta'en awa their life
  Down by yon green wood sidey, O.

She ta'en a napkin frae her neck,
  Hey wi' the Rose and the Lindsay, O;
And she's rolled them up baith head and feet,
  Down by yon green wood sidey, O.

She buried them 'neath a marble stane,
  Hey wi' the Rose and the Lindsay, O;
And she thought she'd gang a maiden hame
  Down by yon green wood sidey, O.

She look'd o'er her father's castle wa',
   Hey wi' the Rose and the Lindsay, O;
And she saw three bonnie boys playing at the ba'
   Down by yon green wood sidey, O.

O bonnie bairnies, if ye were mine,
   Hey wi' the Rose and the Lindsay, O;
I would dress you all in silk so fine
   Down by yon green wood sidey, O.

O cruel mother, when we were thine,
   Hey wi' the Rose and the Lindsay, O;
Ye didna dress us in silk so fine
   Down by yon green wood sidey, O.

Ye took out a little pen-knife,
   Hey wi' the Rose and the Lindsay, O;
And ye did take awa our life
   Down by yon green wood sidey, O.

O bonnie bairns, come tell to me,
   Hey wi' the Rose and the Lindsay, O;
The punishment I'll hae to dree
   For the deeds o' the green wood sidey, O.

Ye'll be seven years a bird in the tree,
   Hey wi' the Rose and the Lindsay, O;
And seven years a fish in the sea
   For the deeds o' the green wood sidey, O.

Ye'll be seven years a tongue to the bell,
   Hey wi' the Rose and the Lindsay, O;
And a' the rest in the flames o' hell,
   For the deeds o' the green wood sidey, O.

Welcome, welcome a bird in the tree,
   Hey wi' the Rose and the Lindsay, O;
And welcome, welcome a fish in the sea,
   For the deeds o' the green wood sidey, O.

Welcome, welcome a tongue to the bell,
   Hey wi' the Rose and the Lindsay, O;
But Guid keep me frae the flames o' hell
   For the deeds o' the green wood sidey, O.

GEORDIE DOWNIE.

HAE ye heard o' a widow in rich attire
    That rode on a weel shod pownie?
She's followed a tinker frae Dee-side,
    His name is Geordie Downie.

    My bonnie love, joe, my dear, you know,
        My bonnie love, Geordie Downie,
        I'll sell my hose, and drink my sheen,
        And follow Geordie Downie.

Downie melts the brass, the brass,
    And Downie melts the tin, O;
And happy, happy is the town,
    That Downie enters in, O.

    My bonnie love, joe, etc.

I ance was Charlie Petrie's wife
    In the auld toon o' Aberdeen, O;
But now I'm tinker Downie's wife,
    Wi' the pearlin' ower my e'en, O.

    My bonnie love, joe, etc.

Adieu to the lads wi' the white cocades,
    Likewise to the leather apron,
For I'm awa wi' Downie the cyaurd,
    He's a brisk lad and a vaporin'.

    My bonnie love, joe, etc.

Hae ye heard what cam' o' the tinker lad,
    Whose name was Geordie Downie?
He killed his wife, then broke his neck
    By fa'en when drunk frae his pownie.

    My bonnie love, joe, etc.

Her love and her joe, her dearie ye know,
    The tinker Geordie Downie,
Took all she had, then killed hersel',
    And died by a fall frae his pownie.

    My bonnie love, joe, etc.

There is an ancient superstition that gipsies have the power by casting spells over the eyes of those with whom they fall in love, so that the latter become mere passive tools in their hands. In this way, a tinker, or gipsy, is said to have " keist " a glamour over a countess of Cassilis and made her follow him. That there are certain powerful mesmeric influences we well know, but whether or not the " glamour " of the gipsies was of that kind, there is no means of ascertaining.

THE RUNAWAY BRIDE.

IF you go to the North Countrie,
    If that you be but ready,
You'll hear how the bride from the blacksmith ran
    To be a liggar lady.
        She ran away, she ran away,
            At home she would not tarry;
        And she has with the sergeant gane
            His halbert for to carry.

The lassies in the North Countrie
    They long to be a bride, man;
But when the wedding day is come
    Wi' the bridegroom they winna bide, man.
        She ran away, etc

In the toun o' Keith, to lie I'm loth,
    The wedding day was set, man;
But when the people gathered were,
    The bride they couldna get, man.
        She ran away, etc.

It's woe to the Low Countrie,
    And a' your men in Banff, man;
Let the laddies frae the Hielan's come
    And play you sic a jamph, man.
        She ran away, etc.

They wrote a letter wi' great speed,
    To the bridegroom sent for fun, man;
And when the tidings he did hear,
    Distracted he did run, man.
        She ran away, etc.

When the bridegroom heard, he cried, "alas!
    For ever I'll away, man;
For this day I am ruined quite,
    My bride she's run away, man."
        She ran away, etc.

His young men and his maidens all
    Unto him did resort, man,
With laughter like to split their sides
    When they heard of such sport, man.
        She ran away, etc.

" All young men, if you please to stay,
Your dinner it is ready;
But I'll go to the toun o' Keith
And seek to find my lady."
She ran away, etc.

His maiden at his right side stands,
And laughing thus did say, man,
" I think myself a happy maid
Since she has run away, man."
She ran away, etc.

His maiden at his right side stands,
And laughing thus did say, man,
" If I live to another year
We'll have our wedding day, man."
She ran away, etc.

Since she's run away, away is gone,
At home she would not tarry;
I'll be a bride to the self-same man,
And with him I will marry.
She ran away, etc.

All you young men, I pray beware,
If ever you are to marry,
Take care your bride don't run away
The halbert for to carry.
She'll run away, etc.

All you young men, I pray beware,
If you be to wed, man,
Take care none of the Hielan' lads
Come down and steal your bride, man.

For they'll away, they'll run away,
At home they will not bide, man;
For the laddies frae the Hielan's come
And steal away your bride, man.

This ballad is founded on an incident in real life which occured about
the end of the eighteenth century, where the bride of a blacksmith in Keith
is reported to have run off with a soldier on the eve of her marriage.

S

THE LORD O' ABOYNE.

THE Lord o' Aboyne to auld England's gane,
    And a' his nobles wi' him;
And sair was the he'rt that the Lady got,
    When she kent she couldna get wi' him.

When she looked owre her castle wa'
    She saw twa bonnie boys rinnin':
" What news, what news, my twa bonnie boys,
    What news hae ye brocht frae Lunnon?"

" Good news, good news, my fair lady,
    Good news hae we frae Lunnon;
The Lord o' Aboyne is but twa miles behin',
    The bells o' his bridle is ringin'."

She turned hersel' richt roon about
    To Jean her gentle woman
Says, " Mak' ready the best in the castle o' Aboyne
    Since the Lord o' Aboyne is comin'."

She turned her about and called her cook,
    Says, " Ha'e a' your pots a-shinin',
And the finest o' roast, and dinna hain the cost
    Since the Lord o' Aboyne is comin'."

She waved her han' and called her groom,
    Says, " Hae a' your stables shinin';
And corn and hay spare none this day,
    For the Lord o' Aboyne is comin'."

She called upon her minstrel boy,
    Says, " Hae a' your pipes a-tunin',
And be ready wi' the springs and dinna hain the strings,
    Since the Lord o' Aboyne is comin'."

Her bonnie page-boy he's run to the door,
    Cries, " Here's my Lord a-comin'."
She gaed to the close and took him frae his horse,
    Says, " Ye're welcome hame frae Lunnon."

" If I be as welcome as ye say,
  Come, kiss me for my comin';
To-morrow should have been my wedding day
  Had I stayed ony langer in Lunnon."

She turned her right roon about
  To Jean her gentle woman—
" To-morrow should have been his wedding day,
  He can kiss his misses in Lunnon."

He turned himsel' richt roon about,
  Says, " I'm sorry for my comin',
But this nicht we'll licht on the bonnie Braes o' Gicht,
  And the morn we'll saddle for Lunnon."

She called on Jean her gentle maid,
  Says, " See if I'll win wi' him ";
" Oh, no, no, no, my lady fair,
  He winna' tak' ye wi' him."

She wept here, and she wept there,
  And doctors wi' her dealin',
And all in a crack her young he'rt did brack,
  And a letter did follow him to Lunnon.

When he saw it sealed in black,
  He fell on his bed a-weepin';
If she be dead that I love best,
  She's got my he'rt a-keepin'.

He turned himsel' richt roon about,
  Says, " Hurry ye hame frae Lunnon;
Frae the horse to the hat, we'll go a' dressed in black,
  And we'll mourn for bonnie Peggie Irvine."

When they drew nigh to the castle o' Aboyne
  They heard the death-bell ringin',
And every knell that the death-bell gied,
  Said, " Come back and bury Peggie Irvine."

There are some versions of this song popular in Aberdeenshire.
Sometimes Aboyne is called the Duke, sometimes the Earl, and at other
times he is only the Laird.

THE SHEPHERD LAD O' RHYNIE.

Come ye, oh, come, my bonnie lass,
   We'll both join hands and marry;
Let all the world say what they may
   We'll both join hands and marry, marry,
   We'll both join hands and marry.

Here's to you my pipes and viols
   To play when you are weary;
And a' that I'll seek back o' thee
   Is a kiss of you, my dearie, dearie,
   Is a kiss o' you, my dearie.

I will not have your pipes and viols
   To play when I am weary;
And a kiss from me you'll never have,
   For I'll never be year dearie, dearie,
   For I'll never be your dearie.

Here is to you, my fleecy flocks,
   Though they were twice as many,
And all that I'll seek back of thee
   Is your hand, my dear, to marry, marry,
   Is your hand, my dear, to marry.

My father keeps me under guard,
   He will not let me take you,
And the only advice that he gives me
   Was always to forsake you, 'sake you,
   Was always to forsake you.

When he did hear what she did say
   He went up to a land called Rhynie,
And threw himself far over a rock,
   And was never seen by any, any,
   And was never seen by any.

When she did hear what he had done,
   You'd have heard her cries lamenting,
You'd have heard her cries far, far away,
   For the shepherd lad of Rhynie, Rhynie,
   For the shepherd lad of Rhynie.

O mother, dear, go make my bed,
　And make it long and narrow;
For my true love died for me to-day,
　And I'll die for him to-morrow, morrow,
　I'll die for him to-morrow.

She has laid her head on her father's breast,
　And oh, she was grieved with sorrow,
She's laid her head in her father's arms,
　But she never saw the morrow, morrow,
　But she never saw the morrow.

JOHNNIE O' COCKLESMUIR.

JOHNNIE raise up in a May morning,
　Called for water to wash his hands,
Says, "Lowse to me my twa grey dogs
　That lie bound in iron bands."

When Johnnie's mother heard o' this,
　Her hands for dule she wrang,
Says, "Johnnie, for my benison,
　To the green wood dinna gang."

But he has taen his guid bend-bow,
　His arrows ane by ane,
And he's awa to the green wood gane
　To hunt the dun deer down.

As he came down by Monymusk,
　And down amang the scrogs,
And there he spied a deer lyin'
　Asleep amang the scrogs.

The dun deer lap, and Johnnie fired,
　And he wounded her on the side;
And atween the water and the wood
　The grey dogs laid her pride.

And Johnnie has bryttled the deer sae weel,
  And cut out her liver and her lungs,
And wi' these he has fed his good grey dogs
  As if they had been earl's sons.

They ate sae much o' the venison,
  And they drank sae much o' the bleed,
That Johnnie and his twa gray dogs
  Fell asleep as they'd been deid.

By there cam' a silly, auld man,
  An ill death may he dee!
And he's awa to Esslemont
  The seven foresters to see.

"What news, what news, my grey auld man,
  What news hae ye to gie?"
"Nae news, nae news," said the silly, auld man,
  "But what my e'en did see.

"As I cam' in by Monymusk,
  And down amang the scrogs,
The bonniest youth that ever I saw
Lay sleeping atween his dogs.

"The sark that was upon his back
  Was o' the Holland fine;
And the doublet that was over that
  Was o' the Lincoln twine.

"The buttons that were on his sleeves
  Were o' the gowd sae guid,
And the twa dogs that he lay atween,
  Their mouths were dyed wi' bleed."

Then out and spak' the first forester,
  He was head man owre them a';
"Gin this be Johnnie o' Cocklesmuir
  Unto him we will draw."

Then out and spak' the second forester,
  A sister's son was he;
"Gin this be Johnnie o' Cocklesmuir,
  We'll better lat him be."

The first shot that the foresters fired
  It wounded him on the knee;
And the next shot that the foresters fired
  His heart's blood blin't his e'e.

Then up rose Johnnie out o' his sleep,
  And an angry man was he;
Says, " Ye micht hae waukened me frae my sleep
  For my heart's blood blins my e'e."

He's lean'd his back against an oak,
  His foot against a stone,
And he has fired at the seven foresters
  And he's killed them a' but one.

He has broken four o' this man's ribs,
  Likewise his collar bone,
And he's laid him twa-fauld owre his steed,
  Bade him carry the tidings home.

They hae made a rod o' the hazel bush,
  Anither o' the slae-thorn tree,
And mony, mony were the men
  At the carrying of our Johnnie.

Then out and spak' his auld mother,
  And fast her tears did fa':
" Ye wadna be warned, my son Johnnie,
  Frae the huntin' to bide awa.

" But wae betide that silly, auld man,
  An ill death shall he dee!
For the highest tree in Monymusk
  Shall be his morning's fee."

Now Johnnie's guid bend-bow is broke,
  And his twa grey dogs are slain,
His body lies in Monymusk,
  And his huntin' days are dune.

Sir Walter Scott published a version of this ballad in which the hero is described as " Johnnie o' Breadislee," and the scene of the tragedy is placed on the Borders.

THE BONNIE HOUSE O' AIRLIE.

It fell upon a day, a bonnie summer day,
    When green grew the aits and the barley,
That there fell out a great dispute
    Between Argyle and Airlie.
Argyle has callèd a hundred o' his men
    To come in the morning early,
And they hae gane doon by the back o' Dunkeld
    To plunder the bonnie house o' Airlie.

Lady Ogilvie look'd frae her window sae hie,
    And oh, but she grat sairly,
To see Argyle and a' his men
    Come to plunder the bonnie house o' Airlie.
Come doon, come doon, Lady Ogilvie, he cried,
    Come doon and kiss me fairly,
Or ere the morning's clear daylicht
    I'll no leave a standin' stane in Airlie.

I'll no' come doon, great Argyle, she cried,
    I will not kiss thee fairly,
I wadna kiss thee, false Argyle,
    Though ye shouldna leave a stanin' stane in Airlie;
But were my ain guid lord at hame,
    As he's this nicht wi' Charlie,
The base Argyle and a' his men
    Daurna enter the bonnie house o' Airlie.

O, I hae seven bonnie sons, she said,
    The youngest has ne'er seen his daddie,
And though I had as mony mair again,
    They'd a' be followers o' Charlie.
Then Argyle and his men attacked the bonnie ha',
    And O, but they plundered it fairly,
In spite o' the tears the lady let fa',
    They brunt doon the bonnie house o' Airlie.

JANET JAMIESON.

Come, all ye pretty, fair maids, and listen to my lay;
Likewise ye gallant ploughmen all, give heed to what I say:
It was a blooming, modest maid was hoeing on the farm,
When she did spy a gentleman with a gun beneath his arm.

The gentleman came up to her, and thus to her did say:
" What is thy name, where is thy hame, my pretty maid, I
      pray?"
" My hame is there, kind sir," she said; " beside yon wood so
      green,
My name is Janet Jamieson, as I've informed been."

" O Janet Jamieson," he said, " thou are a lovely queen,
And fitter far for lordly hall than hoeing neeps I ween,
It's come along with me, sweet maid, and I will busk thee rare
In ribbands, silks, and satinettes, and gold beyond compare.

" It's come along with me, sweet maid, and give to me thy hand,
And thou shall ride a milk-white steed, with servants at
      command."
" Oh no, no, gentle sir," she said, " I fear that cannot be,
I'm not a match for you, kind sir, as you may plainly see.

" And I do love a gallant swain, who drives the cart and plough,
To marry him at Whitsunday, to heaven I've pledged my vow."
" To go with me thou must consent," this gentleman replied,
Or with this gun my life I'll take, this moment by thy side.

" I've sought through all great London town, someone my wife
      to be,
But never maiden have I seen to be compared with thee."
.Oh, then unto his flattering words the maiden gave consent,
And to his hall that very night along with him she went.

But oh! alas! and lack-a-day, a week had not passed o'er,
When this false-hearted gentleman did turn her from his door;
She wandered east, she wandered west, ashamed to be seen,
But never sought her father's cot, beside the wood so green.

She wandered south, she wandered north, she shunned the face
      of men,
Her food the hip and the wild berrie, her home the lonesome
      glen;
She wandered up, she wandered down, and long ere
      Christmastide
A shepherd found her clay-cold corpse upon a bleak hillside.

The cruel gentleman also, he never more did thrive,
For in the wars of Hindustan, it's he was killed alive.
For all ye swains and maidens gay, come, listen every one,
And take a lesson from the fate of Janet Jamieson.

THE SILVERY TIDE.

'Tis of a fair young creature who dwelt by the seaside,
With lovely form and features, she was called the village pride;
There was a young sea captain who Mary's heart did gain,
And true she was to Henry whilst on the raging main.

It was in young Henry's absence a nobleman he came,
A-courting pretty Mary, but she refused the same;
Your vows are vain, for on the main there's one I love, she cried;
Therefore, begone, I love but one, and he's on the silvery tide.

Then, mad with desperation, the nobleman did say,
" To cause their separation I'll take her life away;
I'll watch her late and early, till when alone," he cried;
" I'll send her body floating down along the silvery tide."

The nobleman was walking one morn to take the air,
Down by the rolling ocean he met that lady fair;
Then said the cruel villain, " Consent to be my bride,
Or you'll sink or swim far, far from him that's on the silvery
        tide."

With trembling limbs, said Mary, " My vows I ne'er can break,
For Henry I love dearly, I'd die for his sweet sake ";
With his handkerchief he bound her, and flung her o'er the side,
And, shrieking, she went floating down along the silvery tide.

It happened Mary's true love soon after came from sea,
Expecting to be happy and fix the wedding day.
" Oh, we fear your true love's murdered," her aged parents
        cried,
" Or has caused her own destruction in yonder silvery tide."

Young Henry on his pillow at night could take no rest,
The thoughts of pretty Mary disturbed his wounded breast;
He dreamt that as he was walking down by the ocean side
His true love he saw weeping on the banks of the silvery tide.

With fright then he aroused, and at midnight gloom went he
To wander the sand bank over down by the raging sea;
At day-break in the morning there Mary's corpse he spied,
As to and fro it was rolling down, down in the silvery tide.

He knew it was young Mary by his own ring on her hand;
He unbound the silk handkerchief, which put him to a stand.
The name of her base murderer in full thereon he spied,
Which proved who drown'd young Mary all in the silvery tide.

The nobleman was taken, and the gallows was his doom,
For drowning pretty Mary, who had scarce attain'd her bloom.
Young Henry, quite dejected, did wander till he died,
And his last words were for Mary, drowned in the silvery tide.

HARLAW.

As I cam' in by Garioch land,
    And down by Neitherha',
There were fifty thousand Highlandmen
    A' marching to Harlaw.
        Wi' a drie, drie, drie, did dronilie,
        Drie, did dronilie drie.

As I cam' on and further on,
    And down and by Balquhain,
O, there I met Sir James the Rose,
    Wi' him Sir John the Græme.

" O, cam' ye frae the Hielands, man?
    O, cam' ye a' the wye?
Saw ye Macdonald and his men
    As they cam' in frae Skye?"

" Yes, I cam' frae the Hielands, man,
    And I cam' a' the wye,
And I saw Macdonald and his men
    As they cam' in frae Skye."

" O, were ye near Macdonald's men?
    Did ye their number see?
Come tell to me, John Hielandman,
    What might their number be?"

" Yes, I was near, and near enough,
    And I their number saw,
There were fifty thousand Highlandmen
    A' marching to Harlaw."

" Gin that be true," said James the Rose,
   " We'll no come muckle speed,
We'll cry upon our merry men,
   And turn our horses' head."

" O na, O na," said John the Græme,
   " That thing will never be,
The gallant Græmes were never beat,
   We'll try what we can dee."

As I cam' on, and further on,
   And down and by Harlaw,
They fell fu' close on ilka side,
   Sic straiks ye never saw.

They fell fu' close on ilka side,
   Sic straiks ye never saw,
For ilka sword gaed clash for clash
   At the battle o' Harlaw!

The Hielandmen, wi' their lang swords,
   They laid on us fu' sair,
And they drave back our merry men
   Three acres' breadth and mair.

Braves Forbes to his brother did say:
   " O brither, dinna ye see,
They beat us back on ilka side
   And we'll be forced to flee."

" O na, O na, my brither dear,
   O na, that maunna be!
You'll tak' your gude sword in your hand
   And ye'll gang in wi' me."

Then back to back the brithers brave
   Gaed in amang the thrang,
And they swept down the Hielandmen
   Wi' swords baith sharp and lang.

The first ae straik that Forbes struck
   He gar'd Macdonald reel,
And the next ae straik that Forbes struck
   The brave Macdonald fell.

And siccan a pitlarichie
  I'm sure ye never saw,
As was amang the Hielandmen
  When they saw Macdonald fa'.

And when they saw that he was deid
  They turned and ran awa;
And they buried him at Legates Den,
  A lang mile frae Harlaw.

Some rade, some ran, and some did gang,
  They were o' sma' record,
But Forbes and his merry men,
  They slew them on the road.

On Mononday, at morning,
  The battle it began,
And Saturday at gloamin'
  Ye'd scarce ken'd wha had won.

Of fifty thousand Hielandmen
  Scarce fifty-three went hame,.
And out o' a' the Lowlandmen
  But fifty marched wi' Græme.

And sic a weary burying,
  I'm sure ye never saw,
As was the Sunday after that
  On the muir aneath Harlaw.

Gin onybody speir at ye
  For them we took awa,
Ye tell them plain, and very plain,
  They're sleeping at Harlaw.

    Wi' a drie, drie, drie, did dronilie,
    Drie, did dronilie drie.

The above is the traditional version of the ballad of Harlaw as it is still sung in the farm-kitchens of the North-east of Scotland, and it differs in several respects from the book version. The ballad is not historically correct, as every student of Scottish history knows. Macdonald was not killed, but the chiefs of clans Macintosh and MacLean were. The flower of the Lowland army fell in the fight which lasted a whole day, but victory remained with them. The battle was fought on 24th July, 1411.

Some authorities state that the refrain—Wi' a drie, drie, drie did dronilie—is part of an old druidical chant.

BARBARA ALLAN.

I⋅ fell about the Martinmas time,
  When the green leaves were down-**fallin**',
That Sir John the Græme, o' the North Countrie,
  Fell in love wi' Barbara Allan.

He sent his men down thro' the town
  To the place where she was dwallin';
" O haste and come to my master dear,
  Gin your name be Barbara Allan."

O hooly, hooly rose she up,
  And slowly gaed she till him,
An' when she cam' to his bed-side,
  Said, " Young man I think you're dyin`."

" O, I am sick, and very sick,
  And it's a' for Barbara Allan!"
" O, better for me ye'll never be,
  Though your heart's blood were a-spillin'.

" Remember ye not in the tavern, sir,
  When ye the cups were fillin',
How ye made the healths gie roun' and roun',
  And ye slighted Barbara Allan."

" Put in your hand at my bed-head,
  And there ye'll find a token,
Ye'll find my case but and a ring,
  Gie them to Barbara Allan.

" Put in your hand at my bed-foot,
  An' there you'll find a warran',
An' there ye'll find my bloody shirt,
  That was bled for Barbara Allan."

He turned his face unto the wa',
  And death was with him dealin';
" Adieu, adieu, my dear friends a',
  Be kind to Barbara Allan."

Then hooly, hooly raise she up,
  And slowly, slowly left him,
And sighing, said she could not stay,
  Since death o' life had reft him.

She had not gane a mile but twa,
  When she heard the deid-bell knellin';
And every jow that the deid-bell gied
  Cried, "Wae to Barbara Allan!"

"O mither, mither, mak' my bed,
  An' mak' it saft and narrow;
Since my love died for me to-day
  I'll die for him to-morrow."

This ballad was collated from several copies which came into my hands
as I could not get a perfect copy from any single source. Mr. Pepys, in
his diary, mentions having heard the famous Nell Gwynn singing the English
version of it during the reign of Charles II.

THE LONGFORD MURDERER.

Both young and old, I now make bold,
  I pray you lend an ear;
It's of as cruel a murder
  As ever you did hear.

It's of a pretty female,
  Her age was scarce sixteen;
Her beauty bright made me delight,
  And Satan made me sin.

This fair maid being a servant girl,
  And I a farmer's son,
Her home in County Longford,
  Convenient to my own.

I courted her in private,
  Till I had her beguiled;
And then to take her tender life
  I made this action wild.

'Twas on a Sunday evening,
  As you may plainly see,
I sent for her in secret,
  And soon she came to me.

I said, "My dearest Annie,
  To Longford we will go;
It's there we will get married,
  And no one here shall know."

So late that night we both set out
  Across the dreary plain;
All on the way I talked full gay,
  My action time to gain.

And the tender words she spoke to me
  Would bring tears to your eye;
But I said, "We'll go no further,
  For it's here that you must die."

"O Jamie, think on all your vows,
  And do not me affright;
And do not commit murder
  This dark and dismal night.

"I promise here, all on my knees,
  If you will spare my life,
I'll never seek to trouble you,
  Nor ask to be your wife."

The words she said were all in vain,
  I struck her wondrous sore;
With a heavy whip I took her life,
  And left her in her gore.

Her flowing blood did stain the ground,
  Her moans they pierced my heart;
And thinking I had murdered her,
  From her I quick did part.

But being alive next morning,
   Just at the break of day,
A shepherd's only daughter
   By chance did pass that way.

And seeing her lying in her gore,
   She went to her release;
And Annie told her all my guilt,
   And she sent for the police.

The cor'ner and the officer,
   And the policeman likewise,
They all got information,
   And set out in disguise.

They quickly me surrounded,
   And put me on my trial;
And I was taken prisoner
   And lodged in Longford Jail.

But I lay there with troubled mind
   Until my trial day;
When the judge in passing sentence,
   These words to me did say—

" For murdering of an orphan girl,
   Your countrymen shall see,
On the twenty-fourth of April,
   You'll hang on the gallows-tree."

My name is James M'Donald,
   From life I soon must part
For the murdering of Annie O'Brien—
   It grieves me to the heart.

But I hope the Lord will pardon me;
   And, on my dying day,
When I do mount the scaffold,
   Good Christians, for me pray.

This is an Irish Folk-song introduced into this country by Irish harvesters
at the beginning of the last century.

THE HIREMAN CHIEL.

THERE was a knight, a baron bright,
  A bold baron was he,
And he had only but one son,
  And a comely youth was he.

He brought him up at schools nine,
  So has he at schools ten,
And the boy learned to haud the plough
  Amang his father's men.

But it fell ance upon a day
  The bold baron did say:
" My son, you maun gae court a wife,
  And ane o' high degree.

" Ye hae lands, woods, rents, and bowers,
  Castles and towers three;
Then go, my son, and seek some dame
  To share these gifts wi' thee."

" Yes, I have lands and woods, father,
  Castles and towers three;
But what if she likes my lands and rents
  Far more than she loves me?

" But I will go and seek a wife
  That weel can please my e'e;
And I will fairly try her love
  Before she goes wi' me."

Then he's taen aff his scarlet coat,
  Bedeck'd wi' shinin' gold,
And he's put on the hireman's coat
  To keep him frae the cold.

He's laid past the studded sword
  That he could bravely draw,
And he's gone skippin' down the stair,
  Swift as a bird that flaw.

He took a stick into his hand,
  Which he could bravely wiel',
And he's gane whistling o'er the lan',
  Like ony hireman chiel.

He gaed up yon high, high hill,
  And low in yonder glen,
'Twas there he saw a gay castle
  Wi' turrets nine or ten.

And he's gone on and further on,
  Till to the yett drew he,
And there he saw a lady fair,
  That pleased that young man's e'e.

He went straught to the grieve's chamber,
  And with humilitie
Said, "Hae ye ony kind o' work
  For a hireman chiel like me?"

"What is the wark ye'd tak' in han',
  Or how can we agree?
Can ye plough, sow, and reap the corn,
  And a' for meat and fee?"

"Yes, I can plough, and reap and mow,
  And sow the corn tee,
And I can manage horse and cow,
  And a' for meat and fee."

"If ye can haud the plough richt weel,
  And sow the corn tee,
By faith and troth, my hireman loon,
  We sanna pairt for fee."

He's put his hand in his pocket,
  And ta'en out shillings nine;
Says, "Tak' ye that, my hireman chiel,
  And turn in here and dine."

He acted all he took in hand,
  His master loved him weel;
And the young lady of the land
  Fell in love wi' the hireman chiel.

How oft she tried to drown the flame,
  And oft wept bitterlie;
But still she loved the hireman chiel,
  So weel's he pleased her e'e.

She has written a broad letter,
  And sealed it wi' her hand,
And dropt it at the stable-door
  Where this young man did stand.

"I am in love, my hireman chiel,
  I'm deep in love wi' thee;
And, if ye think me worth your love,
  I' the garden green meet me."

When he read the letter o'er,
  A loud, loud laugh gae he;
Said, "If I manage my business weel,
  I'm sure to get my fee."

At night they met behind a tree,
  Low in the garden green,
To tell the tale among the flowers,
  And view the evenin' scene.

Next morning by the rising sun,
  She, wi' her Maries fair,
Walk'd to the field to see the plough
  And meet the hireman there.

"Good morn, good morn, my lady gay,
  I wonder much at you,
To rise so early in the morn
  While fields are wet wi' dew;
To hear the linnets on the thorn,
  And see the plough-boy plough."

"I wonder much at you, young man,
  I wonder much at you,
That ye no other station have
  Than hold my father's plough."

"I love as weel to rise each morn
  As you can your Maries fair.
I love as weel to hold the plough
  As if I was your father's heir.

"If ye love me as ye protest,
  As I trust weel ye dee,
The morn's nicht at eight o'clock,
  In the guid green-wood meet me."

" Yes, I love you, my hireman chiel,
 And that most tenderlie,
But my maidenhood it feareth me
 So late to meet with thee."

" Tak' ye no dread, my bonnie lass,
 Lat a' your folly be;
If ye come a maiden to the green wood,
 Ye'll return the same for me."

The lady she went home again,
 Wi' a Marie on every hand;
She was so very sick in love,
 Should could not sit or stand.

It was on a dark and dismal night,
 No stars blink'd o'er the lea,
When the lady and her hireman met
 Under the greenwood tree.

He took the lady in his arms,
 Embraced her tenderlie,
And thrice he kissed her rosy lips
 Under the greenwood tree.

" Haud aff your hands, young man," she said,
 " I wonder much at thee;
The man that holds my father's plough
 To lay his hands on me."

" No harm I mean, my winsome dame,
 No impudence at a';
I never laid a hand on you
 Till your libertie I saw.

" But the morning it is coming in,
 The dew is falling down,
An' you must go home again
 Or you'll spoil your satin gown."

" If you are wearied of me so soon,
 Why did you tryst me here?"
" I would not weary with you, my dear,
 Though this night were a year."

When morning beams began to peep
   Among the branches green,
The lovers rose to part, and meet,
   And tell their tale again.

" Ye will go home unto the plough,
   Where often ye hae been;
I'll tak' my mantle folded up
   And walk i' the garden green.

" The baron and my mother dear
   Will wonder what I mean;
They'll think I've been disturbed sair,
   When I am up sae seen ."

But this passed on, and further on,
   For two months and a day,
Till word cam' to the bold baron,
   And an angry man was he.

The baron swore a solemn oath,
   An angry man was he:
" The morn before I eat or drink,
   High hanged he shall be."

" Farewell, my lovely lady fair,
   A long adieu to thee;
Your father has sworn a solemn oath
   That hanged I shall be."

" O woe's me!" the lady said,
   " Yet do not troubled be;
If e'er they touch the hair on thy head
   They'll get no good of me."

He turned him right and round about,
   And a loud, loud laugh gave he:
" That man never stood in a court
   That daur this day hang me."

Her mother spoke from her bower door,
   An angry woman was she:
" What impudence in you to tryst
   Her to the greenwood tree."

He turned him right and round about,
  And a loud, loud laugh gave he:
Says, " If she came a maid to the green, green wood,
  She return'd the same for me.

" If she had not gien her consent,
  She had not gone with me;
Ye may wed your daughter when ye will,
  She's none the worse for me."

He's gone whistling o'er the knowe,
  Swift as the bird that flaw;
The lady stood in her bower door
  And lat the tears downfa'.

But this passed on, and further on,
  Till two months and a day,
When there came a knight, a baron bright,
  To woo this lady gay.

He soon gained the baron's will,
  Likewise the mother gay;
He woo'd and won the lady's love,
  But by a slow degree.

" O weel befa' you, daughter dear,
  And happy may ye be,
To lay your love on that grand knight,
  And let the hireman be."

" O haud your tongue, my father dear,
  And speak not so to me;
For more I love yon hireman chiel
  Than a' the knights I see."

The morn was come, and the bells were rung,
  And all to church repair;
And like a rose among the thorns
  Was this lady and her Maries fair.

But as they walked across the field,
  Among the flowers so fair,
Beneath a tree stood on the plain,
  The hireman chiel was there.

" I wish ye joy, my gay madam,
    And aye weel may ye be;
Here's a ring, a pledge o' love,
    That ance I got from thee."

" O wae befa' you, hireman chiel,
    Some ill death may ye dee;
Ye might hae tauld to me your name,
    Your hame, and your countrie."

" If ye love me, my lady fair,
    As ye protest ye dee,
Then turn your love from this grand knight,
    And reach your hand to me."

Then out it spoke the gay, gay baron,
    And an angry man was he:
" If I had known she was belov'd
    She had ne'er been loved by me."

When she was set on high horse-back,
    And ridin' through the glen,
They saw her father followin' fast
    Wi' fifty armed men.

" Do for yourself, my hireman lad,
    And for your safety flee;
My father he will take me back,
    But married I'll never be."

When they gaed up yon high, high hill,
    There, low down i' the glen,
They saw his father's gilded coach,
    Wi' five hundred gentlemen.

" Come back, come back, my hireman chiel,
    Turn back and speak wi' me;
Ye served me lang for my daughter's sake,
    Come back and get your fee."

" Your blessing give us instantly,
    Is all we crave of thee;
Seven years I served you for her sake,
    And now I've got my fee."

I noted down this ballad from the singing of an old man named Robert
Mellis, West Folds, Huntly, in the autumn of 1908.

INDEX